EXAMKRACKERS MCAT®

INORGANIC CHEMISTY

8TH EDITION

OSOTE
PUBLISHING

ISBN 10: 1-893858-65-0 (Volume 4)
ISBN 13: 978-1-893858-65-7 (5 Volume Set)

8th Edition

To purchase additional copies of this book or the rest of the 5 volume set,
call 1-888-572-2536 or fax orders to 1-859-255-0109.

Examkrackers.com

Osote.com

Audioosmosis.com

Cover/inside layout design/illustrations: Examkrackers' staff

Printed and bound in the United States of America.

Acknowledgements

Although I am the author, the hard work and expertise of many individuals contributed to this book. The idea of writing in two voices, a science voice and an MCAT voice, was the creative brainchild of my imaginative friend Jordan Zaretsky. I would like to thank Scott Calvin for lending his exceptional science talent and pedagogic skills to this project. I also must thank the ExamKrackers students for doggedly questioning every explanation, every sentence, every diagram, and every punctuation mark in the book, and for providing the creative inspiration that helped me find new ways to approach and teach chemistry. Finally, I wish to thank my wife, Silvia, for her support during the difficult times in the past and those that lie ahead.

I also wish to thank the following individuals:

Contributors

Jennifer Birk-Goldschmidt
Patrick Butler
Dr. Scott Calvin
Sam Crayton
Spencer Lewis
Steven Ngai
Mark Pederson
Ahmed Sandu
Shuo Song
Vinita Takiar
Steven Tersigni
Ruopeng Zhu

Read This Section First!

This manual contains all the inorganic chemistry tested on the MCAT and more. It contains more inorganic chemistry than is tested on the MCAT because a deeper understanding of basic scientific principles is often gained through more advanced study. In addition, the MCAT often presents passages with imposing topics that may intimidate the test-taker. Although the questions don't require knowledge of these topics, some familiarity will increase the confidence of the test-taker.

In order to answer questions quickly and efficiently, it is vital that the test-taker understand what is, and is not, tested directly by the MCAT. To assist the test-taker in gaining this knowledge, this manual will use the following conventions. Any term or concept which is tested directly by the MCAT will be written in **red, bold type**. To ensure a perfect score on the MCAT, you should thoroughly understand all terms and concepts that are in **red, bold type** in this manual. Sometimes it is not necessary to memorize the name of a concept, but it is necessary to understand the concept itself. These concepts will also be in **bold and red**. It is important to note that the converse of the above is not true: just because a topic is not in **bold and red**, does not mean that it is not important.

Any formula that must be memorized will also be written in **red, bold type.**

If a topic is discussed purely as background knowledge, it will be written in *italics*. If a topic is written in italics, it is not likely to be required knowledge for the MCAT but may be discussed in an MCAT passage. Do not ignore items in italics, but recognize them as less important than other items. Answers to questions that directly test knowledge of italicized topics are likely to be found in an MCAT passage.

Text written in orange is me, Salty the Kracker. I will remind you what is and is not an absolute must for MCAT. I will help you develop your MCAT intuition. In addition, I will offer mnemonics, simple methods of viewing a complex concept, and occasionally some comic relief. Don't ignore me, even if you think I am not funny, because my comedy is designed to help you understand and remember. If you think I am funny, tell the boss. I could use a raise.

Each chapter in this manual should be read three times: twice before the class lecture, and once immediately following the lecture. During the first reading, you should not write in the book. Instead, read purely for enjoyment. During the second reading, you should both highlight and take notes in the margins. The third reading should be slow and thorough.

The 24 questions in each lecture should be worked during the second reading before coming to class. The in-class exams in the back of the book are to be done in class after the lecture. Do not look at them before class.

Warning: Just attending the class will not raise your score. You must do the work. Not attending class will obstruct dramatic score increases. If you have Audio Osmosis, then listen to the appropriate lecture before and after you read a lecture.

If you are studying independently, read the lecture twice before doing the in-class exam and then once after doing the in-class exam. If you have Examkrackers *MCAT Audio Osmosis With Jordan and Jon*, listen to that before taking the in-class exam and then as many times as necessary after taking the exam.

A scaled score conversion chart is provided on the answer page. This is not meant to be an accurate representation of your MCAT score. Do not become demoralized by a poor performance on these exams; they are not accurate reflections of your performance on the real MCAT. The thirty minute exams have been designed to educate. They are similar to an MCAT but with most of the easy questions removed. We believe that you can answer most of the easy questions without too much help from us, so the best way to raise your score is to focus on the more difficult questions. This method is one of the reasons for the rapid and celebrated success of the Examkrackers prep course and products.

If you find yourself struggling with the science or just needing more practice materials, use the Examkrackers 1001 Questions series. These books are designed specifically to teach the science. If you are already scoring 10s or better, these books are not for you.

You should take advantage of the forums at www.examkrackers.com. The bulletin board allows you to discuss any question in the book with an MCAT expert at Examkrackers. All discussions are kept on file so you have a bank of discussions to which you can refer to any question in this book.

Although we are very careful to be accurate, errata is an occupational hazard of any science book, especially those that are updated regularly as is this one. We maintain that our books have fewer errata than any other prep book. Most of the time what students are certain are errata is the student's error and not an error in the book. So that you can be certain, any errata in this book will be listed as it is discovered at www.examkrackers.com on the bulletin board. Check this site initially and periodically. If you discover what you believe to be errata, please post it on this board and we will verify it promptly. We understand that this system calls attention to the very few errata that may be in our books, but we feel that this is the best system to ensure that you have accurate information for your exam. Again, we stress that we have fewer errata than any other prep book on the market. The difference is that we provide a public list of our errata for your benefit.

Study diligently, trust this book to guide you, and you will reach your MCAT goals.

Table of Contents

PHYSICAL SCIENCES

DIRECTIONS. Most questions in the Physical Sciences test are organized into groups, each preceded by a descriptive passage. After studying the passage, select the one best answer to each question in the group. Some questions are not based on a descriptive passage and are also independent of each other. You must also select the one best answer to these questions. If you are not certain of an answer, eliminate the alternatives that you know to be incorrect and then select an answer from the remaining alternatives. A periodic table is provided for your use. You may consult it whenever you wish.

PERIODIC TABLE OF THE ELEMENTS

1 H 1.0																	2 He 4.0
3 Li 6.9	4 Be 9.0											5 B 10.8	6 C 12.0	7 N 14.0	8 O 16.0	9 F 19.0	10 Ne 20.2
11 Na 23.0	12 Mg 24.3											13 Al 27.0	14 Si 28.1	15 P 31.0	16 S 32.1	17 Cl 35.5	18 Ar 39.9
19 K 39.1	20 Ca 40.1	21 Sc 45.0	22 Ti 47.9	23 V 50.9	24 Cr 52.0	25 Mn 54.9	26 Fe 55.8	27 Co 58.9	28 Ni 58.7	29 Cu 63.5	30 Zn 65.4	31 Ga 69.7	32 Ge 72.6	33 As 74.9	34 Se 79.0	35 Br 79.9	36 Kr 83.8
37 Rb 85.5	38 Sr 87.6	39 Y 88.9	40 Zr 91.2	41 Nb 92.9	42 Mo 95.9	43 Tc (98)	44 Ru 101.1	45 Rh 102.9	46 Pd 106.4	47 Ag 107.9	48 Cd 112.4	49 In 114.8	50 Sn 118.7	51 Sb 121.8	52 Te 127.6	53 I 126.9	54 Xe 131.3
55 Cs 132.9	56 Ba 137.3	57 La* 138.9	72 Hf 178.5	73 Ta 180.9	74 W 183.9	75 Re 186.2	76 Os 190.2	77 Ir 192.2	78 Pt 195.1	79 Au 197.0	80 Hg 200.6	81 Tl 204.4	82 Pb 207.2	83 Bi 209.0	84 Po (209)	85 At (210)	86 Rn (222)
87 Fr (223)	88 Ra 226.0	89 Ac⁼ 227.0	104 Unq (261)	105 Unp (262)	106 Unh (263)	107 Uns (262)	108 Uno (265)	109 Une (267)									

*	58 Ce 140.1	59 Pr 140.9	60 Nd 144.2	61 Pm (145)	62 Sm 150.4	63 Eu 152.0	64 Gd 157.3	65 Tb 158.9	66 Dy 162.5	67 Ho 164.9	68 Er 167.3	69 Tm 168.9	70 Yb 173.0	71 Lu 175.0
⁼	90 Th 232.0	91 Pa (231)	92 U 238.0	93 Np (237)	94 Pu (244)	95 Am (243)	96 Cm (247)	97 Bk (247)	98 Cf (251)	99 Es (252)	100 Fm (257)	101 Md (258)	102 No (259)	103 Lr (260)

Atoms, Molecules and Quantum Mechanics

1.1 Atoms

All mass consists of tiny particles called **atoms**. Each atom is composed of a **nucleus** surrounded by one or more electrons. The radius of a nucleus is on the order of 10^{-4} angstroms (Å). One angstrom is 10^{-10} m. The nucleus contains **protons** and neutrons, collectively called *nucleons*, held together by the *strong nuclear force*. Protons and neutrons are approximately equal in size and mass. (Neutrons are very slightly heavier.) Protons have a positive charge and neutrons are electrically neutral.

Proton

Neutron

Atomic radius
(reduced approximately 500 times relative to the nucleons)

Electron
(magnified 1,000 times relative to the nucleons)

Surrounding the nucleus at a distance of about 1 to 3 Å are **electrons**. The mass of one electron is over 1800 times smaller than the mass of a nucleon. Electrons and protons have opposite charges of equal magnitude. Although for convenience we often think of the charge on an electron as 1– and the charge on a proton as 1+, we should remember that this charge is in electron units '*e*' called the *electronic charge*. A charge of 1 *e* is equal to 1.6×10^{-19} coulombs, the SI unit. An atom itself is electrically neutral; it contains the same number of protons as electrons.

Table 1.1 Composition of an Atom

Particle	Charge	Mass (amu)
Proton	Positive (1+)	1.0073
Neutron	Neutral	1.0087
Electron	Negative (1-)	5.5×10^{-4}

> Of course, you want to know the charges on the particles, but don't memorize the masses in the table shown. Instead, recognize the disparity in size between electrons and nucleons. Also, notice that protons and neutrons have nearly the same mass, about one amu.

Since the nucleons are so small compared to the size of the atom, the atom itself is composed mostly of empty space. If an atom were the size of a modern football stadium, it would have a nucleus the size of a marble.

1.2 Elements

Any given atom must be one of just over 100 **elements**. Elements are the building blocks of all compounds and cannot be decomposed into simpler substances by chemical means. Any element can be displayed as follows in Figure 1.1 where **A** is the **mass number** or number of protons plus neutrons, and **Z** is the **atomic number** or number of protons. The atomic number is the identity number of any element. If we know the atomic number, then we know the element. This is not true of the mass number or the number of electrons. Any element may have any number of neutrons or electrons, but only one number of protons.

Figure 1.1   Atomic Notation

Mass Number
A = protons + neutrons

Elemental Symbol

Atomic Number
Z = protons

Notice that 'A' stands for mass number and NOT atomic number.

Two or more atoms of the same element that contain different numbers of neutrons are said to be **isotopes**. A nucleus of a specific isotope is called a *nuclide*. Isotopes have similar chemical properties. Hydrogen has three important isotopes: ^{1}H (*protium*), ^{2}H (*deuterium*), and ^{3}H (*tritium*). 99.98% of naturally occurring hydrogen is protium. Examples of three isotopes for carbon are:

$$^{12}C, \ ^{13}C, \text{ and } ^{14}C.$$

Each of carbon's isotopes contains 6 protons. Six protons define carbon. ^{12}C (carbon-12) contains 6 neutrons, ^{13}C (carbon-13) contains 7 neutrons, and ^{14}C (carbon-14) contains 8 neutrons.

The number of protons identifies the element. For a given element, the number of neutrons identifies the isotope.

Although the mass number is a good approximation of the mass of an atom, it is not exact. The **atomic weight** or **molar mass** (**MM** or **M**) of an atom is given in **atomic mass units** (abbreviated **amu** or with the less commonly used SI abbreviation **u**). The atomic weight of an element is actually a mass (or in some books a ratio) and not a weight. An amu is defined by carbon-12. By definition, one atom of ^{12}C has an atomic weight of 12 amu. All other atomic weights are measured against this standard. Since carbon naturally occurs as a mixture of its isotopes, the atomic weight of carbon is listed as the weighted average of its isotopes or 12.011 amu. (This is very close to 12 amu because almost 99% of carbon occurs in nature as ^{12}C.)

Think of an amu as approximately the mass of one proton or one neutron.

Biochemists call an amu a dalton.

^{12}C also defines a **mole**. A mole is similar to a dozen or a score. A dozen is 12 of something and a score is 20 of something. So 3 dozen eggs means 3 × 12 = 36 eggs and "four score and seven years ago" means 4 × 20 + 7 = 87 years ago. A mole is just 6.022 × 10^{23} of something, where **6.022 × 10^{23}** is **Avogadro's number**, the number of carbon atoms in 12 grams of ^{12}C. Keeping in mind the relationship between an amu and a gram can be useful:

$$6.022 \times 10^{23} \text{ amu} = 1 \text{ gram}$$

We can read atomic weights from the periodic table as either amu or g/mol.

If we are given the amount of an element or compound in grams, we can divide by the atomic or molecular weight to find the number of moles in that sample.

$$\text{moles} = \frac{\text{grams}}{\text{atomic or molecular weight}}$$

If you can't find moles from molecular or atomic weight, then you better get crackin'. This is basic stuff, but you need to have it down cold!

One mole of carbon.

1.3 The Periodic Table

The **periodic table** lists the elements from left to right in the order of their atomic numbers. Each horizontal row is called a **period**. The vertical columns are called **groups or families**. There are at least two methods used to number the groups. The newer method is to number them 1 through 18 from left to right. An older method, which is still used, is to separate the groups into sections A and B. These sections are then numbered with Roman numerals as shown below.

The periodic table below divides the elements into three sections: 1) nonmetals on the right (green), 2) metals on the left (yellow gold), and 3) metalloids along the blue-shaded diagonal separating the metals from the nonmetals.

Metals are large atoms that tend to lose electrons to form positive ions or form positive oxidation states. To emphasize their loose hold on their electrons and the fluid-like nature of their valence electrons, metals are often described as atoms in a sea of electrons. The easy movement of electrons within metals gives them their metallic character. Metallic character includes ductility (easily stretched), malleability (easily hammered into thin strips), thermal and electrical conductivity, and a characteristic luster. Metal atoms easily slide past each other allowing metals to be hammered into thin sheets or drawn into wires. Electrons move easily from one metal atom to the next transferring energy or charge in the form of heat or electricity. All metals but mercury exist as solids at room temperature. Metals typically form ionic oxides such as BaO. (BeO is one exception that is not ionic.)

One characteristic of metals is malleability. Here, hot iron is hammered into a different shape by a blacksmith.

> Know the characteristics of metals: lustrous, ductile, malleable, thermally and electrically conductive.

Calcium

Magnesium

Lithium

Alkali Metals

Alkaline Earth Metals

> You need to know the names of the following groups: alkali metals, alkaline earth metals, halogens, and noble gases.

Metals

Metalloids

Halogens

Noble Gases

Nonmetals

Lanthanides

| 58 Ce 140.1 | 59 Pr 140.9 | 60 Nd 144.2 | 61 Pm (145) | 62 Sm 150.4 | 63 Eu 152.0 | 64 Gd 157.3 | 65 Tb 158.9 | 66 Dy 162.5 | 67 Ho 164.9 | 68 Er 167.3 | 69 Tm 168.9 | 70 Yb 173.0 | 71 Lu 175.0 |

Actinides

| 90 Th 232.0 | 91 Pa (231) | 92 U 238.0 | 93 Np (237) | 94 Pu (244) | 95 Am (243) | 96 Cm (247) | 97 Bk (247) | 98 Cf (251) | 99 Es (252) | 100 Fm (257) | 101 Md (258) | 102 No (259) | 103 Lr (260) |

Nonmetals have diverse appearances and chemical behaviors. Generally speaking, nonmetals have lower melting points than metals. They form negative ions. Molecular substances are typically made from only nonmetals. Nonmetals form covalent oxides such as SiO_2 or CO_2.

Metalloids have some characteristics that resemble metals and some that resemble nonmetals.

You should also recognize the names of the following four groups: alkali metals, alkaline earth metals, halogens, and noble (or rare) gases. The section A groups are known as the *representative* or *main-group elements* and the section B groups are called the **transition metals**.

Elements in the same family on the periodic table tend to have similar chemical properties. For example, they tend to make the same number of bonds and exist as similarly charged ions.

> Elements in the same family have similar chemical properties. Hydrogen is an exception to the rule.

1.4 Characteristics Within Groups

Hydrogen is unique and its chemical and physical characteristics do not conform well to any family. It is a nonmetal. Under most conditions, it is a colorless, odorless, diatomic gas.

As pure substances, Group 1A or alkali metals are soft metallic solids with low densities and low melting points. They easily form 1+ cations. They are highly reactive, reacting with most nonmetals to form ionic compounds. Alkali metals react with hydrogen to form hydrides such as NaH. Alkali metals react exothermically with water to produce the metal hydroxide and hydrogen gas. In nature, alkali metals exist only in compounds.

> You can remember that alkali metals are Group 1 and alkaline earth metals are Group 2 because alkali comes before alkaline in alphabetical order.

Group 2A or alkaline earth metals are harder, more dense, and melt at higher temperatures than alkali metals. They form 2+ cations. They are less reactive than alkali metals. Heavier alkaline earth metals are more reactive than lighter alkaline earth metals.

All the 4A elements can form four covalent bonds with nonmetals. All but carbon can form two additional bonds with Lewis bases. Of the 4A elements, only carbon forms strong π-bonds to make *strong* double and even triple bonds.

Group 5A elements can form 3 covalent bonds. In addition, all 5A elements except nitrogen can form five covalent bonds by using their *d* orbitals. These elements can further bond with a Lewis base to form a sixth covalent bond. Nitrogen forms strong π-bonds to make double and triple bonds. Phosphorous can form only weak π-bonds to make double bonds. The other 5A elements cannot make π-bonds. Nitrogen can also form four covalent bonds by donating its lone pair of electrons to form a bond.

Group 6A elements are called the *chalcogens*. Oxygen and sulfur are the important chalcogens for the MCAT. Oxygen is the second most electronegative element. Oxygen is divalent and can form strong π-bonds to make double bonds. In nature, oxygen exists as O_2 (*dioxygen*) and O_3 (ozone). Oxygen typically reacts with metals to form metal oxides. Alkali metals form peroxides (Na_2O_2) and *super oxides* (KO_2) with oxygen. The most common form of pure sulfur is the yellow solid S_8. Metal sulfides, such as Na_2S, are the most common form of sulfur found in nature. Sulfur can form two, three, four, five or even six bonds. It has the ability to pi-bond making strong double bonds.

Granulated mineral sulfur

Phosphorus is a multivalent nonmetal of Group 5A and is commonly found in inorganic phosphate rocks.

The radioactively stable Group 7A elements (called halogens) are fluorine, chlorine, bromine, and iodine. Halogens are highly reactive. Fluorine and chlorine are diatomic gases at room temperature; bromine, a diatomic liquid; iodine, a diatomic solid. Halogens like to gain electrons. However, halogens other than fluorine can take on oxidation states as high as +7 when bonding to highly electronegative atoms like oxygen. When in compounds, fluorine always has an oxidation state of –1. This means that fluorine makes only one bond, while the other halogens can make more than one bond. Hydrogen combines with all the halogens to form gaseous hydrogen halides. The hydrogen halides are soluble in water forming the hydrohalic acids. Halogens react with metals to form ionic halides (example NaCl).

Noble gases are nonreactive. They are sometimes called the **inert gases**. Only the noble gas elements are normally found in nature as isolated atoms. They are all gases at room temperature.

The elements that tend to exist as diatomic molecules are hydrogen, oxygen, nitrogen, and the halogens. Typically, when these elements are discussed, it is assumed that they are in their diatomic form unless otherwise stated. In other words, the statement "nitrogen is nonreactive" refers to N_2 and not N.

Notice that the size of an atom has a significant effect on its chemistry. If we examine the smallest element in a Group, we can sometimes see deviations in its behavior due to its size. Small atoms have less room to stabilize charge by spreading it out. This makes them bond more strongly to water resulting in greater heats of hydration. Because beryllium in its ionic form is not large enough to stabilize its charge, it forms a covalent oxide, whereas other alkaline earth metals make ionic oxides. This means that BeO is amphoteric whereas other alkaline earth metal oxides are basic. Small atoms don't have d orbitals available to them for bond formation. Atoms without d orbitals cannot form more than four bonds. Oxygen typically forms two bonds, while the larger sulfur can form up to six. On the other hand, the p orbitals on atoms that are too big don't overlap significantly, so large atoms can't easily form π-bonds. The second period elements carbon, nitrogen, and oxygen are small enough to form strong π-bonds while their larger third row family members form only weak π-bonds, if they form π-bonds at all.

Flasks containing bromine (Br_2) and iodine (I_2).

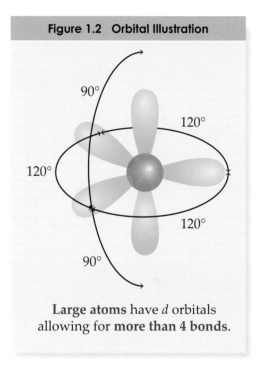

Figure 1.2 Orbital Illustration

Large atoms have d orbitals allowing for **more than 4 bonds.**

Figure 1.3 Pi (π) Bonds

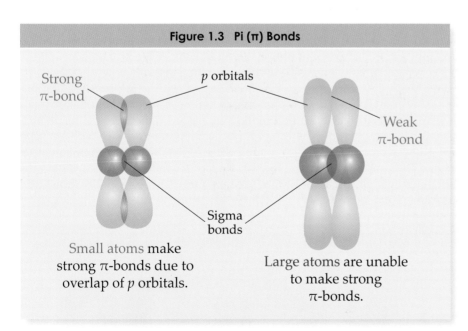

Strong π-bond

p orbitals

Weak π-bond

Sigma bonds

Small atoms **make** strong π-bonds due to overlap of p orbitals.

Large atoms **are unable** to make strong π-bonds.

This is a lot of detail! Knowing some of details of the characteristics of each group on the periodic table will be helpful, but is not required by the MCAT. Don't be too concerned with all this detail.

1.5 Ions

When an element has more or fewer electrons than protons, it becomes an ion. Positive ions are called cations; negative ions, anions. The representative elements make ions by forming the closest noble gas electron configuration. (Electron configurations are discussed later in this Lecture.) Metals form cations; nonmetals form anions. When the transition metals form ions, they lose electrons from their s-subshell first and then from their d-subshell. (Subshells will be discussed later in this lecture.) Below are some common ions formed by metals.

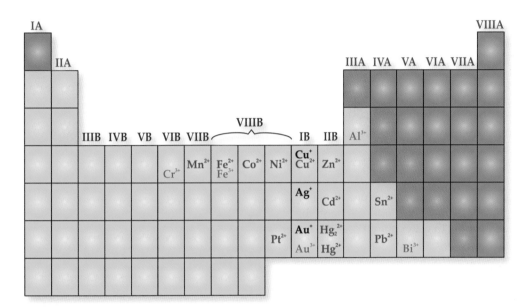

The periodic table to the left shows some of the more common ions formed by the transition metals. Notice that Group 1B makes three 1+ ions. There are five 3+ ions Cr^{3+}, Fe^{3+}, Au^{3+}, Al^{3+}, and Bi^{3+}. The other transition metal ions are 2+.

Cations are significantly smaller than their neutral atom counterparts. For instance, sodium's outermost electron is located by itself on an outer shell. When this outer electron is removed, the sodium cation is significantly smaller because the remaining electrons are located in inner shells. The reverse is true for anions. The additional electrons are added to an outer shell making the anion much larger than its neutral atom counter part. Isoelectronic ions (ions with the same number of electrons) tend to get smaller with increasing atomic number because more protons pull inward on the same number of electrons. The sizes of the oxygen, fluorine, sodium and magnesium ions in Figure 1.4 reflect this trend.

In Figure 1.4 the purple spheres represent the atoms oxygen, fluorine, neon, sodium, and magnesium. The pink and blue spheres show an isoelectronic series. The pink spheres represent the anions O^{2-} and F^-. The blue spheres represent the cations Na^+ and Mg^{2+}. With each ion, moving from left to right, a proton is added but no electron is added. With more protons pulling on the same number of electrons, the ions in an isoelectronic series become increasingly smaller. Figure 1.4 shows an isoelectronic series (a group of ions with the same number of electrons) consisting of oxygen, fluorine, sodium, and magnesium ions. (The size of the neon atom is provided for comparison). Each ion has a total of 10 electrons. The ions tend to get smaller with increasing atom number because more protons pull inward on the same number of electrons.

Figure 1.4   Relative Size in Isoelectronic Series

1.6 Periodic Trends

Coulomb's law, $F = kq_1q_2/r^2$, describes the electrostatic forces holding an electron to its nucleus. The distance between the electron and the nucleus is r. For q_1 we might plug in the positive charge of the nucleus, Z, and for q_2, the charge on an electron, e. This would work fine for hydrogen, where the lone electron feels 100% of the positive charge on the nucleus. However, in helium the first electron shields some of the nuclear charge from the second electron, so that the second electron doesn't *feel* the entire nuclear charge, Z. The amount of charge felt by the second electron is called the effective nuclear charge (Z_{eff}). In complete or perfect shielding, each electron added to an atom would be completely shielded from the attractive force of all the protons except for the last proton added, and the Z_{eff} would be 1 eV for each electron. Without shielding, each electron added would feel the full attractive force of all the protons in the nucleus, and the Z_{eff} would simply be equal to Z for each electron.

Figure 1.5 shows Z_{eff} values (given in electron volts) for the highest energy electron in each element through sodium. Notice the drop in Z_{eff} going from helium to lithium. This is because the last electron added to make lithium is added to an outer shell making the shielding effect strong. To form beryllium, an electron is added to the same shell and the shielding effect is not as great. To form boron, an electron is added to the 2p-subshell, a higher energy subshell, and shielding is stronger again. (We'll discuss subshells later in this lecture.) Going from nitrogen to oxygen, the next electron must share an orbital with one of the three p orbitals resulting in some shielding and a reduction in Z_{eff}. Moving from neon to sodium, the next electron is added to an entirely new shell, the 3s-subshell. This causes a strong reduction in Z_{eff}, but notice that the outermost electron in sodium still experiences a higher Z_{eff} than the outermost electron of the element immediately above it on the periodic table, lithium. Z_{eff} generally increases going left to right across the periodic table and going top to bottom down the periodic table.

You can see in Figure 1.5 that Z_{eff} for the outermost electron of helium is not 2, even though there are two protons in the helium nucleus. The Z_{eff} is the nuclear charge Z minus the average number of electrons between the nucleus and the electron in question. The Z_{eff}, and not Z, should be plugged in for q in Coulomb's law to find the force on the outermost electron. Note that the force is a function of both q (Z_{eff}) and r (the distance from the nucleus).

Must. Shield. Friends. From. Nuclear charge.

Figure 1.5   Graph of Z_{eff} from Hydrogen to Sodium

When considering the effect of Z_{eff}, consider the strength of Z_{eff} and the distance from the nucleus. The force pulling the electron inward goes up with Z_{eff} but goes down with distance according to Coulomb's law: $F = kq_1q_2/r^2$.

e−

Some atoms are better at sharing electrons than others.

With Z_{eff} in mind, we can make general predictions about the elements based upon their positions in the periodic table. These predictions can be summarized as five **periodic trends** concerning:

1. Atomic Radius
2. Ionization Energy
3. Electronegativity
4. Electron Affinity
5. Metallic Character

The **atomic radius** is the distance from the center of the nucleus to the outermost electron. Atomic radius corresponds to the size of the atom. Since the effective nuclear charge increases when moving from left to right on the periodic table, each additional electron is pulled more strongly toward the nucleus. The result is that atoms tend to get smaller when adding electrons across the periodic table. However, when dropping down from atom to atom within a group, each drop represents the addition of a new electron shell, and thus atoms tend to grow as we move down a group.

When an electron is more strongly attached to a nucleus, more energy is required to detach it. The energy necessary to detach an electron from a nucleus is called the **ionization energy**. The energy necessary to detach an electron from a neutral atom and form a +1 cation is called the first ionization energy. (By definition, the atom being ionized is gaseous.) The energy for the removal of a second electron from the same atom to form a +2 cation is called the **second ionization energy**. Third, fourth, fifth, and other ionization energies are named in the same manner. The second ionization energy is always much greater than the first because when one electron is removed, the effective nuclear charge on the other electrons increases. Ionization energy generally increases along the periodic table from left to right and from bottom to top. This trend is related to Z_{eff}. Moving across a period to the right, higher Z_{eff} values hold electrons more tightly to the nucleus requiring more energy to rip them off. Although Z_{eff} also increases when moving down the periodic table, the distance of the electron from the nucleus increases as well. From Coulomb's law, $F = kqq/r^2$, we see that though the electric force, F, holding the electron onto the nucleus goes up proportionally with q (recall that q in this case is Z_{eff}), the same force drops with the square of the distance from the nucleus, r. Less force means less energy required to remove the electron. The distance plays a more important role than the increased Z_{eff} and ionization energy increases moving up a group.

Recall from Organic Chemistry Lecture 1.6, that electrons are shared in a covalent bond. Recall also that these electrons may be shared unequally. **Electronegativity** is the tendency of an atom to attract these shared electrons. The most commonly used measurement of electronegativity is the *Pauling scale*, which ranges from a value of 0.79 for cesium to a value of 4.0 for fluorine. Like ionization energy, electronegativity tends to increase across a period from left to right and up the group. The reasoning for this is similar to the reasoning for the trend of ionization energy. Since noble gases tend not to make bonds, electronegativity values are undefined for the noble gases.

Electronegativity allows us to predict what type of bond will form between two atoms. Atoms with large electronegativity differences (1.4 on the Pauling scale as a rule of thumb) will form ionic bonds with each other. For example, metals and non-metals usually exhibit large electronegativity differences and form ionic bonds to each other. Atoms with more moderate differences in electronegativities will generally form polar covalent bonds. Atoms with very minor electronegativity differences will form nonpolar covalent bonds.

Electron affinity is the willingness of an atom to accept an additional electron. More precisely, it is the energy released when an electron is added to an isolated atom. The sign of electron affinity changes for different atoms because some atoms release energy when accepting an electron and some atoms require energy to force the electron to add. Just like electronegativity (and for the same reasons), electron affinity tends to increase on the periodic table from left to right and from bottom to top. (**Warning:** Many books use the exothermic value for electron affinity, which is the negative of the energy released. We can state this as follows: electron affinity is more exothermic to the right and up on the periodic table.) The noble gases do not follow this trend. Electron affinity values for the noble gases are endothermic.

Some atoms have a very high affinity for electrons.

The final important periodic trend, **metallic character**, tends to increase from right to left and top to bottom.

Li	Be											B	C	N	O	F	Ne
Na	Mg											Al	Si	P	S	Cl	Ar
K	Ca	Sc	Ti	V	Cr	Mn	Fe	Co	Ni	Cu	Zn	Ga	Ge	As	Se	Br	Kr
Rb	Sr	Y	Zr	Nb	Mo	Tc	Ru	Rh	Pd	Ag	Cd	In	Sn	Sb	Te	I	Xe
Cs	Ba	La	Hf	Ta	W	Re	Os	Ir	Pt	Au	Hg	Tl	Pb	Bi	Po	At	Rn
Fr	Ra	Ac	Unq	Unp	Unh	Uns	Uno	Une

H ... He

Energy of Ionization
Electron Affinity
Electronegativity

Atomic Radius
Metallic Character

E

An easy way to remember the 5 periodic trends is as follows: if it begins with an 'E', as shown here, then it increases going to the right and up; if it doesn't begin with an 'E', then it increases in the opposite direction. Be careful! This mnemonic requires that you think of 'ionization energy' as 'energy of ionization' so that it begins with an 'E'. Z_{eff} is not considered a periodic trend for this mnemonic. Keep in mind that the trends are just trends, and are violated frequently.

The noble gases do not follow the trends for electronegativity or for electron affinity.

Notice that hydrogen has moved to a more appropriate position.

1. Which of the following increases with increasing atomic number within a family on the periodic table?

   A. electronegativity
   B. electron affinity
   C. atomic radius
   D. ionization energy

2. Which of the following molecules has the greatest dipole moment?

   A. H_2
   B. O_2
   C. HF
   D. HBr

3. How many carbon atoms exist in 12 amu of ^{12}C?

   A. 1
   B. 12
   C. 6.02×10^{23}
   D. 7.22×10^{24}

4. Silicon has a silvery luster at room temperature. Silicon is brittle, and does not conduct heat or electricity well. Based on its position in the periodic table, silicon is most likely a:

   A. nonmetal
   B. metalloid
   C. metal
   D. chalcogen

5. Which of the following most likely represents the correct order of ion size from greatest to smallest?

   A. O^{2-}, F^-, Na^+, Mg^{2+}
   B. Mg^{2+}, Na^+, F^-, O^{2-}
   C. Na^+, Mg^{2+}, O^{2-}, F^-
   D. Mg^{2+}, Na^+, O^{2-}, F^-

6. A natural sample of carbon contains 99% of ^{12}C. How many moles of ^{12}C are likely to be found in a 48.5 gram sample of carbon obtained from nature?

   A. 1
   B. 4
   C. 12
   D. 49.5

7. In 1869 both Mendeleev and Meyer, working separately, published nearly identical classification schemes for the elements that were the forerunners of the modern periodic table. Although scientists of that time had no knowledge of atomic numbers, both schemes ordered the elements in nearly correct order from lowest to highest atomic number. Which of the following is the most likely explanation?

   A. Both scientists noticed similar patterns in chemical and physical behaviors among the elements.
   B. Atomic number generally increases with atomic weight and the scientist knew the atomic weights of the elements.
   C. The chemical identity was predictable from the number of valence electrons which was known at the time.
   D. Although the number of protons for each element was not known, the number of neutrons was.

8. Which of the following could be a stable molecular structure?

STOP.

SI Units and Prefixes

By international agreement, SI units are used for scientific measurements. "SI Units" stands for *Systeme International d'Unites*. SI units predominate on the MCAT.

There are seven base units in the SI system. The seven are listed in the table below:

Table 1.2 SI Base Units		
Physical Quantity	*Name of Unit*	*Abbreviation*
Mass	Kilogram	kg
Length	Meter	m
Time	Second	s
Electric current	Ampere	A
Temperature	Kelvin	K
Luminous intensity	Candela	cd
Amount of substance	Mole	mol

Other SI units can be derived from these seven, such as a newton: $1\ N = 1\ kg\ m\ s^{-2}$. There are other units still commonly in use that you may also see on the MCAT, such as atm or torr for pressure. All such units will have an SI counterpart that you should know. We will point this out as we come across new units.

1 atm = 760 torr

The SI system also employs standard prefixes for each unit. These prefixes are commonly seen on the MCAT. Table 1.3 lists these standard prefixes:

Table 1.3 Prefixes for SI Units		
Prefix	*Abbreviation*	*Meaning*
Mega-	M	10^6
Kilo-	k	10^3
Deci-	d	10^{-1}
Centi-	c	10^{-2}
Milli-	m	10^{-3}
Micro-	μ	10^{-6}
Nano-	n	10^{-9}
Pico-	p	10^{-12}
Femto-	f	10^{-15}

STOP! You were going to skip this page; weren't you? Memorize the SI units and the prefixes. They will help you in all the sciences.

1.8 | Molecules

Atoms can be held together by **bonds**. In one type of bond, two electrons are shared by two nuclei. This is called a **covalent bond**. The negatively charged electrons are pulled toward both positively charged nuclei by electrostatic forces. This 'tug of war' between the nuclei for the electrons holds the atoms together. If the nuclei come too close to each other, the positively charged nuclei repel each other. These repulsive and attractive forces achieve a balance to create a bond. Figure 1.6 compares the internuclear distance between two hydrogen atoms to their electrostatic potential energy level as a system. The **bond length** is defined as the point where the energy level is the lowest. Two atoms will only form a bond if they can lower their overall energy level by doing so. Nature tends to seek the lowest energy state.

If we separate the atoms by an infinite distance, the forces between them, and thus the energy, go to zero. The energy necessary to achieve a complete separation is given by the vertical distance on the graph between the energy at the bond length and zero. This is called the **bond dissociation energy** or **bond energy**. (Bond dissociation energy and bond energy are very closely related.)

Boron Hydride (BH$_3$)

Figure 1.6   Bond Length in Relation to Potential Energy for H$_2$

This is the bond dissociation energy, the energy needed to break the bond.

The electrons in this bond are very stable. They are at a very low energy state.

Internuclear distance (bond length) ⟶

> Notice from Figure 1.6 that energy is always required to break a bond. Conversely, no energy is ever released by breaking a bond. (Energy from ATP is released when the new bonds of ADP and iP are formed, and not when the ATP bonds are broken.)

A substance made from two or more elements in definite proportions is called a **compound**. In all pure compounds, the relative number of atoms of one element to another can be represented by a ratio of whole numbers. This ratio is called the **empirical formula**. In molecular compounds, groups of atoms form repeated, separate, and distinct units called **molecules**. In molecular compounds, the exact number of elemental atoms in each molecule can be represented by a **molecular formula**. The empirical formula for glucose is CH_2O. The molecular formula is $C_6H_{12}O_6$.

From the empirical formula and the atomic weight of each atom, we can find the percent composition of a compound by mass. To do this, multiply an atom's atomic weight by the number of atoms it contributes to the empirical formula. Divide your result by the weight of all the atoms in the empirical formula. This gives you the mass fraction of the compound represented by the atom. Now multiply this fraction by 100, and you have the percent composition by mass.

Figure 1.7 Percent by Mass of Carbon in Alanine

The percent mass of carbon
in glucose (empirical formula = CH_2O)
is found as follows:

$$\frac{\text{molecular weight of carbon}}{\text{molecular weight of } CH_2O} = \frac{12}{30} = 0.4$$

$$0.4 \times 100 = 40$$

Glucose is 40% carbon by mass.

To find the empirical formula from the percent mass composition, you assume that you have a 100 gram sample. Now the percent translates directly to grams. When you divide the grams by atomic weight, you get moles. Now divide by the greatest common factor. This is the number of atoms represented by each element in the empirical formula. In order to find the molecular formula, we would need more information.

Figure 1.8 Determining an Empirical Formula

If we are asked to find the empirical formula of a compound that is 6% hydrogen and 94% oxygen by mass, we do the following:

From a 100 gram sample:

$$\frac{6 \text{ g hydrogen}}{1 \text{ g/mol}} = 6 \text{ moles}$$

$$\frac{94 \text{ g oxygen}}{16 \text{ g/mol}} = 5.9 \text{ moles}$$

These must be whole numbers

$\frac{6}{6}$ is a one to one ratio

The empirical formula is HO

> This stuff should be easy for you. You have to know it backwards and forwards. It will definitely be on the MCAT, and it should be a couple of fast and easy points. Practice this until you know it well.

1.9 Naming Inorganic Compounds

The MCAT does not ask many questions that directly test your ability to name inorganic compounds. However, it is a good idea to be able to identify compounds when they are referred to.

Ionic compounds are named after their cation and anion. If the cation is metal and capable of having different charges (for example, copper can take on a charge of 1+ or 2+), then its name is followed by a Roman numeral in parentheses, as in copper(I) ion or copper(II) ion. An older method for naming cations that can take on different charges is to add –ic to the ending of the cation with the greater positive charge and –ous to the cation with the smaller charge, as in cupric (Cu^{2+}) and cuprous (Cu^+) ions. If the cation is made from a nonmetal, the cation name ends in –ium, such as ammonium (NH_4^+). A list of the names of important ions for the MCAT is provided in section 4.3 of this book.

This nomenclature stuff is boring. Just memorize this stuff once and for all and get it over with. Don't get too involved in the myriad little rules in nomenclature. Keep it simple because the MCAT sure will.

Monatomic anions and simple polyatomic anions are given the suffix –ide, such as hydride ion (H^-) or hydroxide ion (OH^-). Polyatomic anions with multiple oxygens end with the suffix –ite or –ate depending upon the relative number of oxygens. The more oxygenated species will use the –ate suffix, such as nitrite ion (NO_2^-) versus nitrate ion (NO_3^-). If there are more possibilities, the prefixes hypo- and per- are used to indicate fewest and most oxygens respectively, such as the hypochlorite (ClO^-), chlorite (ClO_2^-), chlorate (ClO_3^-), and perchlorate (ClO_4^-) ions. If an oxyanion has a hydrogen, the word hydrogen is added as in hydrogen carbonate ion (HCO_3^-). The old name would have been bicarbonate ion.

To name an ionic compound, just put the cation name in front of the anion name as in barium sulfate ($BaSO_4$) or sodium hydride (NaH).

For **binary molecular compounds** (compounds with only two elements), the name begins with the name of the element that is farthest to the left and lowest in the periodic table. The name of the second element is given the suffix –ide and a Greek number prefix is used on the each element if necessary (e.g., dinitrogen tetroxide, N_2O_4).

Acids are named based on their anions. If the name of the anion ends in –ide, the acid name starts with hydro- and ends in –ic, as in hydrosulfuric acid (H_2S). If the acid is an oxyacid, the ending –ic is used for the species with more oxygens and –ous for the species with fewer oxygens, as in sulfuric acid (H_2SO_4) and sulfurous acid (H_2SO_3).

Notes:

1.10 Chemical Reactions and Equations

When a compound undergoes a reaction and maintains its molecular structure and thus its identity, the reaction is called a physical reaction. Melting, evaporation, dissolution, and rotation of polarized light are some examples of physical reactions. When a compound undergoes a reaction and changes its molecular structure to form a new compound, the reaction is called a chemical reaction. Combustion, metathesis, and redox are examples of chemical reactions. Chemical reactions can be represented by a chemical equation with the molecular formulae of the reactants on the left and the products on the right.

$$CH_4 + 2O_2 \rightarrow CO_2 + 2H_2O$$

Notice that there is a conservation of atoms from the left to the right side of the equation. In other words, there is the same number of oxygen, hydrogen, and carbon atoms on the right as on the left. This means the equation is balanced. On the MCAT, if the answer is given in equation form, the correct answer will be a balanced equation unless specifically indicated to the contrary.

In the previous equation, O_2 is preceded by a coefficient of two. A coefficient of one is assumed for all molecules not preceded by a coefficient. Methane, then, has a coefficient of one. These coefficients indicate the relative number of molecules. They represent the number of single molecules, moles of molecules, dozens of molecules or any other quantity. They do not represent the mass, the number of grams, or kilograms.

To say that a reaction **runs to completion** means that it moves to the right until the supply of at least one of the reactants is depleted. (Reactions often don't run to completion because they reach equilibrium first.) As indicated by the equation above, two moles of oxygen (O_2) are needed to burn one mole of methane (CH_4). If we were to react four moles of methane with six moles of oxygen, and the reaction ran to completion, we would be left with 1 mole of methane. This is because, from the two to one ratio in the equation, six moles of oxygen are only enough to burn three moles of methane. Since we would run out of oxygen first, oxygen is our **limiting reagent**. Notice that the limiting reagent is not necessarily the reactant of which there is the least; it is the reactant that would be completely used up if the reaction were to run to completion. Also from the balanced equation, the one to one ratio of methane to carbon dioxide and the two to one ratio of methane to water, tells us that burning three moles of methane produces three moles of carbon dioxide and six moles of water.

Potassium reacting with water. Potassium (K) is a highly reactive metallic element of group one of the periodic table. It reacts with water to produce soluble potassium hydroxide (KOH) and hydrogen gas (H_2). The reaction produces enough heat to ignite.

An unbalanced equation is a wrong answer unless specifically asked for. By the way, know the difference between a physical and chemical reaction.

Figure 1.9 Limiting Reactant

$$CH_4 \quad + \quad 2O_2 \quad \rightarrow \quad CO_2 \quad + \quad 2H_2O$$

	CH₄	2O₂	CO₂	2H₂O
Starting amount	4 moles	6 moles	0 moles	0 moles
Amounts used up	3 moles	6 moles	0 moles	0 moles
= Ending amounts	1 mole	0 moles	3 moles	6 moles

The amounts that react must follow the stoichiometry of the reaction.

1 mole remains since all 6 moles of O_2 are used to react the first 3 moles of CH_4.

No O_2 is left to react with the last mole of CH_4. O_2 is the limiting reactant.

If you don't understand where the numbers came from in the table, take another look. You should understand this for the MCAT.

1.11 Chemical Yield

MCAT would probably give you the equation for the percent yield. Just understand the concept.

The amount of product produced when a reaction runs to completion is called the **theoretical yield**. The amount of actual product after a real experiment is the actual yield. As mentioned above, reactions often don't run to completion, and sometimes there are competing reactions that reduce the actual yield. Actual yield divided by the theoretical yield, times 100, gives the **percent yield**.

$$\frac{\text{Actual yield}}{\text{Theoretical yield}} \times 100 = \text{Percent yield}$$

1.12 Fundamental Reaction Types

Nothing to do here but memorize these reaction types in case MCAT asks one question requiring you to identify which type. It won't be worth more than one question on an MCAT.

Reactions can be categorized into types. The following lists four reaction types using hypothetical elements or molecules A, B, C, and D.

Combination: $A + B \rightarrow C$

Decomposition: $C \rightarrow A + B$

Single Displacement: $A + BC \rightarrow B + AC$ (also called single replacement)

Double Displacement: $AB + CD \rightarrow AD + CB$ (also called double replacement or metathesis)

Some other important reaction types shown in Table 1.4 are redox, combustion, Brønsted-Lowry acid-base, and Lewis acid-base. We will cover these types later in this book. Reaction types are not mutually exclusive, so one reaction can fall into more than one type.

Table 1.4 Other Reaction Types	
Reaction Type	*Example*
Redox	$2Au^{3+} + 3Zn \rightarrow 2Au + 3Zn^{2+}$
Combustion	$C_6H_{12} + 9O_2 \rightarrow 6CO_2 + 6H_2O$
Brønsted-Lowry acid-base	$HI + ROH \rightarrow I^- + ROH_2^+$
Lewis acid-base	$Ni^2 + 6NH_3 \rightarrow Ni(NH_3)_6^{2+}$

The decomposition reaction taking place is: $2Ag_2O \rightarrow 4Ag + O_2$. The oxides of unreactive metals, such as silver, are capable of being reduced to their metals by heat alone because less reactive metals do not tend to form stable compounds.

1.13 Reaction Symbols

The symbol 'Δ' usually means "change in" but 'Δ' above or below a reaction arrow indicates that heat is added. When a chemical is written above the reaction arrow, it is often a catalyst. Two arrows pointing in opposite directions (like this '⇌') indicate a reaction that can reach equilibrium. If one arrow is longer than the other, the equilibrium favors the side to which the long arrow points. A single arrow pointing in both directions (like this '↔') indicates resonance structures. Square brackets [ ] around an atom, molecule, or ion indicate concentration. The naught symbol '°' indicates standard state conditions.

1.14 Bonding in Solids

Solids can be *crystalline* or *amorphous*. A crystal has a sharp melting point and a characteristic shape with a well ordered structure of repeating units which can be atoms, molecules or ions. A crystal is classified as *ionic, network covalent, metallic,* or *molecular* depending upon the nature of the chemical bonding and the intermolecular forces in the crystal. Ionic crystals consist of oppositely charged ions held together by electrostatic forces. Salts are ionic crystals. Metallic crystals are single metal atoms bonded together by delocalized electrons. These delocalized electrons allow metallic crystals to efficiently conduct heat and electricity. They also make metallic crystals malleable and ductile. Network covalent crystals consist of an infinite network of atoms held together by polar and nonpolar bonds. Diamond and crystal SiO_2 are common examples of network covalent crystals. It is not possible to identify individual molecules in ionic, metallic, and network covalent crystals. Molecular crystals are composed of individual molecules held together by intermolecular bonds. Ice is an example of a molecular crystal.

An amorphous solid has no characteristic shape and melts over a temperature range. Glass (SiO_2) is an amorphous solid usually with some impurities added to lower the melting point. Some substances are capable of forming both crystalline and amorphous solids.

Polymers are solids with repeated structural units. They consist of individual molecules, but each molecule may be very large. They can be crystalline or amorphous. Generally, rapid cooling of liquid polymers results in amorphous solids and slow cooling results in crystalline solids. There are many polymers found in living systems. Examples of biopolymers are DNA, glycogen, and protein.

Candle wax is an amorphous solid.

Amethyst is a crystalline solid.

> The MCAT does not directly test your knowledge of the structure of solids beyond ionic and molecular solids; however, it is good to at least be aware that atoms can form substances in many ways. Molecular solids are actually less common than other types of solids. There has been an MCAT passage on this topic.

14. Name the following compound: $Cu(ClO_4)_2$.

   A. copper(I) chlorate
   B. copper(II) perchlorite
   C. copper(II) chlorate
   D. copper(II) perchlorate

Questions 9 through 16 are **NOT** based on a descriptive passage.

9. What is the empirical formula of a neutral compound containing 58.6% oxygen, 39% sulfur, 2.4% hydrogen by mass?

   A. HSO_3^-
   B. HSO_4^-
   C. H_2SO_3
   D. H_2SO_4

15. Polyethylene is a flexible plastic with many industrial uses. The synthesis of polyethylene is a radical reaction that follows the equation:

$$nCH_2 = CH_2 \rightarrow (CH_2CH_2)_n$$

   Polyethylene is a(n):

   A. molecular solid.
   B. polymer.
   C. ionic solid.
   D. network solid.

10. Silica is a network solid of silicon and oxygen atoms. The empirical formula for silica is SiO_2. In silica, to how many oxygen atoms is each silicon bonded?

   A. 1
   B. 2
   C. 3
   D. 4

16. What type of reaction is shown below?

$$2Mg(s) + O_2 \rightarrow 2MgO(s)$$

   A. combination
   B. single replacement
   C. metathesis
   D. decomposition

11. What is the percent by mass of carbon in CO_2?

   A. 12%
   B. 27%
   C. 33%
   D. 44%

12. Sulfur dioxide oxidizes in the presence of O_2 gas as per the reaction:

$$2SO_2(g) + O_2(g) \rightarrow 2SO_3(g)$$

   Approximately how many grams of sulfur trioxide are produced by the complete oxidation of 1 mole of sulfur dioxide?

   A. 1 g
   B. 2 g
   C. 80 g
   D. 160 g

13. When gaseous ammonia is passed over solid copper(II) oxide at high temperatures, nitrogen gas is formed.

$$2NH_3(g) + 3CuO(s) \rightarrow N_2(g) + 3Cu(s) + 3H_2O(g)$$

   What is the limiting reagent when 34 grams of ammonia form 26 grams of nitrogen in a reaction that runs to completion?

   A. NH_3
   B. CuO
   C. N_2
   D. Cu

1.15 Quantum Mechanics

You can only move in discrete units.

The MCAT requires a small amount of knowledge concerning quantum mechanics. Everything that you'll need to know is in this Lecture. Quantum mechanics basically says that elementary particles can only gain or lose energy and certain other quantities in discrete units. This is analogous to walking up stairs as opposed to walking up a ramp. If each stairstep is one foot, you can only raise or lower yourself by increments of one foot on the stairs, while on the ramp you can move along until you are raised one half foot or any other fraction of a foot. In quantum mechanics these 'steps' are discrete units of energy. Each 'step' or energy unit is so small that the overall change in energy is insignificant when working in classical physics. Thus quantum mechanic effects are generally only important when dealing with elementary particles.

1.16 Quantum Numbers

A set of four quantum numbers is the address or ID number for an electron in a given atom. The **Pauli Exclusion Principle** states that no two electrons in the same atom can have the same four quantum numbers.

The first quantum number is the **principle quantum number**, n. It designates the shell level for the electron.

The second quantum number is the **azimuthal quantum number**, ℓ. It designates the **subshell**. $\ell = 0$ is the s-subshell, $\ell = 1$ is the p-subshell, $\ell = 2$ is the d-subshell, and $\ell = 3$ is the f-subshell.

The third quantum number is the **magnetic quantum number**, m_ℓ. The magnetic quantum number designates the precise orbital of a given subshell. Each subshell will have orbitals with magnetic quantum numbers from $-\ell$ to $+\ell$. For instance, within the p-subshell ($\ell = 1$), there are three magnetic quantum numbers: -1, 0, and 1. Of these, one designates the p_x-orbital, one the p_y-orbital, and one the p_z-orbital.

The fourth quantum number is the **electron spin quantum number**, m_s. The electron spin quantum number can have values of $-\frac{1}{2}$ or $+\frac{1}{2}$. This final quantum number is used to distinguish the two electrons that may occupy the same orbital, since those electrons will have the same first three quantum numbers.

The number of total orbitals within a shell is equal to n^2. Solving for the number of orbitals for each shell gives 1, 4, 9, 16… Since there are two electrons in each orbital, the number of elements in the periods of the periodic table is 2, 8, 18, and 32.

Let's summarize: The first quantum number is the shell. It corresponds roughly to the energy level of the electrons within that shell. The second quantum number is the subshell. It gives the shape. You need to recognize the shape of s- and p-orbitals. The third quantum number is the specific orbital within a subshell. The fourth quantum number distinguishes between two electrons in the same orbital; one is spin +1/2 and the other is spin −1/2.

Table 1.5 Quantum Numbers				
Number	Name	Symbol	Value	Character
1st	principle	n	n	shell (energy level)
2nd	azimuthal	ℓ	from zero to n-1	subshell (shape: s, p, d, or f)
3rd	magnetic	m_ℓ	between ℓ and $-\ell$	orbital (3D orientation: p_x, p_y, p_z)
4th	spin	m_s	$\frac{1}{2}$ or $-\frac{1}{2}$	spin ($\uparrow\downarrow$)

1.17 The Heisenberg Uncertainty Principle

The **Heisenberg Uncertainty Principle** arises from the dual nature (wave-particle) of matter. It states that there exists an inherent uncertainty in the product of the position of a particle and its momentum, and that this uncertainty is on the order of Planck's constant.

$$\Delta x \Delta p \approx h$$

Here's the story with the Heisenberg uncertainty principle: the more we know about the momentum of any particle, the less we can know about the position. The amount of uncertainty is very small; on the order of Planck's constant (6.63×10^{-34} J s). There are other quantities besides position and momentum to which the uncertainty principle applies, but position and momentum is the pair that you are likely to need to know for the MCAT.

1.18 Energy Level of Electrons

Figure 1.10 S and P Orbitals

1s   2s   3s

2p_x

2p_y

2p_z

The **Aufbau principle** states that with each new proton added to create a new element, the new electron that is also added will occupy the lowest energy level that is available to it. Nature typically prefers a lower energy state. All other things being equal, the lower the energy state of a system, the more stable the system. Thus, electrons look for an available orbital in the lowest energy level whenever they add to an atom. The orbital with the lowest energy will be contained in the subshell with the lowest energy.

For the representative elements the **shell** level of the most recently added electrons is given by period in the periodic table. For instance, the most recently added electron of F is in shell 2 and the most recently added electron for Sr is in shell 5. For transition metals the shell of the most recently added electron lags one behind the period, and for the lanthanides and actinides lags two behind the period. For example, the most recently added electron of Os is in shell 5 and the most recently added electron for Ce is in shell 4.

The **subshells** are the orbital shapes with which we are familiar such as s, p, d, and f. Each subshell has a peculiar shape to its orbitals. The shapes are based on probability functions of the position of the electron. There is a 90% chance of finding the electron somewhere inside the given shape. You should recognize the shapes of the orbitals in the s- and p-subshells (Figure 1.10). By looking at the periodic table, we can tell when each type of subshell is filling. The s-subshells are filling in groups 1 and 2, the p-subshells are filling in groups 13–18, the d-subshells are filling in groups 3–12, and the f-subshells are filling in the lanthanide and actinide series.

We can, therefore, assign a shell and subshell to the most recently added electron for any element simply by looking at the periodic table. For example, the most recently added electron in P is in the 3p energy level; for Ru it is in the 4d energy level; for K it is in the 4s energy level.

Valence electrons, the electrons which contribute most to an element's chemical properties, are located in the outermost shell of an atom. Typically, but not always, only electrons from the *s*- and *p*-subshells are considered valence electrons.

The energy level rises as the electrons move further from the nucleus. To see why, we must consider the attractive force between the negatively charged electrons and the positively charged nucleus. Because the force is attractive, we must do work to separate them; we apply a force over a distance. Work is the transfer of energy into or out of a system. In this case, our system is the electron and the nucleus. We are doing work on the system, so we are transferring energy into the system. This energy shows up as increased electrostatic potential energy. Like the energy between bonding atoms, the energy between the electron and the nucleus increases from a negative number to zero as the electron moves to an infinite distance away from the nucleus.

If, for a given atom, we list the shells and the subshells in order from lowest to highest energy level, and we add a superscript to show the number of electrons in each subshell, we have the **electron configuration** of that atom. (Electron configurations do not have to be from lowest to highest energy subshells, but they usually are.) Electron configurations for several atoms are given below:

$$Na => 1s^2\, 2s^2\, 2p^6\, 3s^1$$
$$Ar => 1s^2\, 2s^2\, 2p^6\, 3s^2\, 3p^6$$
$$Fe => 1s^2\, 2s^2\, 2p^6\, 3s^2\, 3p^6\, 4s^2\, 3d^6$$
$$Br => 1s^2\, 2s^2\, 2p^6\, 3s^2\, 3p^6\, 4s^2\, 3d^{10}\, 4p^5$$

An abbreviated electron configuration can be written by using the configuration of the next smallest noble gas as follows:

$$Na => [Ne]\, 3s^1$$
$$Ar => [Ar]$$
$$Fe => [Ar]\, 4s^2\, 3d^6 \text{ (sometimes written } [Ar]\, 3d^6\, 4s^2)$$
$$Br => [Ar]\, 4s^2\, 3d^{10}\, 4p^5$$

Above are the electron configurations for atoms whose electrons are all at their lowest energy levels. This is called the **ground state**. Electron configurations can also be given for ions and atoms with excited electrons:

$$Na^+ => 1s^2\, 2s^2\, 2p^6 \text{ or } [Ne]$$
$$Fe^{3+} => [Ar]\, 3d^5$$
$$Br^- => [Ar]\, 4s^2\, 3d^{10}\, 4p^6 \text{ or } [Kr]$$
$$Be_{\text{with an excited electron}} => 1s^2\, 2s^1\, 2p^1$$

A simple trick to find the relative energies of the subshells is to use this table. The chart grows like stair-steps. An arrow is drawn down each diagonal as shown. If we follow the arrows as they go down the steps, they show us the order of increasing energy for the subshells. Notice that the energy levels are not exactly in numerical order. For example, the 4s-subshell is at a lower energy level than the 3d.

Be certain that the total number of electrons in your electron configuration equals the total number of electrons in the atom. Notice that for the ions of the representative elements, electron configuration resembles that of a noble gas. The electron configurations of the transition metal ions are not the same as the nearest noble gas. As noted before, for transition metals, ions are formed by losing electrons from the subshell with the highest principle quantum number first. Something else to know about transition metals is that their electron configurations aren't always that easy to predict. For instance, in the fourth period, the electron configurations of Cr and Cu have only one electron in the 4s orbital:

$$Cu => [Ar]\ 4s^1\ 3d^{10}$$

This is because the 4s- and 3d- orbitals of these atoms are degenerate (at the same energy level). You don't have to memorize the electron configuration of each transition metal. Just be aware that they don't always follow the table given above, due to degenerate orbitals.

Also, notice that an electron can momentarily (for a matter of microseconds) absorb energy and jump to a higher energy level creating an atom in an excited state.

Figure 1.11   Orbital Diagrams

Hydrogen $\underset{1s}{\uparrow}$ $\underset{2s}{\rule{1em}{0.4pt}}$ $\underset{2p_x}{\rule{1em}{0.4pt}}\ \underset{2p_y}{\rule{1em}{0.4pt}}\ \underset{2p_z}{\rule{1em}{0.4pt}}$

Helium $\underset{1s}{\uparrow\downarrow}$ $\underset{2s}{\rule{1em}{0.4pt}}$ $\underset{2p_x}{\rule{1em}{0.4pt}}\ \underset{2p_y}{\rule{1em}{0.4pt}}\ \underset{2p_z}{\rule{1em}{0.4pt}}$

Lithium $\underset{1s}{\uparrow\downarrow}$ $\underset{2s}{\uparrow}$ $\underset{2p_x}{\rule{1em}{0.4pt}}\ \underset{2p_y}{\rule{1em}{0.4pt}}\ \underset{2p_z}{\rule{1em}{0.4pt}}$

Beryllium $\underset{1s}{\uparrow\downarrow}$ $\underset{2s}{\uparrow\downarrow}$ $\underset{2p_x}{\rule{1em}{0.4pt}}\ \underset{2p_y}{\rule{1em}{0.4pt}}\ \underset{2p_z}{\rule{1em}{0.4pt}}$

Boron $\underset{1s}{\uparrow\downarrow}$ $\underset{2s}{\uparrow\downarrow}$ $\underset{2p_x}{\uparrow}\ \underset{2p_y}{\rule{1em}{0.4pt}}\ \underset{2p_z}{\rule{1em}{0.4pt}}$

Carbon $\underset{1s}{\uparrow\downarrow}$ $\underset{2s}{\uparrow\downarrow}$ $\underset{2p_x}{\uparrow}\ \underset{2p_y}{\uparrow}\ \underset{2p_z}{\rule{1em}{0.4pt}}$

Nitrogen $\underset{1s}{\uparrow\downarrow}$ $\underset{2s}{\uparrow\downarrow}$ $\underset{2p_x}{\uparrow}\ \underset{2p_y}{\uparrow}\ \underset{2p_z}{\uparrow}$

Oxygen $\underset{1s}{\uparrow\downarrow}$ $\underset{2s}{\uparrow\downarrow}$ $\underset{2p_x}{\uparrow\downarrow}\ \underset{2p_y}{\uparrow}\ \underset{2p_z}{\uparrow}$

Like charges repel each other. If we considered the energy of two particles with like charges, we would find that as the particles near each other, the mutual repulsion creates an increase in potential energy. This is the case when electrons approach each other. It explains why only two electrons can fit into one orbital. It also helps explain Hund's rule: electrons will not fill any orbital in the same subshell until all orbitals in that subshell contain at least one electron, and the unpaired electrons will have parallel spins. Hund's rule can be represented graphically as shown in Figure 1.11. Electrons are represented by vertical arrows. Upward arrows represent electrons with positive spin, and downward arrows represent electrons with negative spin. When going from boron to carbon, the added electron has a choice of sharing the $2p_x$ orbital or taking the $2p_y$ orbital for itself. **Hund's rule** says that the electron prefers to have its own orbital when such an orbital is available at the same energy level.

Notes:

Max Planck is considered the father of quantum mechanics. Planck's quantum theory demonstrates that electromagnetic energy is quantized (i.e. it comes only in discrete units related to the wave frequency). In other words, if we transfer energy from one point to another via an electromagnetic wave, and we wish to increase the amount of energy that we are transferring without changing the frequency, we can only change the energy in discrete increments given by:

$$\Delta E = hf$$

where h is Planck's constant (6.6×10^{-34} J s).

Einstein showed that if we considered light as a particle phenomenon with each particle as a photon, the energy of a single photon is given by the same equation: $E_{photon} = hf$. Neils Bohr applied the quantized energy theory to create an electron ladder model for hydrogen with each rung representing an allowed energy level for the electron. His model explained the line spectra for hydrogen but failed for atoms with more than one electron. *Louis de Broglie* then showed that electrons and other moving masses exhibit wave characteristics

$$\lambda = \frac{h}{mv}$$

that follow the equation:

The energy levels of electrons are quantized as well. The possible energy levels of an electron can be represented as an energy ladder. Each energy level is analogous to a rung on a ladder or the spheres shown in Figure 1.12. The electrons may occupy any rung, but do not occupy the space between rungs because this space represents forbidden energy levels.

When an electron falls from a higher energy rung to a lower energy rung, energy is released from the atom in the form of a photon. The photon must have a frequency which corresponds to the change in energy of the electron as per $\Delta E = hf$. Of course the reverse is also true. If a photon collides with an electron, it can only bump that electron to another energy level rung and not between energy level rungs. If the photon doesn't have enough energy to bump the electron to the next rung, the electron will not move from its present

Notes:

Figure 1.12 Photoelectric Effect

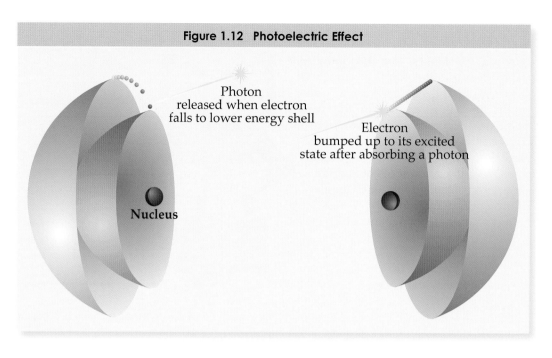

Photon
released when electron
falls to lower energy shell

Electron
bumped up to its excited
state after absorbing a photon

Nucleus

rung and the photon will be reflected away.

With the **photoelectric effect** Einstein demonstrated this one-to-one, photon to electron collision. He showed that the one-to-one collision proved that light was made up of particles. Einstein's reasoning went as follows: Light shining on a metal may cause the emission of electrons (sometimes called *photoelectrons* in the photoelectric effect). Since the energy of a wave is proportional to its intensity, we would expect that when the intensity of light shining on a metal is increased by increasing the number of photons, the kinetic energy of an emitted electron would increase accordingly. This is not the case. Instead, the kinetic energy of the electrons increases only when intensity is increased by increasing the frequency of each photon. If the frequency is low enough, no electrons at all will be emitted regardless of the number of photons. This demonstrates that the electrons must be ejected by one-to-one photon-electron collisions and not by the combined energies of two or more photons. It also shows that if a single photon does not have sufficient energy, no electron will be emitted. The minimum amount of energy required to eject an electron is called the *work function*, Φ, of the metal. The kinetic energy of the ejected electron is given by the energy of the photon minus the work function ($K.E. = hf - \Phi$).

> Note that for the photoelectric effect, the kinetic energy of the electrons inceases only when the frequency is increased.

Early photoelectric cell. Photoelectric cells make use of an effect whereby metals emit electrons when exposed to light (photo-emissivity). A metal plate of either rubidium, potassium or sodium (the cathode) is enclosed in a vacuum and connected to the negative pole of a battery. A loop of wire (the anode) faces the plate. When exposed to light, electricity crosses the gap between the cathode and anode more easily, enabling the cell to produce impulses of electricity dependent on the intensity of the light falling on it.

1.19 Equation Summary

Equations	
Moles	$\text{moles} = \dfrac{\text{grams}}{\text{atomic or molecular weight}}$
Percent Yield	$\dfrac{\text{Actual yield}}{\text{Theoretical yield}} \times 100 = \text{Percent yield}$
Planck's Quantum Theory	$\Delta E = hf$

1.20 Terms You Need To Know

Terms		
6.022×10^{23}	Electronegativity	Mole (mol)
amu	Electron Configuration	Molecular Formula
Avogadro's Number	Electrons	Molecules
Atomic Number	Elements	Nonmetals
Atomic Radius	Empirical Formula	Nucleus
Atomic Weight	First Ionization Energy	Period
Atoms	Ground State	Periodic Table
Bond Dissociation Energy	Groups or Families	Periodic Trends
	Hund's Rule	Photoelectric Effect
Bond Energy	Inert Gases	Protons
Bond Length	Ionization Energy	Second Ionization Energy
Bonds	Isotopes	
Compound	Mass Number	Shell
Covalent Bond	Metallic Character	Shielding
Effective Nuclear Charge (Z_{eff})	Metalloids	Subshells
	Metals	Transition Metals
Electron Affinity	Molar Mass (MM or M)	Valence Electrons

17. Which of the following species has an unpaired electron in its ground-state electronic configuration?

    A. Ne
    B. Ca^+
    C. Na^+
    D. O^{2-}

18. What is the electron configuration of chromium?

    A. $[Ar]\ 3d^6$
    B. $[Ar]\ 4s^1\ 3d^5$
    C. $[Ar]\ 4s^2\ 3d^3$
    D. $[Ar]\ 4s^2\ 4p^4$

19. In reference to the photoelectric effect, which of the following will increase the kinetic energy of a photoelectron?

    A. Increasing the work function
    B. Increasing the frequency of the incident light
    C. Increasing the number of photons in the incident light
    D. Increasing the mass of photons in the incident light

20. When an electron moves from a $2p$ to a $3s$ orbital, the atom containing that electron:

    A. becomes a new isotope.
    B. becomes a new element.
    C. absorbs energy.
    D. releases energy.

21. Compared to an electron with a principal quantum number of 1, an electron with a principal quantum number of 2 will have:

    A. a lower energy.
    B. a higher energy.
    C. a negative spin.
    D. a positive spin.

22. Which of the following best explains why sulfur can make more bonds than oxygen?

    A. Sulfur is more electronegative than oxygen.
    B. Oxygen is more electronegative than sulfur.
    C. Sulfur has $3d$ orbitals not available to oxygen.
    D. Sulfur has fewer valence electrons.

23. Hund's rule says that unpaired electrons in the same subshell:

    A. have opposite spins.
    B. have parallel spins.
    C. occupy the same orbital.
    D. cannot exist.

24. Aluminum has only one oxidation state, while chromium has several. Which of the following is the best explanation for this difference?

    A. Electrons in the d orbitals of Cr may or may not be used to form bonds.
    B. Electrons in the p orbitals of Cr may or may not be used to form bonds.
    C. Electrons in the d orbitals of Al may or may not be used to form bonds.
    D. Electrons in the p orbitals of Al may or may not be used to form bonds.

GASES, KINETICS AND CHEMICAL EQUILIBRIUM

2.1 Gases

A typical real gas is a loose collection of weakly attracted atoms or molecules moving rapidly in random directions. In a gas, the volume of the molecules accounts for about 0.1 percent of the total volume occupied by the gas. By comparison, molecules in a liquid account for about 70 percent of the total volume occupied by the liquid. 0°C and 1 atm is called **standard temperature and pressure (STP)**. At STP, the average distance between gas molecules is about 35 Å. This is small on a macroscopic scale, but typically amounts to over a dozen molecular diameters on the microscopic scale. For instance, an oxygen molecule is about 2.5 Å from end to end. Gas molecules move at tremendous speeds. At STP, the average speed of oxygen molecules is about 1,078 mph (481 m/s). The **mean free path** is the distance traveled by a gas molecule between collisions. The mean free path of oxygen at STP is about 1600 Å, about 1 ten thousandth of a millimeter. Moving such small distances at such high speed results in one oxygen molecule making about 2,500,000,000 collisions with other molecules each second. This explains why some chemical reactions can appear to occur instantaneously.

This is an optical image of the Crab Nebula also known as Messier 1, which consists mainly of hydrogen gas (H_2).

Gases will mix

Liquids will separate

Oil (nonpolar) and water (polar) mixture.

If a gas is a mixture of compounds, then unlike liquids, the mixture will be homogeneous regardless of polarity differences. For instance, liquid gasoline and liquid water don't mix because gasoline is nonpolar while water is polar; however, water and gasoline vapors form a homogeneous mixture.

Although polarity differences do not cause gases to separate, when temperatures are low enough gravity causes denser gases to settle beneath less dense gases. Cold CO_2 gas from a fire extinguisher is heavier than air and smothers a fire by settling over the fire and displacing the air upward. Hot air rises because it is less dense than cold air.

> Unlike liquids, all gases are miscible with each other; they mix regardless of polarity differences. However, given time and low temperatures, heavier gases tend to settle below lighter gases.

2.2 Kinetic Molecular Theory

To better understand the complex behavior of gases, scientists have theorized a model of an **ideal gas**. This model is called the **kinetic molecular theory**. In the kinetic molecular theory, an ideal gas lacks certain real gas characteristics. Ideal gas has the following four characteristics not shared by a real gas:

1. Gas molecules have zero volume;
2. Gas molecules exert no forces other than repulsive forces due to collisions;
3. Gas molecules make completely elastic collisions;
4. The average kinetic energy of gas molecules is directly proportional to the temperature of the gas.

Ideal gas obeys the **ideal gas law**:

$$PV = nRT$$

where P is the pressure in atmospheres, V is the volume in liters, n is the number of moles of gas, T is the temperature in Kelvin, and R is the universal gas constant (0.08206 L atm K^{-1} mol^{-1} or 8.314 J K^{-1} mol^{-1}). Special cases of the ideal gas law include: *Charles' law*: The volume of a gas is proportional to temperature at constant pressure; *Boyle's law*: The volume of a gas is inversely proportional to pressure at constant temperature; and *Avogadro's law*: The volume of a gas is proportional to the number of moles at constant temperature and pressure.

This balloon has been cooled from 300 Kelvin to 75 Kelvin using liquid nitrogen. The pressure remains approximately constant at 1 atm. According to Charles' law how many times smaller is the cold balloon?

Rather than memorizing Charles', Boyle's, and Avogadro's laws, you should have a good understanding of the ideal gas law. The equations associated with these laws have been left out purposely, so that you won't waste time memorizing them. The equations create confusion in the sense that they are true only within certain limitations. For instance, Charles' law requires constant pressure.

$PV = nRT$ will solve any problem that the other three laws might solve. By the way, you won't need to memorize the name of each law either.

Notice that there are four variables needed to define the state of a gas: P, V, n, and T. R is a constant, not a variable. Four variables in one equation can be confusing. For instance, it is possible to cool a gas by increasing the volume, even though the equation $PV = nRT$ indicates that temperature is directly proportional to volume. When a gas expands in a container, the gas does work on its surrounding by pushing outward on the walls of the container. The force on the walls times the distance that the walls expand is the work done by the gas. This work represents a transfer of energy from the gas to the surroundings. The energy comes from the kinetic energy of the gas molecules. Both the temperature and the pressure are related to the kinetic energy of the molecules. The pressure is related to the kinetic energy per volume, and the temperature is related to the average kinetic energy per mole. When the gas expands, the pressure decreases due to both the loss in kinetic energy and the increase in volume. The temperature decreases due to the loss in kinetic energy via work done. So, if the volume of a gas were doubled, and the kinetic energy remained the same, the pressure would be reduced by a factor of two. But if no heat were added, the kinetic energy would be reduced. If the kinetic energy were reduced as the volume doubles, the pressure would be reduced by more than a factor of two. Thus the temperature would also decrease to preserve the equality in $PV = nRT$.

Notice that the ideal gas law does not change for different gases behaving ideally. (Of course not, it's written for an ideal gas.) This means that all gases (behaving ideally) will have the same volume, if they have the same temperature, pressure, and number of molecules. At STP one mole of any gas (behaving ideally) will occupy the **standard molar volume of 22.4 liters**.

Thought Provoker

Roger is filling balloons with helium gas for a birthday party. He knows that the volume of his helium tank is 2L. How many moles of helium are in the tank if the pressure is 730 torr and the temperature is 25 degrees Celsius? (Assume all the helium is in a gaseous state)

Answer: See page 55

22.4 L	22.4 L	11.2 L
0°C (273 K)	0°C	0°C
1 mole	2 moles	2 moles
1 atm	2 atm	4 atm

You must recognize the standard molar volume and understand what it means. Learn to use this volume with the ideal gas law. For instance, 2 moles of gas at 0°C occupying 11.2 liters will have a pressure of 4 atm. To get this result, we start with the standard molar volume, 22.4 L, at STP. First, we double the number of moles, so, according to the ideal gas law, the pressure doubles. Second, we halve the volume, so pressure doubles again.

22.4 L
0°C
1 mole
1 atm

As well as pure gases, we can apply the kinetic molecular theory to mixtures of gases. In a mixture of gases, each gas contributes to the pressure in the same proportion as it contributes to the number of molecules of the gas. This makes sense, given the kinetic molecular theory, because molecules have no volume, no interactive forces other than collisions, and kinetic energy is conserved when they collide. Thus, each gas in a mixture essentially behaves as if it were in its container alone.

The amount of pressure contributed by any gas in a gaseous mixture is called the partial pressure of that gas. The **partial pressure** of a particular gas is the total pressure of the gaseous mixture times the mole fraction of the particular gas. The equation for the partial pressure is:

$$P_a = \chi_a P_{total}$$

where P_a is the partial pressure of gas 'a', and χ_a is the mole fraction of gas 'a'. (The mole fraction is the number of moles of gas 'a' divided by the total number of moles of gas in the sample.)

Dalton's law states that the total pressure exerted by a gaseous mixture is the sum of the partial pressures of each of its gases.

$$P_{total} = P_1 + P_2 + P_{3...}$$

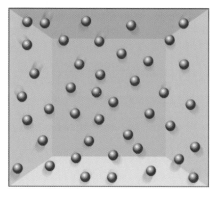

22.4 L
0°C
2 moles
2 atm

> Dalton's law is a good way to understand an ideal gas. Each gas behaves like it is in the container by itself so all the partial pressures added together equal the total pressure.

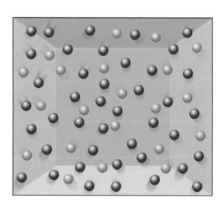

22.4 L
0°C
3 moles

$\chi_{green} = \frac{1}{3}$, $\chi_{blue} = \frac{2}{3}$
$P_{green} = 1$ atm
$P_{blue} = 2$ atm
$P_{total} = 3$ atm

Scuba divers during the last minutes of their decompression time after a deep dive.

From the ideal gas law, we can derive the following equation relating average translational kinetic energy and the temperature of a gas:

$$K.E._{avg} = \frac{3}{2}RT$$

where the average translational kinetic energy is found from the root-mean-square (rms) velocity. (rms velocity is the square root of the average of the squares of the molecular velocities. rms velocity is slightly greater than the average speed.) $K.E. = 3/2\ RT$ is valid for any fluid system, including liquids. Notice that the kinetic energy derived from this equation is the average kinetic energy for <u>one mole</u> of gas molecules at a given moment. It does not represent the energy of every gas molecule or perhaps even any single gas molecule at any given moment. A gas molecule chosen at random may have almost any kinetic energy associated with it.

> When you imagine a fluid warming up, you should visualize the fluid molecules moving faster.

Since the temperature dictates the average kinetic energy of the molecules in a gas, the gas molecules of each gas in any gaseous mixture must have the same average kinetic energy. For instance, the air we breathe is made up of approximately 21% O_2 and 79% N_2 by number. The molecules of O_2 and N_2 in a sample of air have the same average kinetic energy. However, since O_2 and N_2 have different masses, their molecules have different rms velocities. By setting their kinetic energies equal to each other, we can derive a relationship between their rms velocities. This relationship, which gives the ratio of the rms velocities of two gases in a homogeneous mixture, is called **Graham's law**:

> In a sample of gas, the kinetic energy of the molecules will vary from molecule to molecule, but there will be an average kinetic energy of the molecules that is proportional to the temperature and independent of the type of gas.

$$\frac{v_1}{v_2} = \frac{\sqrt{m_2}}{\sqrt{m_1}}$$

Where v_1 and v_2 are the rms velocities of the molecules of the respective gases and m_1 and m_2 are the masses of the molecules of the respective gases. Notice that the subscripts are inverted from one side of the equation to the other (i.e. the left side is 1 over 2, and the right side is 2 over 1).

Graham's law also tells us that the average speed of the molecules of a pure gas is inversely proportional to the square root of the mass of the gas molecules.

Interestingly, Graham's law gives information about the rates of two types of gaseous spreading: effusion and diffusion. **Effusion** is the spreading of a gas from high pressure to very low pressure through a 'pinhole'. (A 'pinhole' is defined as an opening much smaller than the average distance between the gas molecules.) Because molecules of a gas with higher rms velocity will experience more collisions with the walls of a container, the rate at which molecules from such a gas find the pinhole and go through is likely to be greater. In fact, Graham's law predicts the comparative rates of effusion for two gases at the same temperature. The ratio of the rates of effusion of two gases is equal to the inverse of the ratio of the square roots of their molecular weights and equal to the ratio of their rms velocities.

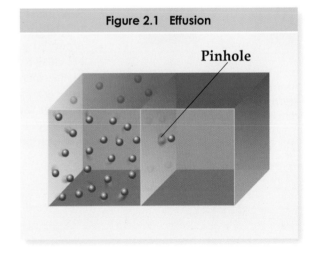

Figure 2.1 Effusion

Pinhole

$$\frac{\text{effusion rate}_1}{\text{effusion rate}_2} = \frac{\sqrt{M_2}}{\sqrt{M_1}}$$

where M_1 and M_2 are the molecular weights of the respective gases.

Diffusion is the spreading of one gas into another gas or into empty space. The ratio of the diffusion rates of two gases (acting ideally) is approximated by Graham's law. The diffusion rate is much slower than the rms velocity of the molecules because gas molecules collide with each other and with molecules of other gases as they diffuse. For example, if we wet two cotton balls, one with aqueous NH_3 and the other with aqueous HCl, and place them into opposite ends of a glass tube, gaseous NH_3 and HCl will diffuse toward each other through the air inside the tube. Where they meet, they will react to form NH_4Cl, which will precipitate as a white solid. Graham's law accurately predicts that NH_3 will travel 1.5 times further than HCl. However, any particular molecule is far more crooked than even those shown in the diagram. Recall that the mean free path of a gas molecule is on the order of a few hundred nanometers.

Figure 2.2   Diffusion

$$\frac{\text{Diffusion rate of } NH_3}{\text{Diffusion rate of HCl}} = \frac{\sqrt{M_{HCl}}}{\sqrt{M_{NH_3}}} = \sqrt{\frac{36.5}{17}} = 1.5$$

2.3   Real Gases

Real gases deviate from ideal behavior when their molecules are close together. When this happens, the volume of the molecules become significant compared to the volume around the molecules. Also, as can be seen by Coulomb's law ($F = kqq/r^2$), when molecules are close together, the electrostatic forces increase and become significant. High pressure pushes gas molecules together causing deviations from ideal behavior. Low temperatures cause gas molecules to settle close together also resulting in deviations from ideal behavior. Gases generally deviate from ideal behavior at pressures above ten atmospheres and temperatures near their boiling points. Substances that we typically think of as gases closely approximate ideal behavior.

Figure 2.3   Real gases

Ammonia (NH_3), left, reacting with hydrochloric acid (HCl), right. NH_3 diffuses at a faster rate than HCl.

You should be aware of how real gases deviate from ideal behavior. Van der Waals equation:

$$\left[P+\left(\frac{n^2 a}{V^2}\right)\right](V - nb) = nRT$$

approximates the real pressure and real volume of a gas, where a and b are constants for specific gases. The variable b is a measure of the actual volume occupied by a mole of gas. The variable a reflects the strength of intermolecular attractions. The values of a and b generally increase with the molecular mass and molecular complexity of a gas.

You do not need to know van der Waals equation for the MCAT. It is more important that you have a qualitative understanding of real gas deviations from ideal behavior. First, since molecules of a real gas do have volume, their volume must be added to the ideal volume. Thus:

Nonideal behavior

$$V_{real} > V_{ideal}$$

where V_{ideal} is calculated from $PV = nRT$.

Once again, be careful about the confusion with $PV = nRT$. It seems like increasing pressure also increases temperature, so how can ideal behavior deviations occur with either an increase in pressure or a decrease in temperature? The answer is that to create deviations in ideal behavior, we just want to move the molecules closer together; in other words, decrease the volume. We can decrease the volume by squeezing the molecules together with high pressure, or by lowering the temperature and letting the molecules settle close together. From $PV = nRT$, we see that volume decreases with either increasing pressure or decreasing temperature.

Second, molecules in a real gas do exhibit forces on each other, and those forces are attractive when the molecules are far apart. In a gas, repulsive forces are only significant during molecular collisions or near collisions. Since the predominant intermolecular forces in a gas are attractive, gas molecules are pulled inward toward the center of the gas, and slow before colliding with container walls. Having been slightly slowed, they strike the container wall with less force than predicted by the kinetic molecular theory. Thus a real gas exerts less pressure than predicted by the ideal gas law:

$$P_{real} < P_{ideal}$$

where P_{ideal} is calculated from $PV = nRT$.

Figure 2.4   Deviations from Ideal Gas Law

Positive deviation due mainly to molecular volume.

$\frac{PV}{RT}$

N_2 CH_4

H_2

1.0

P

Negative deviation due mainly to attractive intermolecular forces.

From $PV = nRT$, we expect PV/RT to equal one for one mole of ideal gas at any temperature and pressure. Since volume deviates positively from ideal behavior and pressure deviates negatively, if PV/RT is greater than one for one mole of gas, then the deviation due to molecular volume must be greater than the deviation due to the intermolecular forces. If PV/RT is less than one for one mole of gas, then the deviation due to intermolecular forces must be greater than the deviation due to molecular volume.

25. A 13 gram gaseous sample of an unknown hydrocarbon occupies a volume of 11.2 L at STP. What is the hydrocarbon?

    A. CH
    B. C_2H_4
    C. C_2H_2
    D. C_3H_3

26. If the density of a gas is given as ρ which of the following expressions represents the molecular weight of the gas?

    A. $P\rho/RT$
    B. $\rho RT/P$
    C. $nRT/P\rho$
    D. $P\rho/RT$

27. Ammonia burns in air to form nitrogen dioxide and water.

$$4NH_3(g) + 7O_2(g) \rightarrow 4NO_2(g) + 6H_2O(l)$$

If 8 moles of NH_3 are reacted with 14 moles of O_2 in a rigid container with an initial pressure of 11 atm, what is the partial pressure of NO_2 in the container when the reaction runs to completion? (Assume constant temperature.)

    A. 4 atm
    B. 6 atm
    C. 11 atm
    D. 12 atm

28. At moderately high pressures, the *PV/RT* ratio for one mole of methane gas is less than one. The most likely reason for this is:

    A. Methane gas behaves ideally at moderate pressures.
    B. The temperature must be very low.
    C. At such pressures, molecular volume causes a greater deviation to ideal behavior than intermolecular forces for methane.
    D. At such pressures, intermolecular forces cause a greater deviation to ideal behavior than molecular volume for methane.

29. A force is applied to a container of gas reducing its volume by half. The temperature of the gas:

    A. decreases.
    B. increases.
    C. remains constant.
    D. The temperature change depends upon the amount of force used.

30. Equal molar quantities of oxygen and hydrogen gas were placed in container *A* under high pressure. A small portion of the mixture was allowed to effuse for a very short time into the vacuum in container *B*. Which of the following is true concerning partial pressures of the gases at the end of the experiment?

    A. The partial pressure of hydrogen in container *A* is approximately four times as great as the partial pressure of oxygen in container *A*.
    B. The partial pressure of oxygen in container *A* is approximately four times as great as the partial pressure of hydrogen in container *A*.
    C. The partial pressure of hydrogen in container *B* is approximately four times as great as the partial pressure of oxygen in container *B*.
    D. The partial pressure of oxygen in container *B* is approximately four times as great as the partial pressure of hydrogen in container *B*.

31. HCl gas and NH_3 gas form NH_4Cl precipitate according to the following equation:

$$HCl(g) + NH_3(g) \rightarrow NH_4Cl(s)$$

When cotton balls are moistened with the aqueous solutions of the respective gases and inserted into either end of a glass tube, the gases diffuse toward the middle of the glass tube to form the precipitate. If a 10 cm glass tube is used, at what distance *x* will the precipitate form?

Cotton ball with NH_3 NH_4Cl precipitate   Cotton ball with HCl

    A. 1.5 cm
    B. 2.5 cm
    C. 3.0 cm
    D. 4.0 cm

32. At STP, one liter of which of the following gases contains the most molecules?

    A. H_2
    B. He
    C. N_2
    D. Each gas contains the same number of molecules at STP.

2.4 Chemical Kinetics

Chemical kinetics is the study of reaction mechanisms and rates. As of yet, there are no unifying principles of kinetics, which means kinetics is a complicated field with many opposing theories as to how reactions proceed. Additionally, the mathematics of kinetics is complicated and well beyond the scope of MCAT. MCAT will address kinetics only in its simplest form. Keep in mind that kinetics deals with the rate of a reaction typically as it moves toward equilibrium, while thermodynamics deals with the balance of reactants and products after they have achieved equilibrium. Kinetics tells us how fast equilibrium is achieved, while thermodynamics tells us what equilibrium looks like. The two disciplines are intricately related, but they should not be confused.

2.5 The Collision Theory

The **collision model** of reactions provides an enlightening method for visualizing chemical reactions. In order for a chemical reaction to occur, the reacting molecules must collide. However, for most reactions, the rate of a given reaction is found to be much lower than the frequency of collisions. This indicates that most collisions do not result in a reaction.

There are two requirements for a given collision to create new molecules in a reaction. First, the relative kinetic energies of the colliding molecules must reach a threshold energy called the **activation energy**. The relative kinetic energy refers to the kinetic energy due to relative velocity only. In other words, velocity in a direction away from another molecule decreases the relative kinetic energy of a collision. Second, the colliding molecules must have the proper spatial orientation.

Artwork made of a particle collision. Collisions like this take place in particle accelerators at high energies near the speed of light. The new particles produced in such collisions allow particles physicists to test their theories on the fundamental nature of matter.

Figure 2.5 Proper Energy, Proper Orientation

1 Impending collision

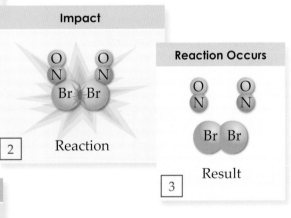

2 Reaction — Impact

3 Result — Reaction Occurs

Figure 2.6 Proper Energy, Wrong Orientation

1 Impending collision

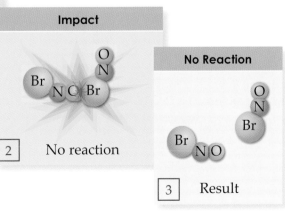

2 No reaction — Impact

3 Result — No Reaction

The product of the collision frequency z, the fraction of collisions having the effective spatial orientations p (called the *steric factor*), and the fraction of collisions having sufficient relative energy $e^{-E_a/RT}$ (where E_a is the activation energy) gives the rate constant k of a reaction. This relationship is called the *Arrhenius equation*:

$$k = zpe^{-E_a/RT}$$

(often written as $k = Ae^{-E_a/RT}$). The value of the rate constant depends upon pressure, catalysts, and temperature. Pressure dependence is typically negligible. Catalysts will be discussed later in this Lecture. The temperature dependence is seen in the Arrhenius equation. The rate constant generally doubles to triples with each increase of 10°C. Since the effect of temperature on E_a is negligible for most reactions, the fraction of collisions that have at least the activation energy ($e^{-E_a/RT}$) increases with the temperature. This, in turn, indicates that the rate constant k increases with increasing temperature for nearly all reactions. As demonstrated by the rate law (discussed later in this lecture), the rate constant is directly proportional to the rate of a reaction. The rate of a reaction increases with temperature mainly because more collisions with sufficient relative kinetic energy occur each second.

The temperature dependence of rate is demonstrated by the graph in Figure 2.6, which compares two samples of identical gaseous mixtures reacting at different temperatures. The area under any section of the curve represents the relative number of collisions in that energy range. Notice the area to the right of the activation energy is greater at higher temperature. (i.e. The blue area for the higher temperature reaction is much larger and even includes the striped area of the lower temperature reaction.) At higher temperature there are more collisions with enough energy to create a reaction. Notice that the energy of activation does not change with temperature. (Actually, E_a is temperature dependent, but for most reactions the dependence is extremely small, and, for the MCAT, E_a should be considered independent of temperature.)

Figure 2.7 Temperature Dependence in Relation to Rate

Reaction at lower temperature

Reaction at higher temperature

Relative number of collisions

Energy of collisions E_a

Thought Provoker

Hank is doing a chemistry experiment in his university lab. He puts a 3.0 g strip of magnesium in a 0.5 M solution of HCl:

$$Mg\,(s) + 2HCl\,(aq) \rightarrow MgCl_2\,(aq) + H_2\,(g)$$

The lab manual instructs him to perform the reaction many times, increasing the rate of reaction each time. What are some ways that Hank can increase his rate of reaction for his experiment?

Hint: (Use collision theory to explain why there would be a rate increase.)

Answer: See page 55.

2.6 Equations for Reaction Rates

For MCAT purposes we will consider only reactions occurring in gases and ideally dilute liquids at constant temperature. The rate of a reaction tells us how quickly the concentration of a reactant or product is changing. Rates are most often given in terms of molarity per second (mol L^{-1} s^{-1}). Factors affecting the rate of a reaction are temperature, pressure, and concentration of certain substances in the reacting system; however, pressure effects on reaction rates are usually small enough to be ignored.

Potassium Chlorate and Phosphorous mix to ignite a match.

The rate of a reaction can be viewed in terms of the change in concentration of any one of the reacting participants. Consider the following elementary reaction where the lower case letters are the stoichiometric coefficients of the balanced equation:

$$a\mathbf{A} + b\mathbf{B} \rightarrow c\mathbf{C} + d\mathbf{D}$$

An *elementary reaction* is a reaction that occurs in a single step. The stoichiometric coefficients of an elementary equation give the *molecularity* of the reaction. The molecularity is the number of molecules colliding at one time to make a reaction. There are three possible molecularities: *unimolecular*, *bimolecular*, and *termolecular*. Since the reaction above is elementary, its molecularity is given by $a + b$. Chemical equations often represent multistep reactions called complex or composite reactions. There is no way to distinguish an elementary reaction from a complex reaction by inspection of the chemical equation. On the MCAT, the only way to know if a reaction is elementary is if you are told that it is elementary.

> In an elementary reaction, the coefficient tells you how many molecules participate in a reaction producing collision.

The average reaction rate for any brief time interval t during the above reaction is:

$$rate = -\frac{1}{a}\frac{\Delta[A]}{t} = -\frac{1}{b}\frac{\Delta[B]}{t} = \frac{1}{c}\frac{\Delta[C]}{t} = \frac{1}{d}\frac{\Delta[D]}{t}$$

'Δ' means "change in". The negative signs indicate that the reactant concentrations are decreasing as the reaction moves forward. Although the rate equation above is strictly correct only for an elementary reaction, it is a good approximation for a multistep reaction if the concentration of any intermediates is kept low. **Intermediates** are species that are products of one reaction and reactants of a later reaction in a reaction chain. The concentration of intermediates is often very low because they are often unstable and react as quickly as they are formed.

> Don't confuse the rate constant with the rate of the reaction. They are proportional, but they are NOT identical.

Chemical reactions are reversible; as the products are formed, products begin to react to form the reactants. This reverse reaction complicates the study of kinetics. For the time being, we will consider only the forward reactions. If we consider only the forward reaction, we can write a **rate law** for the reaction $a\mathbf{A} + b\mathbf{B} \rightarrow c\mathbf{C} + d\mathbf{D}$ as:

$$rate_{\text{forward}} = k_f[\mathbf{A}]^{\alpha}[\mathbf{B}]^{\beta}$$

where k_f is the rate constant for the forward reaction. α and β are the **order of each respective reactant** and the sum $\alpha + \beta$ is the **overall order** of the reaction. If the reaction is elementary, $\alpha = a$ and $\beta = b$.

> **Warning:** Never assume that you can use the coefficients of the balanced equation in a rate law unless you know that the reaction is elementary.
>
> Also, since the rate law shown here is for a particular reaction, you should not memorize it. Instead, you should recognize its form and its relationship to an elementary reaction.

2.7 Determining the Rate Law by Experiment

Both the order of the reactants and the value of the rate constant must be determined through experiment. Finding the rate law on the MCAT is a relatively simple matter. Consider the hypothetical reaction:

$$2A + B + C \rightarrow 2D$$

In this case, we will assume that no reverse reaction occurs. We are given the following table with experimental data:

Table 2.1   Experimental Data

Trial	Initial Concentration of A (mol L^{-1})	Initial Concentration of B (mol L^{-1})	Initial Concentration of C (mol L^{-1})	Measured Initial Rate (mol L^{-1})
1	0.1	0.1	0.1	8.0×10^{-4}
2	0.2	0.1	0.1	1.6×10^{-3}
3	0.2	0.2	0.1	6.4×10^{-3}
4	0.1	0.1	0.4	8.0×10^{-4}

We can find the order of each reactant by comparing the rates between two trials in which only the concentration of one of the reactants is changed. For instance, comparing Trial 1 to Trial 2, the initial concentration of A is doubled and the concentrations of B and C remain the same. The reaction rate also doubles. Thus the rate of this reaction is directly proportional to the concentration of A. In the rate law, [A] receives an exponent of 1, and the reaction is considered first order with respect to reactant A.

Table 2.2   Comparison of Trial 1 and 2

Trial	Initial Concentration of A (mol L^{-1})	Initial Concentration of B (mol L^{-1})	Initial Concentration of C (mol L^{-1})	Measured Initial Rate (mol L^{-1})
1	0.1	0.1 Same	0.1 Same	8.0×10^{-4}
2	2x 0.2	0.1	0.1	1.6×10^{-3}

Increase
$2x = 2^1$

Comparing Trials 2 and 3 we find that when only the concentration of B is doubled, the reaction rate is quadrupled. This indicates that the rate is proportional to the square of the concentration of B. [B] receives a 2 for its exponent in the rate law and the reaction is second order with respect to B.

	Table 2.3 Comparison of Trial 2 and 3			
Trial	Initial Concentration of A (mol L⁻¹)	Initial Concentration of B (mol L⁻¹)	Initial Concentration of C (mol L⁻¹)	Measured Initial Rate (mol L⁻¹)
2	0.2 Same	0.1	0.1 Same	1.6×10^{-3}
3	0.2	0.2 2×	0.1	6.4×10^{-3}

Increase $4\times = 2^2$

Comparing Trials 1 and 4, the concentration of C is quadrupled, but there is no resulting change in the rate. The rate is independent of the concentration of C, so [C] receives an exponent of zero in the rate law. The reaction is zero order with respect to C.

	Table 2.4 Comparison of Trial 1 and 4			
Trial	Initial Concentration of A (mol L⁻¹)	Initial Concentration of B (mol L⁻¹)	Initial Concentration of C (mol L⁻¹)	Measured Initial Rate (mol L⁻¹)
1	0.1 Same	0.1 Same	0.1	8.0×10^{-4}
4	0.1	0.1	0.4 4×	8.0×10^{-4}

No change.

The complete rate law for our hypothetical reaction is:

$$rate_{forward} = k_f[A]^1[B]^2[C]^0$$

also written:

$$rate_{forward} = k_f[A][B]^2$$

By adding the exponents we find that the reaction overall is third order (1 + 2 + 0 = 3). Notice that the coefficients in the balanced chemical equation were not used to figure out the order.

Once we have derived the rate law from the experimental data, we can plug in the rate and concentrations from <u>any</u> of the experiments into the rate law, and solve for the rate constant k.

Notice that the rate may be increased by increasing the concentration of the reactants. If we consider the collision model, this makes sense. The greater the concentration of a species, the more likely are collisions.

The Rate Law WILL be determined by experiment!

Figure 2.8 Reaction Orders

Zero order

First order

Second order

Third order

The different orders of reactions have recognizably different characteristics. Keeping in mind that we are assuming that there is no reverse reaction taking place, we can compare graphs of the different orders of reaction for a single reactant. Plotting [A] with respect to time t for a zeroth order reaction results in a straight line with a slope $-k_f$.

In a first order reaction of the form:

$$A \rightarrow products \qquad rate = k_f[A]$$

where there is no reverse reaction, [A] decreases exponentially. A graph of a first order reaction comparing ln[A] with time t gives a straight line with a slope of $-k_f$. The same first order reaction has a constant half life that is independent of the concentration of A. The molecularity of a first order reaction implies that no collision takes place since there is only one molecule reacting. However, current theory requires a collision with any other molecule, boosting the reactant to a higher energy state resulting in a reaction. Although this is a two step process, it exhibits first order kinetics (except under low pressure). This is referred to as *pseudo-first order kinetics*.

For a graph of an irreversible second order reaction with a single reactant of the form:

$$2A \rightarrow products \qquad rate = k_f[A]^2$$

plotting 1/[A] gives a straight line with a slope of k_f. The half life of this type of second order reaction is dependent upon the concentration of A. It has the interesting characteristic that each consecutive half-life is twice as long as the last. For instance, the time required to reduce the concentration of A from 100% to 50% is half as long as the time required to reduce the concentration from 50% to 25%.

The second order reaction of the form:

$$A + B \rightarrow products \qquad rate = k_f[A][B]$$

does not reveal the same graph, and does not have an easily predictable half life.
For a graph of an irreversible third order reaction with a single reactant of the form:

$$3A \rightarrow products \qquad rate = k_f[A]^3$$

plotting $1/(2[A]^2)$ gives a straight line with a slope of k_f.

To avoid the complications of reverse reactions, the technique of initial rates is often employed. In the initial moments of a reaction starting with all reactants and no products, the rate of the reverse reaction is zero. The rate law in section 2.7 was determined with initial rates.

> For the MCAT, just be concerned with the graphs for the zero order and first order rate laws. Note that, like a rate constant, the slope is a straight line and remains constant throughout the reaction. A typical MCAT question might draw your attention to the descending green line and ask you if the value of the rate constant decreases over time. Of course, it does not. It remains constant.

2.9 Rates of Multiple Step Reactions

Any complex reaction can be separated into elementary steps. The rate of the slowest elementary step determines the rate of the overall reaction and is called the **rate determining step**. If the slow step is the first step, the rate law can be derived directly from this step and no other. If the slow step is other than the first step, the slow step is still the rate determining step, but steps prior to the slow step will contribute to the rate law. Steps after the slow step will make no contribution to the rate law.

Consider the following reaction:

$$NO_2(g) + CO(g) \rightarrow NO(g) + CO_2(g)$$

This reaction has two elementary steps:

1. $NO_2(g) + NO_2(g) \rightarrow NO_3(g) + NO(g)$ *slow step*

2. $NO_3(g) + CO(g) \rightarrow NO_2(g) + CO_2(g)$ *fast step*

Notice that if we add these two equations together, we arrive at the original equation. Elementary steps must add to give the complex reaction. Since the first step is the slow step, the rate law for the overall reaction is given by this step and is:

$$rate = k_1[NO_2]^2$$

We know that the exponent for $[NO_2]$ is 2 because we derived the rate law from an elementary equation, and in the elementary equation two NO_2 molecules collide to create a reaction. Automatically using the coefficient of the balanced equation for the exponent in the rate law works only if the equation is elementary. Don't forget, the rate law above assumes negligible contribution from the reverse reaction, and it also assumes a sufficient concentration of CO for the fast step to occur.

When the first step of a reaction series is the fast step, things can be a little tricky. If the first reaction is the fast reaction, the rate of the overall reaction is still equal to the rate of the slowest step. However, now one of the products of the fast step is a reactant in the slow step. Such a species is called an intermediate. The concentration of the intermediate is tricky to predict. An intermediate is usually not stable. If we assume that the fast reaction reaches equilibrium very quickly, the concentration of the intermediate remains at its equilibrium concentration. We can use the equilibrium concentration of the intermediate in predicting the slow step. For instance:

$$2NO(g) + Br_2(g) \rightarrow 2NOBr(g)$$

This reaction has two elementary steps:

1. $NO(g) + Br_2(g) \rightarrow NOBr_2(g)$ *fast step*

2. $NOBr_2(g) + NO(g) \rightarrow 2NOBr(g)$ *slow step*

The rate law for this reaction is:

$$rate = k_2[NOBr_2][NO]$$

To better understand a rate determining step, let's consider a bridge with two consecutive tolls A and B. Imagine toll A has only one open lane and toll B has many open lanes. Traffic backs up at toll A. Once through toll A, there is no waiting at toll B. The rate at which cars cross the bridge is limited only by the rate at which cars pass toll A. If instead, toll A had many open lanes and toll B had only one open lane, toll B would limit the rate at which cars crossed the bridge. The slowest step in a multistep reaction limits the overall rate of the reaction.

> Remember that the slow step determines the rate.

However, the concentration of $NOBr_2$ depends upon the first step. If we assume that the first step reaches equilibrium very quickly, the concentration of $NOBr_2$ can be written in terms of the equilibrium constant K_c for step 1, $[NOBr_2] = K_c[NO][Br_2]$. Alternatively, since the first step is considered to be in equilibrium, we can set the forward reaction rate, $k_1[NO][Br_2]$, equal to the reverse rate, $k_{-1}[NOBr_2]$, and solve for $[NOBr_2]$. $[NOBr_2] = k_1/k_{-1} [NO][Br_2]$. The resulting rate law is:

$$rate = \frac{k_2 k_1}{k_{-1}} [NO]^2 [Br_2]$$

This method is called the *equilibrium approximation*, which assumes that all steps prior to the rate limiting step are in equilibrium. The equilibrium approximation requires that the slow step be significantly slower than the fast steps. Since $k_2 k_1/k_{-1}$ is a constant, it is usually replaced by a single constant, $k_{observed}$.

If there is not a step that is significantly slower than the others, we can use the steady state approximation. In the *steady state approximation*, the concentration of the intermediate is considered to be small and hardly changing. This leads to the same result as the equilibrium approximation.

2.10 Catalysis

A **catalyst** is a substance that increases the rate of a reaction without being consumed or permanently altered. Catalysts increase the rate of both the forward and the reverse reactions and are capable of enhancing product selectivities and reducing energy consumption. A catalyst may lower the activation energy, E_a, or increase the steric factor (p from the Arrhenius equation) or both. Increasing the steric factor increases the number of favorable collisions. Most catalysts work by lowering the activation energy. The reaction rate depends exponentially on the activation energy. When the activation energy is lowered, more collisions have sufficient relative kinetic energy to create a reaction. This leads to more reactions and an increase in the overall reaction rate. This effect is shown in the energy vs. reaction coordinate diagram in Figure 2.8.

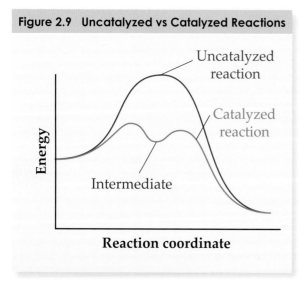

Figure 2.9 Uncatalyzed vs Catalyzed Reactions

Uncatalyzed reaction

Catalyzed reaction

Intermediate

Energy

Reaction coordinate

A catalyst works by providing an alternative reaction mechanism that competes with the uncatalyzed mechanism. **A catalyst cannot alter the equilibrium constant** of a reaction, so it must increase the rate of both the forward and the reverse reaction. Although a catalyst cannot change the equilibrium constant, it can, in some cases, change the composition of the mixture at equilibrium; however, the effect is usually very small and should be ignored for the MCAT. For the MCAT, catalysts do not change the equilibrium composition.

A catalyst can be either heterogeneous or homogeneous. A **heterogeneous catalyst** is in a different phase than the reactants and products. Heterogeneous catalysts are usually solids while the reactants and products are liquids or gases. A reactant may physically adsorb (via van der Waals forces) or, more often, chemically adsorb (usually via covalent bonds) to the surface of a solid catalyst. (Adsorption is the binding of molecules to a surface as opposed to absorption which refers to the uptake of molecules into an interior.) Molecules bind to a metal surface because, unlike metal atoms in the interior, metal atoms at the surface have unfulfilled valence requirements. The binding is almost always exothermic and the rate of catalysis depends upon the strength of the

bond between the reactant and the catalyst. If bonds are too weak, not enough adsorption occurs; if bonds are too strong, too much energy is required to remove the reactant. Depending on the reaction, reactant molecules may bind to any of the atoms at the surface, or they may bind only to surface imperfections. Once adsorbed, molecules migrate from one adsorption site to the next. The more binding that occurs, the greater the reaction rate. Thus, reaction rates can be enhanced by increasing the surface area of a catalyst. Often this is done by grinding the solid into a powder. However, the concentration of a solid catalyst does not change so the concentration of a solid catalyst won't appear in the rate law.

A **homogeneous catalyst** is in the same phase as the reactants and products, usually in the gas or liquid phase. Aqueous acid or base solutions often act as homogeneous catalysts. Some reactions exhibit autocatalysis by generating the catalyst as a product. The acid catalyzed hydrolysis of an ester is an example of autocatalysis, where the carboxylic acid product acts as a catalyst to the reaction.

In the lab, concentrations of catalysts are usually small compared to the concentration of the reactants and products. In such cases, increasing the concentration of the catalyst increases the rate of the reaction. When this happens, the concentration of the catalyst will be found in the rate law. If the concentration of the catalyst is large compared to the reactants and products, the rate changes little or not at all with the catalyst concentration. In this case, the concentration of the catalyst may not be included in the rate law. Since catalysts alter reaction mechanisms, reactions with catalysts require separate rate constants. Remember, a catalyst doesn't prevent the original reaction from proceeding, so the total rate is given by the sum of the rates for both reactions. For instance, a first order uncatalyzed reaction may follow the rate law:

$$rate = k_0[\text{A}]$$

When the same reaction is catalyzed by acid, the new rate law would be:

$$rate = k_0[\text{A}] + k_{\text{H}+}[\text{H}^+][\text{A}]$$

Typically, the rate of the original reaction is negligible compared to the catalyzed rate.

Almost every chemical reaction in the human body is quickened by a protein catalyst called an enzyme. Enzymes are far more effective than inorganic catalysts. The number of reactions occurring at one active site on one enzyme is typically 1,000 per second and can be tens of thousands of times greater for the fastest enzymatic reactions. This number is called the *turnover number*.

> Remember that a catalyst increases the rate of a reaction by lowering the activation energy of that reaction. A catalyst doesn't change equilibrium and is not used up.

Figure 2.10   Catalyzed vs Uncatalyzed Reactions

Indigestion tablets react in water producing carbon dioxide gas.

2.11 | Effects of Solvent on Rate

Roughly speaking, liquid molecules make around 100 times more collisions per second than gas molecules because liquid molecules are much closer to each other. However, most of the collisions in a liquid are with the solvent resulting in no reaction.

The rate constant in a liquid is a function of the solvent as well as the temperature. The reactant in a liquid is solvated. These solvent-reactant bonds must be broken before a reaction can take place. In addition, the bonds may stabilize an intermediate. The degree of solvation affects k. Solvents can electrically insulate reactants reducing the electrostatic forces between them. The dielectric of the solvent affects k. Solvent viscosity can affect k as per the 'cage effect' described below.

Reactants in a liquid can be trapped in a cage of solvent molecules. They rattle around in such a cage at tremendous rates making hundreds of collisions before squeezing between solvent molecules and into a new solvent cage. If they are trapped in the cage with another reactant, many of their collisions are with the other reactant and a reaction is likely to occur, but if there is not another reactant in the solvent cage, they cannot react until they escape the cage. The net result is that reactants in a liquid make an approximately equal number of collisions with other reactants as they would in a gas with equal concentrations; collisions in a liquid occur at about the same rate as in a gas.

For liquids, stirring or shaking may greatly increase the reaction rate.

Notes:

33. Which of the following changes to a reaction will always increase the rate constant for that reaction?

    A. decreasing the temperature
    B. increasing the temperature
    C. increasing the concentration of the reactants
    D. increasing the concentration of the catalyst

34. All of the following may be true concerning catalysts and the reaction which they catalyze EXCEPT:

    A. Catalysts are not used up by the reaction.
    B. Catalysts lower the energy of activation.
    C. Catalysts increase the rate of the reverse reaction.
    D. Catalysts shift the reaction equilibrium to the right.

35. The table below shows 3 trials where the initial rate was measured for the reaction:

    $$2A + B \rightarrow C$$

    Which of the following expressions is the correct rate law for the reaction?

T	Molarity of A	Molarity of B	Initial Rate
1	0.05	0.05	5×10^{-3}
2	0.05	0.1	5×10^{-3}
3	0.1	0.05	1×10^{-2}

    A. rate = 0.1[A]
    B. rate = [A]
    C. rate = [A][B]
    D. rate = $[A]^2[B]$

36. The reaction below proceeds via the two step mechanism as shown.

    Overall Reaction: $2NO_2 + F_2 \rightarrow 2NO_2F$
    Step 1: $NO_2 + F_2 \rightarrow NO_2F + F$
    Step 2: $NO_2 + F \rightarrow NO_2F$

    X is the rate of step 1, and Y is the rate of step 2. If step 1 is much slower than step 2, then the rate of the overall reaction can be represented by:

    A. X
    B. Y
    C. $X + Y$
    D. $X - Y$

37. As temperature is increased in an exothermic gaseous reaction, all of the following increase EXCEPT:

    A. reaction rate.
    B. rate constant.
    C. activation energy.
    D. rms molecular velocity.

38. A container holds a pure sample of compound X shown at $t = 0$ min. Compound X undergoes a first order reaction to form compound Y. The same container is shown at $t = 15$ min. (Compound X is shown as white circles and compound Y is shown as black circles.)

    If the rate of the reverse reaction is negligible, which of the following might represent the container at t = 30 min?

    A.   C.

    B.   D.

39. The conversion of cis-2-butene to trans-2-butene takes place in a reaction that is first-order with respect to cis-2-butene. The conversion was observed in two separate trials under identical conditions except that in the second trial, the concentration of cis-2-butene was doubled. In the second trial:

    A. the reaction rate will be halved.
    B. the reaction rate will be doubled.
    C. the rate constant will be halved.
    D. the rate constant will be doubled.

40. When a radioactive isotope undergoes nuclear decay, the concentration of the isotope decreases exponentially with a constant half-life. It can be determined from this that radioactive decay is a:

    A. zeroth order reaction.
    B. first order reaction.
    C. second order reaction.
    D. third order reaction.

Chemical reactions are reversible. As reactants are converted to products, the concentration of the reactants decreases, and the concentration of the products increases. Since rates are related to concentrations, the rate of the forward reaction begins to slow, and the rate of the reverse reaction quickens as a reaction proceeds. Eventually, the two rates become equal. This condition, where the forward reaction rate equals the reverse reaction rate, is called **chemical equilibrium**. At chemical equilibrium, there is no change in the concentration of the products or reactants. Equilibrium will be reached from either direction, beginning with predominantly reactants or predominantly products.

If the two faucets flow at different rates, the bucket will empty or overflow. However, if the faucets flow at the same rate, an equilibrium will be reached and the water level will remain constant.

The object of this game is to get all the balls to the opponent's side. However, no one can win because inevitably an equilbrium will be reached. Although there are more players on one side, as fewer balls become available, more time is required to find a ball to throw. Thus, the rate at which balls are thrown from that side slows. On the other hand, as my side fills with balls, I am able to grab and throw balls more quickly, and the rate at which I throw increases. Eventually these rates equalize. The game has reached an equilibrium with no winner. Reactions work in a similar fashion.

Equilibrium is the point of greatest entropy. From the second law of thermodynamics we know that nature wants to increase entropy. This is why a reaction moves toward and then stays at equilibrium.

Figure 2.11   Nature Trends Toward Equilibrium

When concentrated nitric acid and copper react the system moves toward equilibrium and greatest entropy.

Consider the hypothetical first order elementary reaction:

$$A \rightarrow B$$

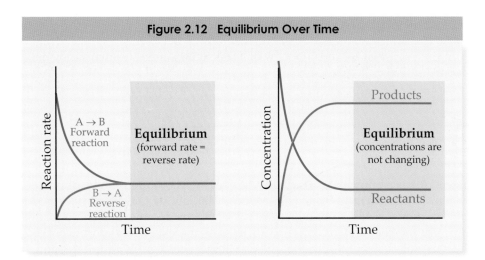

Figure 2.12   Equilibrium Over Time

Notice that by the rate definition:

$$rate = -\frac{1}{a}\frac{\Delta[A]}{t}$$

the rate at equilibrium is zero. Understand that zero is the net reaction rate, but there is a forward and a reverse reaction rate at equilibrium. Equilibrium is a dynamic process.

Notice from Figure 2.11 that the forward rate changes faster than the reverse rate as the reaction proceeds. This indicates that the forward rate constant is greater than the reverse rate constant. The rate law for the forward and reverse reactions are rate = $k_f[A]$ and rate = $k_r[B]$ respectively. The rate of the forward reaction is directly proportional to [A]. From the diagram, the rate of the forward reaction is reduced by more than half, so [A] is also reduced by more than half. For every molecule of A lost, a molecule of B is created, so at equilibrium [B] must be greater than [A]. Setting the rates equal, $k_f[A] = k_r[B]$, we see that k_f must be greater than k_r if [B] is greater than [A] at equilibrium.

This is elementary!

For a homogeneous reaction, where all species are in the same phase, there will always be some of each species present at equilibrium; however, in some cases, the rate constant for the forward reaction is so much greater than the rate constant for the reverse reaction that, for all practical purposes, the reaction runs to completion. Alternatively, if a product is continually removed as the reaction proceeds (perhaps in the form of a gas leaving an aqueous solution), the reaction can run to completion.

Consider the hypothetical elementary reaction: $aA + bB \rightarrow cC + dD$. Since the reaction is elementary, we can use the stoichiometric coefficients for the forward and reverse rate laws:

$$rate_{forward} = k_f[A]^a[B]^b$$

$$rate_{reverse} = k_r[C]^c[D]^d$$

(**WARNING:** For the MCAT, never use the coefficients as the exponents in the rate law. We do it here because we are told that the reaction is elementary.) Since equilibrium occurs when these two rates are equal, then, for equilibrium conditions only, we set them equal to each other as shown below:

$$k_f[A]^a[B]^b = k_r[C]^c[D]^d$$

With a little algebraic manipulation we have:

$$\frac{k_f}{k_r} = \frac{[C]^c[D]^d}{[A]^a[B]^b}$$

In the equilibrium expression we use the coefficients as exponents; in the rate law we <u>cannot</u> use the coefficients as exponents unless we know the reaction is elementary

Since both k's are constants, we can replace them with a new constant called the **equilibrium constant K**. (**2nd WARNING:** This simple relationship between K equilibrium and k rate is only true for elementary equations.) The relationship between a chemical equation and the equilibrium constant is called the **Law of Mass Action** and is written as an equilibrium expression as follows:

$$K = \frac{[C]^c[D]^d}{[A]^a[B]^b} = \frac{Products^{cofficients}}{Reactants^{cofficients}}$$

The equilibrium constant depends upon temperature only. Don't confuse the equilibrium constant with equilibrium.

The value of K has no dimensions because the concentrations are actually approximations for a dimensionless quantity called an *activity*. The law of mass action is good for all chemical equations, including non-elementary equations. In other words, for equilibrium constants, use the chemical equation coefficients as the exponents of the concentrations regardless of molecularity. Notice that the equilibrium constant is a capital K and the rate constant is represented by lowercase k. Also notice that the equilibrium constant for the reverse reaction is the reciprocal of the equilibrium constant of the forward reaction. This is true regardless of whether or not the reaction is elementary. Following this same line of reasoning will demonstrate that the equilibrium constant for a series of reactions is equal to the product of the equilibrium constants for each of its elementary steps. Since the rate constant depends upon temperature, the equilibrium constant must also depend upon temperature.

The concentration of a pure liquid or a pure solid is usually given a value of one for the equilibrium expression. Concentrations are only approximations for activities. Activities for pure solids and pure liquids are like 'effective' mole fractions. The mole fraction of a pure solid or liquid is one. Although solvents are not actually pure, they are usually considered ideally dilute on the MCAT, which means that their mole fraction is one. The activity of a pure solid or liquid is approximately one. Be aware that pure solids or liquids can still participate in the equilibrium. When they do, they must be present in order for equilibrium to exist.

Don't use solids or pure liquids such as water in the law of mass action.

Thought Provoker

The manufacturing of cement involves the decomposition of limestone. The reaction is as follows:

$CaCO_3(s) \rightarrow CaO(s) + CO_2(g)$

What is the equilibrium constant for this process?

Answer: See page 55.

Notes:

For reactions with more than one pathway, and for reactions with more than one step, *the principle for detailed balance* states that, at equilibrium, the forward and reverse reaction rates for each step must be equal, and any two or more single reactions or series of reactions resulting in the same products from identical reactants must have the same equilibrium constant for a given temperature. The equilibrium constant does not depend upon whether or not other substances are present.

For reactions involving gases, the equilibrium constant can be written in terms of partial pressures. For the all gas reaction $a\text{A} + b\text{B} \rightarrow c\text{C} + d\text{D}$, the partial pressure equilibrium expression is written as:

$$K_p = \frac{P_c P_d}{P_a P_b} = \frac{\text{products}^{\text{coefficients}}}{\text{reactants}^{\text{coefficients}}}$$

where K_p is the partial pressure equilibrium constant and P_a, P_b, P_c, and P_d are the partial pressures of the respective gases. The concentration equilibrium constant and the partial pressure equilibrium constant do not have the same value, but they are related by the equation:

$$K_p = K_c(RT)^{\Delta n}$$

where K_p is the partial pressure equilibrium constant and n is the sum of the coefficients of the products minus the sum of the coefficients of the reactants. This equation is not required for the MCAT, but you must be able to work with partial pressure equilibrium constants.

Figure 2.13 Air Composition

- Nitrogen   78%
- Oxygen   21%
- Other   1%

Thought Provoker

An experiment is performed which requires a specific greenhouse air environment of 3.0 mol percent CO_2, 20.0 mol percent O_2, and 77.0 mol percent Ar.

1. What is the partial pressure of the CO_2 in the greenhouse if the total pressure is 750 torr?

2. If the greenhouse capacity is 145 L, how many moles of CO_2 are found in the greenhouse at 25 degrees Celsius?

Answer: See page 55

2.14 *The Reaction Quotient*

The equilibrium constant describes only equilibrium conditions. If a reaction is at equilibrium, the concentrations of the products and reactants, when plugged into the equilibrium expression, must equal the equilibrium constant. However, it is possible to momentarily change those concentrations by adding a reactant or product. When we do so, for a moment the reaction is not at equilibrium, and, of course, when the concentrations of the products and reactants are plugged into the equilibrium expression, they will NOT equal the equilibrium constant. In such cases, we substitute a <u>variable</u> Q for the equilibrium <u>constant</u> K. Q is called the reaction quotient and is given by a formula identical to the equilibrium expression.

$$Q = \frac{\text{Products}^{\text{coefficients}}}{\text{Reactants}^{\text{coefficients}}}$$

Q may have any positive value.

Since reactions always move toward equilibrium, Q will always change toward K. Thus we can compare Q and K for a reaction at any given moment, and learn in which direction the reaction will proceed.

> Use the reaction quotient Q to predict the direction in which a reaction will proceed.

- If Q *is equal to* K, then the reaction is at equilibrium.

- If Q *is greater than* K, then the ratio of the concentration of products to the concentration of reactants (as given by the reaction quotient equation above) is greater than when at equilibrium, and the reaction increases reactants and decreases products. In other words, the reverse reaction rate will be greater than the forward rate. This is sometimes called a leftward shift in the equilibrium. Of course, the equilibrium constant does not change during this type of equilibrium shift.

- If Q *is less than* K, then the ratio of the concentration of products to the concentration of reactants (as given by the reaction quotient equation above) is less than when at equilibrium, and the reaction increases products and decreases reactants. In other words, the forward reaction rate will be greater than the reverse rate. This is sometimes called a rightward shift.

Figure 2.14 *K* vs *Q* Relationship

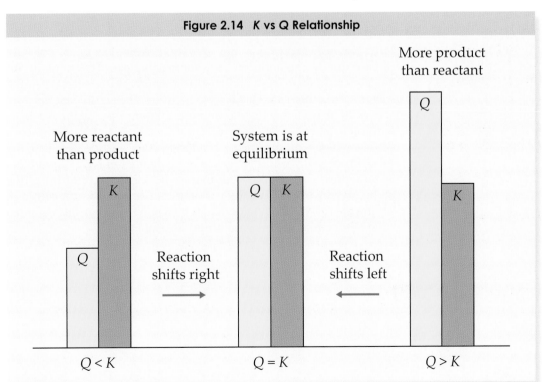

2.15 Le Châtelier's Principle

There is a general rule called Le Châtelier's principle that can often be applied to systems at equilibrium. **Le Châtelier's principle** states that when a system at equilibrium is stressed, the system will shift in a direction that will reduce that stress.

There are three types of stress that usually obey Le Châtelier's principle: 1) addition or removal of a product or reactant, 2) changing the pressure of the system, 3) heating or cooling the system.

The Haber process is important today because the fertilizer generated from ammonia is responsible for sustaining one-third of the Earth's population.

> Systems like equilibrium; so, when a system at equilibrium is stressed, the system will shift in a direction to reduce that stress.

The Haber Process is an all gas reaction commonly used on the MCAT to test Le Châtelier's principle. The Haber Process is an exothermic reaction, so it creates heat. For Le Châtelier purposes, we can think of heat as a product in the Haber Process:

$$N_2(g) + 3H_2(g) \rightarrow 2NH_3(g) + \text{Heat}$$

Imagine a rigid container with N_2, H_2, and NH_3 gas at equilibrium. If we add N_2 gas to our system, the system attempts to compensate for the increased concentration of nitrogen by reducing the partial pressure of N_2 with the forward reaction. The forward reaction uses up H_2 as well, reducing its partial pressure. NH_3 and heat are created by the forward reaction.

If we raise the temperature by adding heat, the reaction is pushed to the left. The concentrations of N_2 and H_2 are increased, while the concentration of NH_3 is decreased.

If the size of the container is reduced at constant temperature, total pressure increases. Since there are four gas molecules on the left side of the reaction and only 2 on the right, the equilibrium shifts to the right producing heat and raising the NH_3 concentration. Interestingly, a similar effect is found when a solution is concentrated or diluted. If one side contains more moles than the other, the equilibrium shifts to the side with fewer moles when the solution is concentrated.

Warning: Le Châtelier's principle does not always predict the correct shift. Notable exceptions are solvation reactions, and pressure increase due to the addition of a nonreactive gas. The solubility of salts generally increase with increasing temperature, even when the reaction is exothermic. This is largely due to the significant entropy increase that occurs with dissolution. The entropy factor becomes more important as the temperature increases. An example of a pressure increase where equilibrium is not affected is the addition of He to the Haber Process. If we add He gas to our container of N_2, H_2, and NH_3, the total pressure increases, but there is no shift in equilibrium. This can be seen by examining the partial pressure equilibrium constant. Adding He to a rigid container, does not change the partial pressures of the other gases, so the equilibrium does not shift.

The following reaction follows Le Châtlier's principle.

$$\text{Light} + 2Ag^+ + 2Cl^- \rightleftharpoons 2Ag + Cl_2$$

The compound silver chloride is found in adjustable shading sunglasses. When light strikes the sunglasses, this reaction shifts right producing metallic silver, Ag, and darkening the glasses. In the absence of light, the reaction shifts left and the glasses lighten.

Examples of Le Châtelier's Principle

$$N_2(g) + 3H_2(g) \rightarrow 2NH_3(g) + \text{Heat}$$

Figure 2.15   Normal Conditions

Figure 2.16   Heat Added

Figure 2.17   N₂ Added

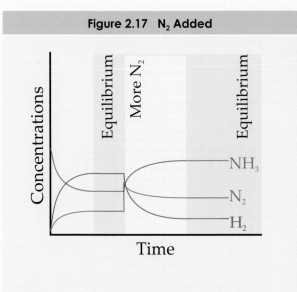

Figure 2.18   Pressure Added

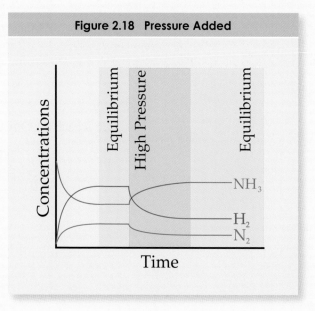

2.16 Equation Summary

Equations	
Ideal Gas Law $$PV = nRT$$	**Partial Pressure** $$P_a = \chi_a P_{total}$$

Dalton's Law

$$P_{total} = P_1 + P_2 + P_{3\ldots}$$

Average Translational Kinetic Energy and the Temperature of a Gas

$$K.E._{\cdot avg} = \frac{3}{2}RT$$

Graham's Law

$$\frac{v_1}{v_2} = \frac{\sqrt{m_2}}{\sqrt{m_1}}$$

Effusion

$$\frac{\text{effusion rate}_1}{\text{effusion rate}_2} = \frac{\sqrt{M_2}}{\sqrt{M_1}}$$

Deviations from Ideal Gas Law

Volume of Gases $\qquad\qquad$ Pressure of Gases

$$V_{real} > V_{ideal} \qquad\qquad P_{real} < P_{ideal}$$

Rate Law

$$rate_{forward} = k_f [\text{A}]^\alpha [\text{B}]^\beta$$

The Law of Mass Action

$$K = \frac{[\text{C}]^c [\text{D}]^d}{[\text{A}]^a [\text{B}]^b} = \frac{\text{Products}^{cofficients}}{\text{Reactants}^{cofficients}}$$

The Reaction Quotient

$$Q = \frac{\text{Products}^{coefficients}}{\text{Reactants}^{coefficients}}$$

Terms	
Activation Energy	Kinetic Molecular Theory
Catalyst	Le Châtelier's Principle
Chemical Equilibrium	Mean Free Path
Collision Model	Order Of Each Respective Reactant
Dalton's Law	Overall Order
Diffusion	Partial Pressure
Effusion	Rate Determining Step
Equilibrium Constant K	Rate Law
Graham's Law	Reaction Quotient
Heterogeneous Catalyst	Standard Molar Volume
Homogeneous Catalyst	Standard Temperature And Pressure (STP)
Ideal Gas	
Ideal Gas Law	
Intermediates	

Thought Provoker Answers

Answer from page 29:

This is a pretty straightforward PV=nRT question. P=730 torr (approx. 0.96 atm), V=2L, n=?, R=constant, and T= 25 °C (298 K). Solving for moles we get 0.078 moles.

Answer from page 36:

1. *Heat the reaction, which would cause the molecules to move more at a higher energy, thereby increasing the collision rate.*

2. *Increase the concentration of HCl, increasing collisions between magnesium and H^+ ions.*

3. *Increase the surface area of the magnesium, creating more locations for potential collisions.*

Answer from page 49:

The equilibrium constant (K) for this process only includes the gas phases for this case, making it K= [CO_2].

Answer from page 50:

1. *A mole percent is the mole fraction times 100. The mole fraction of CO_2 is 0.030. Therefore, using the partial pressure equation, (0.030)(750 torr)= 22.5 torr.*

2. *To determine moles needed of CO_2, we simply use the PV=nRT equation.P=partial pressure CO_2, 22.5 torr, converted to atm=0.029 atm V= 145 L,R=Constant (0.08206 L*atm/mol*K), T= 25+273= 298K, Ans= 0.17 mol CO_2*

41. As temperature is increased, the equilibrium of a gaseous reaction will always:

A. shift to the right.
B. shift to the left.
C. remain constant.
D. The answer cannot be determined from the information given.

42. All of the following are true concerning a reaction at equilibrium EXCEPT:

A. The rate of the forward reaction equals the rate of the reverse reaction.
B. There is no change in the concentrations of both the products and the reactants.
C. The activation energy has reached zero.
D. The Gibbs free energy has reached a minimum.

43. Nitric acid is produced commercially by oxidation in the Oswald process. The first step of this process is shown below.

$$4NH_3(g) + 5O_2(g) \rightleftharpoons 4NO(g) + 6H_2O(g)$$

A container holds 4 moles of gaseous ammonia, 5 moles of gaseous oxygen, 4 moles of gaseous nitric oxide, and 6 moles of water vapor at equilibrium. Which of the following would be true if the container were allowed to expand at constant temperature?

A. Initially during the expansion the forward reaction rate would be greater than the reverse reaction rate.
B. The equilibrium would shift to the left.
C. The partial pressure of oxygen would increase.
D. The pressure inside the container would increase.

44. Nitrous oxide is prepared by the thermal decomposition of ammonium nitrate.

$$NH_4NO_3(s) \rightarrow N_2O(g) + 2H_2O(g)$$

The equilibrium constant for this reaction is:

A. $[NH_4NO_3]/[N_2O][H_2O]^2$
B. $[N_2O][H_2O]^2/[NH_4NO_3]$
C. $[N_2O][H_2O]^2$
D. $[N_2O][H_2O]$

45. Which of the following is true concerning a reaction that begins with only reactants and moves to equilibrium?

A. The rate of the forward and reverse reactions decreases until equilibrium is reached.
B. The rate of the forward and reverse reactions increases until equilibrium is reached.
C. The rate of the forward reaction decreases, and the rate of the reverse reaction increases until equilibrium is reached.
D. The rate of the forward reaction increases, and the rate of the reverse reaction decreases until equilibrium is reached.

Calcium carbonate decomposes to calcium oxide and carbon dioxide gas via the following reversible reaction:

$$CaCO_3(s) \leftrightarrows CaO(s) + CO_2(g)$$

Beaker I contains pure $CaCO_3$ and Beaker II contains pure CaO. The container is sealed.

46. Which of the following statements could be true about the system upon achieving equilibrium?

   A. Beaker I is empty.
   B. The number of calcium atoms in Beaker II has decreased.
   C. The number of calcium atoms in Beaker II has increased.
   D. Beaker II contains a mixture of $CaCO_3$ and CaO.

47. What is the equilibrium expression for the reaction?

   A. $K = [CO_2]$

   B. $K = [CaO][CO_2]$

   C. $K = \dfrac{[CaO][CO_2]}{[CaCO_3]}$

   D. $K = \dfrac{[CO_2]}{[CaCO_3]}$

48. The partial pressure equilibrium constant for the decomposition of $CaCO_3$ is K_p. If Beaker II is removed, under which of the following conditions would equilibrium NOT be achieved?

   A. K_p is less than the partial pressure of CO_2.
   B. K_p is greater than the partial pressure of CO_2.
   C. K_p is equal to the partial pressure of CO_2.
   D. Equilibrium could not be achieved under any conditions because solid CaO is required to achieve equilibrium.

Notes:

THERMODYNAMICS

3.1 Systems and Surroundings

Thermodynamics is the study of energy and its relationship to macroscopic properties of chemical systems. Thermodynamic functions are based on probabilities, and are valid only for systems composed of a large number of molecules. In other words, with few exceptions, the rules of thermodynamics govern complex systems containing many parts, and they cannot be applied to specific microscopic phenomena such as a single collision between two molecules.

Thermodynamic problems divide the universe into a **system** and its **surroundings**. The system is the section of the universe under study. The remainder of the universe outside the system is the surroundings. There are three systems: *open*, *closed*, and *isolated*. System definitions are based upon mass and energy exchange with the surroundings. Open systems exchange both mass and energy with their surroundings; closed systems exchange energy but not mass; and isolated systems do not exchange energy or mass (see Figure 3.1).

Figure 3.1 Types of Systems

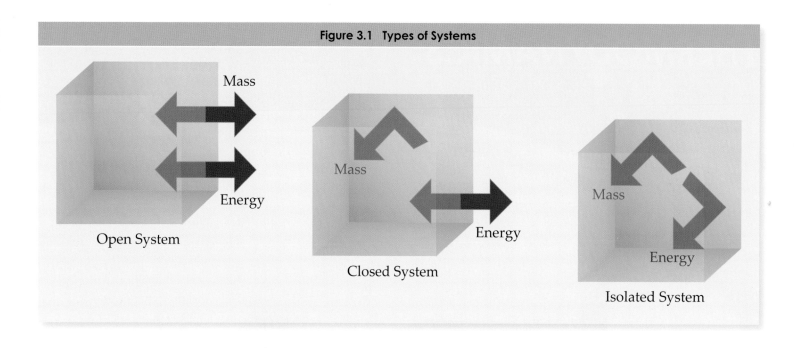

3.2 State Functions

A state is the physical condition of a system described by a specific set of thermodynamic property values. There are two types of properties that describe the macroscopic state of a system: 1) *extensive* and 2) *intensive*. Extensive properties are proportional to the size of the system; intensive properties are independent of the size of the system. If you combine two identical systems and a property is the same for both the single system and the combined system, that property is intensive. If a property doubles when the systems are combined, the property is extensive. If you divide one extensive property by another, the result is an intensive property. Volume V and number of moles n are examples of extensive properties. Pressure P and temperature T are examples of intensive properties.

The macroscopic state of any one-component fluid system in equilibrium can be described by just three properties, at least one of which is extensive. All other properties of the state of the same system can be derived from these three properties. For instance, if for a single component gas in equilibrium, pressure, temperature, and volume are known, all other properties which describe the state of that gas (such as number of moles, internal energy, enthalpy, entropy, and Gibbs energy) must have a specific single value. Since the state of a system can be described exactly by specific properties, it is not necessary to know how the state was formed or what reaction pathway brought a state into being. Such properties that describe the state of a system are called **state functions**. Properties that do not describe the state of a system, but depend upon the pathway used to achieve any state, are called *path functions*. Work and heat are examples of path functions.

> Extensive properties change with amount; intensive properties do not.
>
> You need to know what a state function is. State functions are pathway independent. They describe the state of a system. In other words, the change in a state property going from one state to another is the same regardless of the process used to change it.
>
> If you know three macroscopic properties of a one component system in equilibrium and at least one of which is extensive, then you know all the other properties.

3.3 Heat

There are only two ways to transfer energy between systems: **heat** (*q*) and **work** (*w*). Heat is the natural transfer of energy from a warmer body to a cooler body. Any energy transfer that is not heat is work.

Heat has three forms: conduction, convection, and radiation. **Conduction** is thermal energy transfer via molecular collisions. Conduction requires direct physical contact. In conduction, higher energy molecules of one system transfer some of their energy to the lower energy molecules of the other system via molecular collisions. Heat can also be conducted through a single object. An object's ability to conduct heat is called its thermal conductivity *k*. The thermal conductivity of an object depends upon its composition and, to a much lesser extent, its temperature. A slab of a given substance with face area *A*, length *L*, and thermal conductivity *k* will conduct heat *Q* from a hot body at temperature T_h to a cold body at temperature T_c in an amount of time *t* (Figure 3.2).

> Heat is movement of energy via conduction, convection, or radiation always from hot to cold.

Figure 3.2 Thermal Conductivity

$$\frac{Q}{t} = kA\frac{T_h - T_c}{L}$$

> Given what we know about heat flow we can also understand Newton's Law of cooling, which states that the rate of cooling of a body is approximately proportional to the temperature difference between the body and its environment. A fresh cup of coffee initially cools quickly, since its temperature is much hotter than the surroundings, then cools more slowly as its temperature approaches room temperature.

Q/*t* is the rate of heat flow or *heat current I*. The resistance to heat flow *R* can be written as *L*/(*kA*). A little algebra results in $\Delta T = IR$, an equation similar in form to Ohm's law in electricity. Like fluid flow in an ideal fluid (see Physics Lecture 6) or the flow of electric current through resistors in series (see Physics Lecture 7), in a steady state system the rate of heat flow is constant across any number of slabs between two heat reservoirs. In other words, if a series of slabs were lined up end to end between hot and cold reservoirs, the rate of heat flow, *Q*/*t*, would be the same in all slabs even if they each had different lengths, thicknesses, and different thermal conductivities (right side of Figure 3.2). Conservation of energy explains why. If the rate of energy transfer were not steady across all slabs, the slab that conducted heat the fastest would become cold. This is an impossibility. A cold slab could not conduct heat to warmer slabs because heat moves from hot to cold. It also follows that since the rate of energy transfer is the same for each slab, the order in which we place the slabs does not affect the overall conductivity. Finally, since the rate of heat flow is the same through each slab, a higher conductivity results in a lower temperature difference across any slab of a given length.

> The temperature difference in thermal conductivity is like the pressure difference in fluids or the potential difference in electricity. The rate of heat flow is like volume flow rate or current. Notice the similarity in these equations for the conduction of heat, fluids, and electricity.
>
> $$\Delta T = IR$$
> $$\Delta P = QR$$
> $$\Delta V = iR$$
>
> You can use this similarity to help you understand heat flow, fluid flow, and electron flow. For instance, in all cases, thicker conduits allow for greater flow, longer conduits impede flow, and flow rate depends upon the difference in a property of the reservoirs at either end of the conduit.

Let's see how well you understand thermal conductivity. If I have a heavy blanket and a light blanket, which blanket should I place on top in order to stay warmer? The answer is: the order of the blankets will not make any difference since it will not change the rate of conduction.

3 Types of Heat

Convection

Radiation

Conduction
(hand warming the glass)

Convection is thermal energy transfer via fluid movements. In convection, differences in pressure or density drive warm fluid in the direction of cooler fluid. For instance, on a warm sunny day at the beach the air above the land heats up faster than the air above the water. As the air above the land warms, it becomes less dense and rises carrying its thermal energy with it. The cool air over the ocean moves in to fill the space over the land. The net result is circular current of air carrying the heat generated by the hot beach up and out to the cooler ocean. Ocean and air currents are common examples of convection (Figure 3.3).

Radiation is thermal energy transfer via electromagnetic waves. When metal is heated, it glows red, orange-yellow, white, and finally blue-white. The hot metal radiates visible electromagnetic waves. But even before the metal begins to glow, it radiates electromagnetic waves at a frequency too low to be visible to the human eye. In fact, all objects with a temperature above $0 \, K$ radiate heat. The rate at which an object radiates electromagnetic radiation (its power P) depends upon its temperature and surface area, and is given by the *Stefan-Boltzman law*:

$$P = \sigma \varepsilon A T^4$$

where A is the surface area of the object, T is the temperature of the object in kelvins, σ is the Stefan-Boltzman constant (5.67×10^{-8} W m^{-2} K^{-4}), and ε is the emissivity of the object's surface, which has a value between 0 and 1. If we substitute the temperature of the environment for the temperature of the object, we find the rate at which the object absorbs radiant heat from its environment. The net rate of heat transfer is the rate at which the body emits energy minus the rate at which it absorbs energy. The heat transfer will always be from hot to cold, and is given by:

$$P = \sigma \varepsilon A (T_e^4 - T_o^4)$$

where the T_e is the temperature of the environment and T_o is the temperature of the object

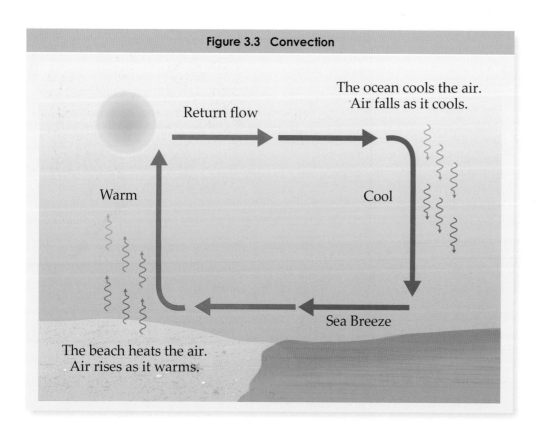

Figure 3.3   Convection

The ocean cools the air.
Air falls as it cools.

Return flow

Warm

Cool

Sea Breeze

The beach heats the air.
Air rises as it warms.

Newton's law of cooling states that the rate of cooling of a body is approximately proportional to the temperature difference between the body and its environment.

> *P in the two equations is power, not pressure. Don't memorize these equations. Just recognize the relationships between power, temperature, and surface area.*

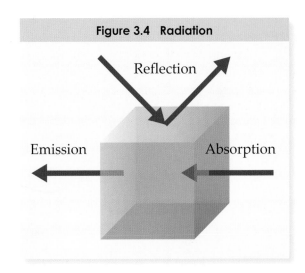

Figure 3.4 Radiation

Reflection

Emission

Absorption

When radiation strikes an opaque surface, only a fraction is absorbed. The remainder is reflected. The fraction absorbed is indicated by the emissivity ε of the surface. The emissivity depends upon surface composition. As stated above, the emissivity of any surface is between 0 and 1. An object with an emissivity of 1 is called a blackbody radiator and is possible only in theory. All other objects reflect as well as absorb and radiate. Dark colors tend to radiate and absorb better than light colors, which tend to reflect.

Radiation is the only type of heat that transfers through a vacuum.

Thought Provoker

Notice that an object that radiates heat faster also absorbs heat faster. This means that an object that is a more efficient radiator comes to equilibrium with its environment more quickly. With this in mind, is it better to paint your house black or white?

Answer: See page 85

3.4 Work

From our discussion of heat, we know that work is any energy transfer that is not heat. In Physics Lecture 3 we defined work as an energy transfer due to a force. In physics problems, work typically changes the motion or position of a body. However, now we want to look at work as it applies to a chemical system at rest. A chemical system at rest can do two types of work, PV work and nonPV work. NonPV work done by a system at rest can take various forms, the most important of which for our purposes is electrical work. For now, we will examine PV work.

A system at rest may change its size or shape, but does not translate or change its position. A system at rest may still be able to do *PV* **work**. Imagine a cylinder full of gas compressed by a piston. If we place two blocks of mass m on the top of the piston and allow the gas pressure to lift the masses to a height h, the system has done work on the mass in the amount of the gravitational energy change $2mgh$. Thus negative work has been done on the system. This work is called *PV* work because, at constant pressure, it is equal to the product of the pressure and the change in the volume ($P\Delta V$).

Figure 3.5 PV Work

Piston

gas

h

Piston

gas

From Newton's second law $F=ma$, we know that if the masses are lifted at constant velocity, the force on the masses is constant and equal to $2mg$ (Figure 3.6, Case 1). From the definition of pressure $P = F/A$, we know that if the force remained constant, the pressure also remained constant. Constant pressure conditions allow us to calculate the work done using:

$$w = P\Delta V_{\text{(constant pressure)}}$$

> *This equation shows the work done by the gas. The work done on the gas is just the negative of the work done by the gas, so you might see this equation written with a negative sign as $w = -P\Delta V$.*

The start point and end point of the expansion could also have been achieved by removing one mass, allowing the piston to rise, increasing the pressure to $2mg/A$ while holding the piston steady, and then replacing the second mass. This would have been a different pathway to achieve the same result. Since work is a path function, a different pathway results in a different amount of work; in this case the work would have been *mgh* (Figure 3.6, Case 2).

Finally, the start and end point of the expansion could have been achieved by changing the pressure as the piston rose. In this case, *PV* work is done, but it does not equal $P\Delta V$. To calculate the work in this case, you would need to use calculus (Figure 3.6, Case 3).

If we examine a pressure vs. volume graph for each case, the work done is given by the area under the curve. Notice that the area is different for each case.

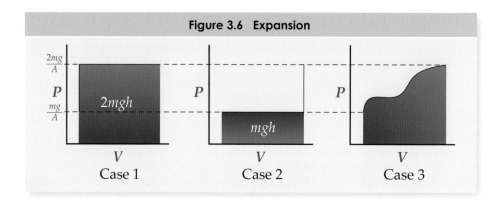

Figure 3.6 Expansion

3.5 The First Law of Thermodynamics

The First Law of Thermodynamics states that energy of the system and surroundings is always conserved. Thus any energy change to a system must equal the heat flow into the system plus the work done on the system.

$$\Delta E = q + w$$

Warning: We have chosen the convention where work on the system is positive. It is possible that an MCAT passage could define work done by the system as positive, in which case the formula would be $\Delta E = q - w$.

3.6 Heat Engines

Since all things contain internal energy, why not use that energy to do work? In other words, why not find hot objects, remove their internal energy as heat and do work with that internal energy? To do this, we need to design a heat engine. Let's start with our cylinder and piston system that we used to do *PV* work. First we turn the cylinder on its side. Now, instead of weights on the piston, we hold and move the piston with a force that we control. For simplicity we imagine a heat reservoir that has so much internal energy that the change in its temperature is negligible when it gives off heat to the gas in our piston. We adjust the force on our piston so that the external pressure is equal to the pressure of the gas, and we set the temperature of the gas equal to the temperature of our heat reservoir. Now our system, the gas, is in equilibrium with the surroundings. Without this equilibrium, we cannot proceed with a reversible process.

The cold reservoir shown in Figure 3.7 is not yet in contact with our system. Now we are ready to do work with internal energy from our heat reservoir.

Figure 3.7 Cylinder and Piston System

Piston

Hot

q_h

q_c

Force

Cylinder

Cold

Step 1: Reversible isothermal expansion – from A to B. We decrease the force on our piston by an infinitesimal amount allowing the cylinder to expand infinitesimally slowly. Our system does PV work on the surroundings. Since energy leaves the gas as work, if this were the only energy transfer, the energy per mole of gas would be reduced, and the temperature of the gas would decrease; however, we have our system in thermal equilibrium with the heat reservoir, so the energy leaving the heat reservoir as work is replaced exactly by energy transferred as heat from the heat reservoir. Thus the temperature of the gas remains constant. The pressure of the gas, energy per volume, drops because the volume is expanding as energy remains constant. Since everything is done infinitely slowly, everything stays in equilibrium.

At first, it seems like we have solved the world's energy crisis! We are changing heat completely into work; we are able change the disordered energy of the random motion of molecules and completely into work. Since energy is never destroyed, if we could just continue this process indefinitely, we could do an endless amount of work continually recycling internal energy into useful work. But, of course, there are problems. The friction between the piston and the cylinder dissipates energy, but let's imagine that is negligible. Nevertheless, our cylinder doesn't go on forever; it has a finite length. Eventually, we have to push our piston back to the original starting point. If we just push the piston back to its starting point, we will have to do more work on the gas than the work that we got out of the gas because as the volume decreases the pressure will increase requiring a greater force over the same distance. Our work done will have been lost. This brings us to step 2.

Step 2: Reversible adiabatic expansion – from B to C. If we cool the gas before we push the piston back to its starting point, less work will be required to reset the piston, and our whole process will result in a net amount of work done on the surroundings. To cool the gas, we separate the heat reservoir from the gas, so no heat can be transferred to or from the gas. Now we continue to expand our gas infinitely slowly. This time, our gas must cool as we expand it because it is still transferring energy as work to the surroundings but no heat is replacing the transferred energy. Since the energy is decreasing and the volume is increasing, pressure, which is energy per volume, is also decreasing. At some point we stop the expansion and go to step 3.

Figure 3.8   Net Work Completed

Step 3. Reversible isothermal compression – from C to D. Now our gas is at a lower pressure and temperature. We connect it to a cold reservoir at the same low temperature. We begin pushing the piston toward its original position by infinitesimally increasing the force. This force applied over a distance transfers energy to the gas via work; however, all the added energy transfers to cold reservoir as heat and the temperature, energy per mole, remains constant. The cold reservoir is so big that any change in its temperature is negligible. The pressure (energy per volume) rises because, although the energy remains constant, the volume is decreasing.

Step 4. Reversible adiabatic compression – from D to A. At a specific point before the piston reaches its original starting position, we will need to separate the cold reservoir from the gas. This is because we still need to increase the temperature of the gas back to its starting temperature. Once the cold reservoir is removed, the extra energy due to the work done on the gas has no place to go. As the energy per mole increases, the temperature increases. As the energy increases and the volume decreases, the pressure increases even faster. Finally, we arrive at the original starting point of the piston.

The four steps just described take the gas system through a complete cycle. By the end of each cycle the gas returns to its original volume, pressure, temperature, internal energy, and all other original state function values; there is no net change to the gas after one complete cycle. The result to the surroundings is that disordered random molecular energy has been ordered; <u>some</u> heat has been changed to work.

But there is another result. Some random molecular energy has also been transferred as heat from the hot reservoir to the cold reservoir. This energy is at a lower temperature. It is in the cold reservoir and, unless work is done, it can never be reused in the same heat reservoir from which it came. This energy has been 'downgraded'; it is less useful. Recall that this 'downgrading' occurred in Steps 3 and 4 of the cycle when we were returning the piston to its original condition. The 'downgrading' was the only way to complete the cycle and still get some net work done on the surroundings. So whenever we use energy, we 'downgrade energy'. Even though energy can never be destroyed, it cannot be endlessly reused. We haven't solved the world's energy crisis after all. This is the first of three ways to state the second law of thermodynamics: heat cannot be changed completely into work in a cyclical process.

Any machine that turns heat into work is called a heat engine. A heat engine can be diagrammed as shown in Figure 3.10. Notice that, via conservation of energy, the heat entering the engine q_h must equal the net work done by the engine w plus the heat leaving the engine q_c ($q_h = w + q_c$).

We can reverse a heat engine to create a refrigerator. If we change the direction of the arrow in heat engine in Figure 3.10, the inside of the refrigerator is represented by the cold reservoir. Notice that the refrigerator requires work, and therefore the heat generated by the refrigerator is greater than the heat that it removes from the cold reservoir. This is the second of three ways to state **the second law of thermodynamics**: work is required to transfer energy from a cold reservoir to a hot reservoir.

Figure 3.9 Heat Engine

The heat engine processes described earlier (isothermal expansion, adiabatic expansion, isothermal compression, and adiabatic compression) are all described as reversible. They are reversible because they are done in infinitesimal increments while the system is maintained in equilibrium. Such a process is called a Carnot cycle and such a heat engine is called a Carnot engine. The Carnot engine is an impossible ideal. It represents a maximum hypothetical efficiency for any heat engine. Because real processes are not infinitely slow, do not take place under perfect equilibrium conditions, and do have friction, no heat engine can be as efficient as a Carnot engine in converting heat to work. But even under the ideal conditions of the Carnot engine, heat cannot be completely converted to work.

A Sterling engine converts heat energy to mechanical work.

The efficiency of a heat engine is the ratio of how much work it produces to how much heat input it requires to produce that work. The efficiency is given by:

$$e = \frac{w}{q_h} \qquad \text{or} \qquad e = 1 - \frac{T_c}{T_h}$$

(*Carnot* engine only)

where e is the efficiency, w is the work done by the engine, q_h is the heat input into the system, and T_h and T_c are the temperatures of the hot and cold reservoirs respectively. The second equation applies only to a Carnot engine. From the equations, notice that the efficiency of any heat engine will be between 0 and 1 where 1 is perfect efficiency. Notice also from the second equation that the efficiency of an ideal heat engine gets closer to 1 as the T_c becomes much colder than T_h, and could only reach 1 if T_c is absolute zero or T_h is infinitely large. Remember, the second equation applies only to an ideal engine, a Carnot Engine. All other heat engines will be less efficient. *Carnot's theorem* states that no engine operating between two heat reservoirs can be more efficient that a Carnot engine operating between the same two heat reservoirs.

By the way, as long as the processes are reversible, the engine is a Carnot engine regardless of how it is constructed or of what substance it is made or what kind of work it does; all Carnot engines are reversible engines with the same efficiency when placed between the same two heat reservoirs.

Even under ideal conditions, heat cannot be completely converted to work. The second law of thermodynamics is not due to friction or man's inability to create a perfect machine. It is a result of the natural direction of energy flow.

The heat engine stuff is given here in order to help you understand the relationship between heat and work. If it is on the MCAT, it will be explained in a passage. However, don't just ignore it. It is a possible passage topic and a good way to learn to understand heat and work. At the very least, know the second law of thermodynamics in terms of heat and work: heat cannot be completely converted to worked in a cyclical process.

Thought Provoker

If we put a running refrigerator in a small closet, close the closet door and open the refrigerator door what will happen to the temperature of the closet?

Answer: See page 85

49. Which of the following is true concerning an air conditioner that sits inside a thermally sealed room and draws energy from an outside power source?

    A. It requires more energy to cool the room than if part of the air conditioner were outside the room.
    B. It will require more time to cool the room than if part of the air conditioner were outside the room.
    C. It will require less energy to cool the room than if part of the air conditioner were outside the room.
    D. It cannot cool the room on a permanent basis.

50. Three blocks made from the same insulating material are placed between hot and cold reservoirs as shown below.

    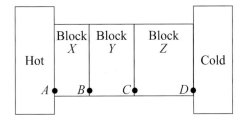

    Which of the following must be true?

    I. The temperature difference between points A and B is less than the temperature difference between points C and D.
    II. The rate of heat flow through Block X is greater than the rate of heat flowing through Block Z.
    III. Switching the positions of Block X and Block Z would decrease the rate of heat flow.

    A. I only
    B. III only
    C. I and III only
    D. I, II, and III

51. Immediately upon bringing a hot piece of metal into a room, the heat is felt from 5 meters away. The type of heat transfer is probably:

    A. convection
    B. transduction
    C. radiation
    D. conduction

52. A box sliding down an incline increases in temperature due to friction. The name for this type of heat is:

    A. convection
    B. conduction
    C. radiation
    D. The energy transfer here is due to work and not to heat.

53. Which of the following gas properties is needed to calculate the work done by an expanding gas?

    I. The initial and final pressures
    II. The initial and final volumes
    III. The path followed during the expansion.

    A. I only
    B. II only
    C. I and II only
    D. I, II, and III

54. The heating bill for a homeowner is directly proportional to the rate at which heat is conducted out of the house and into the surroundings. The average temperature inside and outside of a house is measured on different months and recorded in Table 1.

Month	Temperature outside (°C)	Temperature inside (°C)
Nov	8	22
Dec	5	25
Jan	3	20
Feb	13	26

    For which month would the homeowner expect to have the largest heating bill?

    A. November
    B. December
    C. January
    D. February

55. A rigid container of constant volume is used to store compressed gas. When gas is pumped into the container, the pressure of the gas inside the container is increased and the temperature of the container also increases. Which statement is true of the work done on the container?

   A. The work is equal to the increase in the pressure inside the container.

   B. The work is equal to the increase in the temperature inside the container.

   C. The work is equal to the sum of the pressure and temperature increases.

   D. There is no work done on the container.

56. Under the best possible conditions, a steam engine will have an efficiency of slightly more than 20 percent. A normal steam engine has an efficiency of about 10 percent. This means that for a normal steam engine:

   A. 10 percent of the input energy contributes to the work done by the engine.

   B. 90 percent of the input energy contributes to the work done by the engine.

   C. the internal temperature will increase by 10 percent during operation.

   D. the internal temperature will increase by 90 percent during operation.

3.7 Thermodynamic State Functions

To understand thermodynamics, you must be familiar with seven state functions:

Table 3.1 Thermodynamic State Functions

Title	State Function	Prefix
1	Internal energy	U
2	Temperature	T
3	Pressure	P
4	Volume	V
5	Enthalpy	H
6	Entropy	S
7	Gibbs energy	G

Thermodynamic state functions are macroscopic properties of a system. Heat and work, which are also thermodynamic functions, are not state functions. Thermodynamic functions cannot be applied to systems on a molecular scale. The microscopic world (the motions of the individual molecules) is related to thermodynamic functions by statistics. Statistical predictions become more accurate as the number of subjects within a sample space increases. For instance, the more times you flip a coin, the more likely the total number heads will approach 50%. There are many millions of molecules within any macroscopic sample space making the statistically based thermodynamic functions highly useful for predictions on a macroscopic scale. However, if we try to apply thermodynamic functions to individual molecules, the sample space is far too small and our predictions will not be reliable.

3.8 Internal Energy

Internal energy is the collective energy of molecules measured on a microscopic scale. This energy includes vibrational energy, rotational energy, translational energy, electronic energy, intermolecular potential energy, and rest mass energy. Internal energy does not include macroscopic mechanical energies such as the kinetic energy of the entire system moving as one unit, or the gravitational energy of the entire system raised off the ground. In other words, internal energy is all the possible forms of energy imaginable on a molecular scale.

Perhaps because it is stationary, a glass of water sitting on a table appears to have no energy; however, it contains internal energy as well as gravitational potential energy.

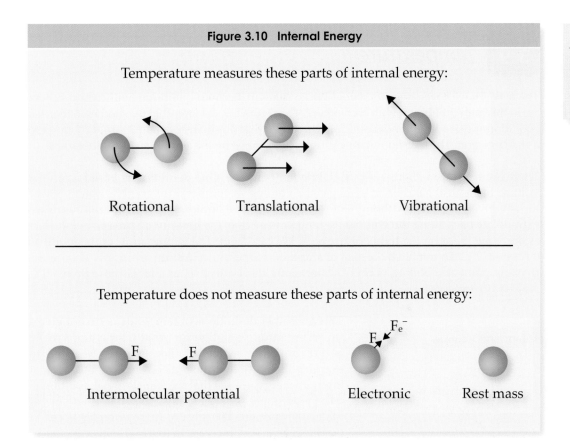

Figure 3.10   Internal Energy

Temperature measures these parts of internal energy:

Rotational   Translational   Vibrational

Temperature does not measure these parts of internal energy:

Intermolecular potential   Electronic   Rest mass

Thought Provoker

How does internal energy
manifest in an ideal gas?

Answer: See page 85

Vibrational energy is created by the atoms vibrating within a molecule. Vibrational energy makes an insignificant contribution to internal energy for light diatomic molecules at temperatures below a few hundred Kelvin. Atoms in a monatomic gas have no vibrational energy.

Rotational energy is molecular movement where the spatial orientation of the body changes, while the center of mass remains fixed and each point within a molecule remains fixed relative to all other points. Atoms in a monatomic gas have no rotational energy.

Translational energy is the movement of the center of mass of a molecule.

Electronic energy is the potential electrical energy created by the attractions between the electrons and their respective nuclei. At temperatures below 5000 K, nearly all molecules are at their lowest electronic energy level. In a chemical reaction, the electronic energy accounts for the greatest change in internal energy. If no chemical reaction occurs, electronic energy remains nearly constant.

Intermolecular potential energy is the energy created by the intermolecular forces between molecular dipoles. For a gas at room temperature and pressure, intermolecular potential energy makes only a small contribution to internal energy, but at higher pressures, the contribution becomes significant. In liquids and solids, intermolecular potential energy is a substantial portion of internal energy.

Rest mass energy is the energy predicted by Einstein's famous equation $E = mc^2$. The sum of these energies for a very large group of molecules is called the internal energy.

If we have a closed system at rest with no electric or magnetic fields, the only energy change will be in internal energy, and the first law of thermodynamics can be rewritten as: $\Delta U = q + w$. For a reaction within such a system involving no change in volume, there is no work of any kind and the change in internal energy is equal to the heat: $\Delta U = q$.

Internal energy is a state function. For an ideal gas, any state function can be expressed as a function of temperature and volume only. For an ideal gas, internal energy is independent of volume and is a function of temperature only.

The MCAT may refer to internal energy as 'heat energy', 'thermal energy', or even 'heat'. Heat energy and thermal energy are really the vibrational, rotational, and translational parts of internal energy. They are called thermal energy because they affect temperature. Heat is a transfer of energy, and using it as another name for internal energy can create confusion. Unfortunately, this is a common mistake.

3.9 Temperature

The *zeroth law of thermodynamics* states "Two systems in thermal equilibrium with a third system are in thermal equilibrium with each other." The zeroth law declares that two bodies in thermal equilibrium share a thermodynamic property, and that this thermodynamic property must be a state function. The thermodynamic property described by the zeroth law is temperature.

There are several methods used to define temperature. One definition is based upon the volume of an ideal gas. For an ideal gas the volume vs. temperature graph is exactly linear for any given pressure. Although all real gases become liquids at low temperatures, if we extrapolate back along the volume vs. temperature line, the lines for all pressures intersect at the same point on the temperature axis. We can define the temperature of this point as 0 K or –273°C. To establish the size of a unit of temperature, we can arbitrarily choose the freezing point and boiling point of water along the 1 atm line, and label those points 0°C and 100°C respectively.

This and other definitions of temperature do not give a satisfying intuitive notion for what temperature really is. For an intuitive feel of temperature, we need to examine the motion of the molecules. When we look at internal energy, we see that the translational, rotational, and vibrational energies describe the energies of molecular motion. The sum of these energies is called *thermal energy*. Any increase in thermal energy increases temperature.

For a fluid, temperature is directly proportional to the translational kinetic energy of its molecules. Translational motion can be divided into three *degrees of freedom* or *modes*: 1) along the x axis 2) along the y axis and 3) along the z axis. The *equipartition theory* states that for a normal system each mode of motion will have the same average energy and that the energy will be equal to $\frac{1}{2}kT$, where T is the temperature, and k is the Boltzmann constant $(1.38 \times 10^{-23} \text{ J K}^{-1})$. The Boltzmann constant k is related to the ideal gas constant R by Avagadro's number N_A: $R = N_A k$. Since there are three modes of kinetic energy each averaging $\frac{1}{2}kT$ joules, the average kinetic energy of a single molecule in any fluid (real or ideal) is given by: This is the same equation found in Lecture 2.

$$K.E._{\text{avg per mole}} = \frac{3}{2}RT$$

Figure 3.11 Gas Temperature and Volume

Volume vs. Temperature for one mole of N_2 gas extrapolated back to zero volume

If we multiply this equation by Avogadro's number we arrive at the average translational kinetic energy for a mole of molecules in any fluid: The equipartition theorem is derived from classical physics and breaks down when quantum effects are significant. Quantum effects are greater for rotation than for translation, and greater still for vibration. The molecules of a solid do not translate or rotate; they vibrate. For solids at high temperatures where quantum effects are less important, temperature is proportional to the average kinetic energy of the vibration of molecules about their equilibrium position. For solids at low temperatures, there is deviation from this rule due to quantum effects.

Molecules in a solid vibrate faster as temperature increases.

The greater the random translational kinetic energy of gas molecules per mole, the greater the temperature. So loosely speaking, temperature can be thought of as the thermal energy per mole of molecules. Recall that when we divide one extensive property by another, we get an intensive property. Energy and number of moles are extensive properties. This makes temperature an intensive property, so when we connect two identical systems the temperature does not change; we double the thermal energy, but we also double the number of moles, so thermal energy per mole remains constant.

The MCAT will use two measurement systems for temperature: degrees Celsius and Kelvin. Celsius is just the centigrade system with a new name. At 1 atm, water freezes at 0°C and boils at 100°C. The lowest possible temperature is called absolute zero, and is approximately –273°C. To find approximate Kelvin from degrees Celsius, simply add 273. An increase of 1°C is equivalent to an increase of 1 K.

Virtually all physcial properties change with temperature.

When in doubt, use kelvin. In chemistry, you are always safe using the Kelvin scale because the Kelvin scale is absolute.

Changing the temperature changes nearly everything.

It is not completely accurate, but accurate enough for the MCAT to think of temperature as a measure of the thermal energy per mole of molecules. The greater the thermal energy per mole, the greater the temperature.

3.10 Pressure

Loosely speaking, pressure of an ideal gas is the random translational kinetic energy per volume. Pressure is an intensive state function. Pressure and volume are discussed in depth in Chemistry Lecture 2 and Physics Lecture 5.

The greater the random translational kinetic energy of gas molecules per volume, the greater the pressure.

Notes:

Enthalpy cannot be intuited. You must rely completely on the equation.

For an ideal gas, enthalpy and internal energy depend ONLY on temperature. Enthalpy increases with temperature.

Enthalpy is defined as an equation rather than as a description of a property. Enthalpy H is defined as:

$$H \equiv U + PV$$

where U represents internal energy. From our inexact but intuitive concept of pressure as the random translational kinetic energy per unit volume, we see that enthalpy actually counts random translational kinetic energy twice! Although enthalpy is measured in units of energy (joules), enthalpy itself is not conserved like energy. Enthalpy of the universe does not remain constant.

Since U, P, and V are state functions, enthalpy is also a state function. Like internal energy, for an ideal gas enthalpy depends only on temperature. Enthalpy is an extensive property, so when we connect two identical systems the total enthalpy doubles.

As with many state functions, we are interested in the *change* in enthalpy and not its absolute value. For the MCAT, we will be interested in the change in enthalpy under constant pressure conditions only:

$$\Delta H = \Delta U + P \Delta V \quad (const.\ P)$$

For a system at rest recall that the first law of thermodynamics can be written as $\Delta U = w + q$. Work can be either nonPV work (w_{nonPV}) or PV work (w_{PV}), so we have $\Delta U = w_{nonPV} + w_{PV} + P\Delta V + q$. At constant pressure in a reversible process, PV work done by the system reduces energy in the system and is given by $w = -P\Delta V$. Substituting for ΔU in our equation for change in enthalpy gives:

$$\Delta H = [w_{nonPV} - P\Delta V + q] + P\Delta V$$

$$\Delta H = w_{nonPV} + q_{(const.\ P,\ closed\ system\ at\ rest,\ PV\ work\ only)}$$

So at constant pressure, enthalpy change of a system at rest is a measure of nonPV work and heat. These are the conditions inside a living cell. NonPV work is mainly electrical work such as that done by contracting muscles, firing neurons, and batteries. If no nonPV work is performed, and only PV work is performed, enthalpy change is the heat flow into the system at constant pressure.

$$\Delta H = q_{(constant\ pressure,\ closed\ system\ at\ rest)}$$

Many liquid and solid chemical reactions performed in the lab take place in systems at rest at constant pressure (1 atm). Remember that at constant volume $\Delta U = q$, which means that at constant volume and constant pressure $\Delta U \cong \Delta H$.

Heat of hydration of copper sulphate. Water being poured from a test tube onto anhydrous copper (II) sulphate (white). The copper (II) sulphate forms hydration bonds with the water in an exothermic reaction, resulting in hydrated copper (II) sulphate (blue). The heat of the reaction is enough to produce steam and disturb the powder.

Thought Provoker

Galvanic cells (Chemistry Lecture 7) do nonPV work, so we cannot use ΔH = q for such reactions.

For reactions at constant volume, the internal energy change is equal to the heat, so for reactions that have both constant volume and constant pressure, enthalpy change approximately equals internal energy change.

What if we mix two chemicals and the reaction produces a gas to the open air? Can we still use ΔH = q?

Answer: See page 85

There are no absolute enthalpy values, so scientists have assigned enthalpy values to compounds based upon their standard state. Standard state should not be confused with STP. Standard state is a somewhat complicated concept that varies with phase and other factors and even has diffrnet values based upon which convention you choose to follow. As usual, we can simplify things greatly for the MCAT. Recall that a 'state' is described by a specific set of thermodynamic property values. For a pure solid or liquid, the standard state is the reference form of a substance at any chosen temperature T and a pressure of 1 bar (about 750 torr or exactly 105 pascals). The reference form is usually the form that is most stable at 1 bar and T. For a pure gas there is an additional requirement that the gas behave like an ideal gas. An element in its standard state at 25°C is arbitrarily assigned an enthalpy value of 0 J/mol. From this value we can assign enthalpy values to compounds based upon the change in enthalpy when they are formed from raw elements in their standard states at 25°C. Such enthalpy values for compounds are called standard enthalpies of formation. The standard enthalpy of formation ΔH°_f is the change in enthalpy for a reaction that creates one mole of that compound from its raw elements in their standard state. The symbol '°' (called naught) indicates standard state conditions. Standard enthalpies of formation can be found by experiment, and are available in books. An example of the enthalpy of formation of water is:

$$H_2(g) + \tfrac{1}{2}O_2(g) \rightarrow H_2O(l) \quad \Delta H^\circ_f = -285.8 \text{ kJ/mol}$$

$$\Delta H = q \quad \text{(const. } P\text{, closed system at rest, } PV \text{ work only)}$$

Since, in many reactions in the lab, enthalpy approximates heat, the change in enthalpy from reactants to products is often referred to as the heat of reaction.

$$\Delta H^\circ_{reaction} = \Delta H^\circ_{f\ products} - \Delta H^\circ_{f\ reactants}$$

Since enthalpy is a state function, the change in enthalpy when converting one group of compounds to another is not dependent upon what reaction or even series of reactions take place. The change in enthalpy depends only on the identities and thermodynamic states of the initial and final compounds. Thus, in any reaction, the steps taken to get from reactants to products do not affect the total change in enthalpy. Hess' law states "The sum of the enthalpy changes for each step is equal to the total enthalpy change regardless of the path chosen." For example:

$N_2 + O_2 \rightarrow 2NO$	$\Delta H = 180$ kJ	step 1
$2NO + O_2 \rightarrow 2NO_2$	$\Delta H = -112$ kJ	$+$ step 2
$N_2 + 2O_2 \rightarrow 2NO_2$	$\Delta H = 68$ kJ	$=$ complete reaction

Hess's law also indicates that a forward reaction has exactly the opposite change in enthalpy as the reverse. If the enthalpy change is positive, the reaction is said to be endothermic; if it is negative, it is said to be exothermic. If we consider a reaction where the change in enthalpy is equal to the heat (a constant pressure reaction), then an exothermic reaction produces heat flow to the surroundings, while an endothermic reaction produces heat flow to the system.

Don't confuse standard state and STP.

If MCAT says 'standard state', you assume 1 bar (about 1 atm). The temperature will probably be 25°C but it doesn't have to be. If it is a gas, adjust the volume for ideal behavior. Now just ask yourself, "Under these conditions is it a gas, liquid, or solid?" Your answer to this question is the reference form.

Figure 3.12 A One Step Reaction

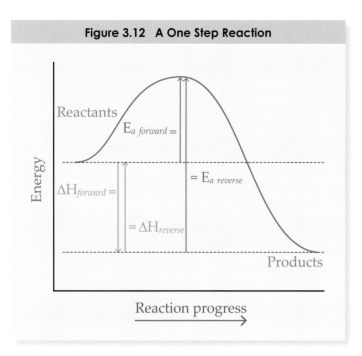

We can see this graphically if we compare the progress of a reaction with the energy of the molecules. (Due to the close relationship between internal energy and enthalpy, the term energy is used loosely for these types of graphs. You may see the y axis labeled as enthalpy, Gibbs free energy, or simply energy.) You can see from the graph that if the reaction progress is reversed, the enthalpy change is exactly reversed. Notice that there is an initial increase in energy regardless of which direction the reaction moves. This increase in energy is called the **activation energy** (the same activation energy as in Chemistry Lecture 2). The peak of this energy hill represents the molecules in a **transition state** where the old bonds are breaking and new bonds are forming. The transition state occurs during the reaction collision. Do not confuse the transition state with intermediates, which are the products of the first step in a two step reaction. A two step reaction has two humps as shown in Figure 2.8 in Chapter 2. The intermediates exist in the trough between the two humps.

Notice, on an energy diagram, how a catalyst lowers the activation energy. The activation energy for both the forward and the reverse reactions is lowered. Although the relative amount by which the activation energies are lowered is different, if we used the Arrhenius equation (Chemistry Lecture 2) to find the new rate constants, we would find that the rate constants are raised by the same relative amounts; thus, equilibrium is unaffected by a catalyst. For the MCAT you must remember that a catalyst affects the rate and not the equilibrium. Notice that a catalyst does not affect the enthalpy change either.

Figure 3.13 Effect of Catalyst

A computer interfaced sensor measuring the temperature change of an exothermic/exergonic reaction between aluminum foil and cupric chloride. The graph shows a steady increase in the temperature of the system after the aluminum foil was added. The reaction occurs spontaneously in water. The enthalpy change indicates that it is chemically an exothermic process. The release of free energy in the form of heat indicates that the reaction is exergonic.

How will you know what ΔH is for a reaction on the MCAT? There are five possible ways:

1. The problem or passage just tells you the ΔH for the reaction (Salty's favorite).
2. The heat can be measured with a calorimeter (see Lecture 5.3), and the heat is the ΔH.
3. For some reactions, the sign of ΔH can be intuited, even if the MCAT doesn't expect you to know the magnitude. For example, we know combustion reactions release heat, so they have a negative ΔH. We can also do this for phase changes (see Lecture 5.4). For example, we know that in order to melt something, you have to add heat to it. Melting, therefore, has a positive ΔH.
4. If given a table of bond energies, you can keep track of how many of each type of bond is broken and formed during the course of a reaction. Since forming bonds releases energy and breaking bonds requires the input of energy, you can total up the net energy (heat) absorbed or released during the reaction.
5. You can calculate the ΔH for a reaction using standard enthalpies of formation (ΔH_f°).

Notes:

57. What is the enthalpy change in the following reaction?

Compound	ΔH_f°
$CH_4(g)$	–75 kJ/mol
$CO_2(g)$	–394 kJ/mol
$H_2O(l)$	–286 kJ/mol

$$CH_4(g) + 2O_2(g) \rightarrow CO_2(g) + 2H_2O(l)$$

A. –755 kJ
B. –891 kJ
C. –1041 kJ
D. 891 kJ

58. Which of the following properties of a gaseous system affect its enthalpy?

I. pressure
II. volume
III. internal energy

A. III only
B. I and II only
C. II and III only
D. I, II, and III

59. A catalyst will change all of the following EXCEPT:

A. enthalpy
B. activation energy
C. rate of the forward reaction
D. rate of the reverse reaction

60. In an exothermic reaction, which of the following will most likely increase the ratio of the forward rate to the reverse rate?

A. adding thermal energy to the system
B. removing thermal energy from the system
C. using a catalyst
D. lowering the activation energy

61. The heats of combustion for graphite and diamond are as follows:

$$C_{graphite}(s) + O_2(g) \rightarrow CO_2(g) \quad \Delta H = -394 \text{ kJ}$$

$$C_{diamond}(s) + O_2(g) \rightarrow CO_2(g) \quad \Delta H = -396 \text{ kJ}$$

Diamond spontaneously changes to graphite. What is the change in enthalpy accompanying the conversion of two moles of diamond to graphite?

A. –790 kJ
B. –4 kJ
C. 2 kJ
D. 4 kJ

62. The standard enthalpy of formation for liquid water is:

$$H_2(g) + \tfrac{1}{2}O_2(g) \rightarrow H_2O(l) \quad \Delta H^{\circ}_f = -285.8 \text{ kJ/mol}$$

Which of the following could be the standard enthalpy of formation for water vapor?

A. –480.7 kJ/mol
B. –285.8 kJ/mol
C. –241.8 kJ/mol
D. +224.6 kJ/mol

63. For a particular reversible reaction, the forward process is exothermic and the reverse process is endothermic. Which of the following statements must be true about this reaction?

A. The forward reaction will be spontaneous under standard conditions.
B. The reverse reaction will be spontaneous under standard conditions.
C. The activation energy will be greater for the forward reaction than for the reverse reaction.
D. The activation energy will be greater for the reverse reaction than for the forward reaction.

64. Sulfur dioxide reacts with oxygen in a reversible reaction to form sulfur trioxide as shown.

$$2SO_2(g) + O_2(g) \rightleftharpoons 2SO_3(g) \quad \Delta H^{\circ} = -200 \text{ kJ}$$

If the temperature at which the reaction takes place is increased, which of the following will take place?

A. The rates of both the forward and reverse reactions will increase.
B. Only the rate of the forward reaction will increase.
C. Only the rate of the reverse reaction will increase.
D. The rates of neither the forward nor reverse reactions will increase.

3.12 Entropy

If you have studied entropy before, you have probably heard the following example: "Over time, a clean room will tend to get dirty. This is entropy at work." Entropy is nature's tendency toward disorder. A better definition of entropy incorporates the concept of probability. **Entropy (S)** is nature's tendency to create the most probable situation that can occur within a system. For instance, imagine four identical jumping beans that bounce randomly back and forth between two containers. If we label each bean A, B, C, and D respectively, we will find that the most likely situation is to have two beans in each container. The least likely situation is to have all four beans in either of the containers. For example, if we choose the left container, there is only one way for all four beans to be in the left container, but there are 6 possible ways that two beans can be in each container. Two beans in each container is six times more likely than four beans in the left container. Since the two-bean container situation is more likely, it has greater entropy.

If we replace the four jumping beans with millions of molecules moving randomly back and forth between two glass spheres connected by a glass tube, you should be able to see how the odds against having all the molecules in one sphere become astronomical. The odds are so poor, in fact, that the second law of thermodynamics states that it will never happen without some outside intervention, namely work. The third way to state **the second law of thermodynamics** is "The entropy of an isolated system will never decrease."

We can apply the second law of thermodynamics to any type of system if we recall that the surroundings of any system include everything that is not in the system. Thus, the system and the surroundings together make up the entire universe. The universe itself is an isolated system. Therefore, the sum of the entropy changes of any system and its surroundings equals the entropy change of the universe, which must be equal to or greater than zero.

$$\Delta S_{system} + \Delta S_{surroundings} = \Delta S_{universe} \geq 0$$

So the entropy of a system can decrease, only if, at the same time, the entropy of the surroundings increases by a greater or equal magnitude. Entropy is a state function and an extensive property.

Entropy, and not energy, dictates the direction of a reaction.

Figure 3.14 Probability in Relation to Entropy

1	A B	C D
2	A C	B D
3	A D	B C
4	C B	A D
5	D B	A C
6	C D	A B
	Left	Right

Six possible situations with two beans in one pan.

| 1 | C D A B | |
| | Left | Right |

Only one possible situation with four beans in the left pan.

The second law of thermodynamics is a funny law because it could be violated, but it is so unlikely to be violated that we say it won't be violated no matter what.

An intuitive way to view entropy is as nature's effort to spread energy evenly between systems. Nature likes to decrease the energy of a system when energy is high relative to the nearby surroundings and to increase energy of a system when energy is low relative to the energy of the nearby surroundings. A warm object will lose energy to its surroundings when placed in a cool room, but the same object will gain energy when placed in a hot room. If we consider the energy of the universe, no energy is gained or lost in either process. Instead, energy is just spread out. This means that it is entropy and not energy that drives reactions in a given direction. The second law of thermodynamics tells us that entropy of the universe is the driving force that dictates whether or not a reaction will proceed. A reaction can be unfavorable in terms of enthalpy, or even energy, and still proceed, but a reaction must increase the entropy of the universe in order to proceed.

Entropy is an extensive property; It increases with amount of substance. All other factors being equal, entropy increases with number, volume, and temperature. On the MCAT, if a reaction increases the number of gaseous molecules, then that reaction has positive entropy (for the reaction system, not necessarily for the surroundings or the universe). The greater the temperature of a substance the greater its entropy.

The third law of thermodynamics assigns by convention a zero entropy value to any pure substance (either an element or a compound) at absolute zero and in internal equilibrium. At absolute zero, atoms have very little motion. Absolute zero temperature is unattainable.

The units for entropy are J/K. Entropy change is defined mathematically by the infinitesimal change in heat q_{rev} per kelvin in a reversible process. So at constant temperature, we have:

$$\Delta S = \frac{q_{rev}}{T}$$

Notice that change in entropy is defined for a reversible process. In an irreversible process between the same two states this equation will not apply. The heat q will be different for an irreversible process because heat is pathway dependent. However, the entropy change ΔS will be the same for any process between the same two states, reversible or not. Thus ΔS for an irreversible process can be found by imagining a reversible process between the same two states and finding the heat transfer for that reversible process. Since entropy is a state function, the change in entropy for any process will be the same as the change in entropy for a reversible process between the same two states.

A time lapse photo of the forces of nature working to increase entropy.

Imagine what happens when you slide a box across the floor. The kinetic energy of the box is dissipated into internal energy of the box and floor via molecular collisions collectively called friction. Of course, energy is conserved; the increase in internal energy equals the initial kinetic energy. Now imagine the reverse reaction: the molecules of the floor and the box happen to be moving in a coordinated fashion so as to collide and make the stationary box suddenly start moving. The internal energy of the molecules becomes kinetic energy. Why doesn't this happen in real life? Energy is still conserved in the reverse reaction, so there is no violation of the first law of thermodynamics. The only reason boxes don't spontaneously start sliding across the floor is due to the decrease in entropy which would accompany such a reaction.

3.13 Reversibility

From universal entropy change, we have a *thermodynamic definition of reversibility*. Imagine a reaction in an isolated system. Since the system is isolated, the forward reaction does not affect the surroundings and can change the entropy of only the system and not the surroundings. Entropy is a state function, so, if we run the reaction exactly in reverse, we bring the system back to its original state. Now the system must have the same entropy as when it started the forward reaction. However, the second law of thermodynamics says that the entropy of an isolated system cannot decrease for any reaction, so in order to be able to run the reaction both in the forward and the reverse direction, the entropy change must be zero in both directions. Thus, for any reversible reaction within an isolated system, the entropy change must be zero. The universe is an isolated system, so the entropy change of the universe must be zero for any reversible reaction.

In real life, reversible reactions do not happen; all known reactions and processes are accompanied by a positive change in the entropy of the universe. In the real world, all reactions are thermodynamically irreversible. However, hypothetically we can imagine a reversible reaction. A hypothetical reversible reaction will be a quasi-static process; one where the system is in equilibrium with the surroundings at all times. Any heat transfer must occur while the system and surroundings are at the same temperature. Pressure differences where PV work is done must be infinitesimal. All changes to the system will be infinitesimal and require an infinite amount of time.

Unfortunately, *alternative definitions of reversibility* are also used outside thermodynamics. Recall that thermodynamics deals with macroscopic properties, large numbers of molecules. If, instead, we examine a system microscopically, on the scale of two molecules reacting with each other, entropy is undefined. The second law of thermodynamics does not work on this scale and all reactions on a microscopic scale must be considered reversible from the stand point of classical mechanics. From the microscopic point of view, collisions

If the entropy of an isolated system cannot decrease, the universal entropy change for any reversible reaction must be zero in both directions.

The equilibrium point is the point of maximum universal entropy.

between individual molecules are exact opposites of their reverse collisions and there is no law in classical physics that favors one direction over another. All molecular collisions are reversible. On the microscopic scale, this definition of reversibility is contradictory to the thermodynamic definition. The macroscopic principles of thermodynamics should not be applied to the microscopic world. However, the reverse is not true; predictions about the macroscopic world can be made based upon microscopic conditions. Recall from Chemistry Lecture 2 that equilibrium is achieved when the rate of the forward reaction equals the rate of the reverse reaction. This is the point of greatest universal entropy. Reactions at equilibrium have achieved maximum universal entropy.

But there is still another *alternative to the meaning of reversibility*. Any chemical reaction has a threshold activation energy that must be reached before a reaction can take place. This threshold energy is related to the energy required to break chemical bonds before new bonds can be formed. Since products and reactants may be at different energy levels, more energy is required to reach the threshold energy from one side of the reaction than from the other. If the required energy is much greater, the reaction may be considered irreversible. This definition of irreversibility focuses on the system, and not on the universe. It is subjective and not directly related to the exact thermodynamic definition of reversibility as we have defined it.

3.14 Gibbs Free Energy

Just for a moment, let's define three types of equilibrium: mechanical, material, and thermal. A system is in mechanical equilibrium when it is not accelerating. A system is in material equilibrium when no net chemical reaction is occurring, and there is no matter transferring within the system. A system is in thermal equilibrium when its temperature is the same throughout. A system can also be in thermal equilibrium with its surroundings, which simply means that it is the same temperature as its surroundings. For a system to be in thermodynamic equilibrium it must be in mechanical, material, and thermal equilibrium.

The equilibrium achieved by maximizing the entropy of the universe, $\Delta S_{univ} = \Delta S_{surr} + \Delta S_{sys}$, is material equilibrium. A closed system undergoing an irreversible chemical reaction at constant pressure and temperature is in thermal and mechanical equilibrium, but not material equilibrium. The surroundings at the same temperature as the system are not undergoing an irreversible reaction and are in thermal, mechanical, and material equilibrium. If heat flows into the system, the heat flow is reversible from the standpoint of the surroundings, thus $\Delta S_{surr} = q_{surr}/T$. We also know that $q_{surr} = -q_{sys}$, so $\Delta S_{surr} = -q_{sys}/T$. Pressure is constant, so $\Delta H_{sys} = q_{sys}$. Substituting we have $\Delta S_{surr} = -\Delta H_{sys}/T$. Plugging the result into $\Delta S_{univ} = \Delta S_{surr} + \Delta S_{sys}$ gives:

$$\Delta S_{universe} = \frac{-\Delta H_{system}}{T} + \Delta S_{system}$$

If we multiply through by $-T$, and substitute ΔG for $-\Delta S_{universe}T$, we have the important MCAT equation for **Gibbs free energy (G)**:

$$\Delta G = \Delta H - T\Delta S \qquad \boxed{\text{Important MCAT equation!}}$$

All state functions in this equation refer to the system and not the surroundings. Notice that $\Delta G_{sys} = -T\Delta S_{universe}$. Since any real process moves in the direction of increasing $\Delta S_{universe}$, we say that a reaction that increases $\Delta S_{universe}$ is spontaneous. Since we require a positive $\Delta S_{universe}$ for a spontaneous reaction, it follows that a negative ΔG is required for a spontaneous reaction. Since $\Delta S_{universe} = 0$ indicates equilibrium, $\Delta G=0$ is required for equilibrium. However, there are limitations attached to ΔG that were created when we derived our equation. At constant temperature and pressure, PV work only, for a closed system G decreases as the reaction approaches equilibrium. Nevertheless, for the MCAT, a negative ΔG will be good enough to indicate a spontaneous reaction.

The different kinds of equilibrium will not be tested by the MCAT. It is given here only to help you understand Gibbs Energy.

Do you remember that enthalpy is a man-made concept? Here's a reason why scientists made up enthalpy: It is easier to measure changes in your chosen system than in the entire universe of your surroundings. Measuring the enthalpy change of the system sometimes allows you to calculate the entropy change of the surroundings. Under certain conditions $\Delta S_{surr} = -\Delta H_{sys}/T$

$\Delta G = 0$ means equilibrium. Negative ΔG indicates a spontaneous reaction.

Gibbs energy is an extensive property and a state function. It is not conserved in the sense of the conservation of energy law. An isolated system can change its Gibbs energy. The Gibbs energy represents the maximum non-*PV* work available from a reaction, hence the name 'free energy'. Again, contracting muscles, transmitting nerves, and batteries are some examples of things that do only non-*PV* work, making Gibbs energy a useful quantity when analyzing these systems.

You must know the Gibbs function, and, most importantly, that a negative ΔG indicates a spontaneous reaction. Realize that the terms ΔG, ΔH, and ΔS in the Gibbs function refer to changes in the system and not the surroundings. Also realize that since Gibbs energy is a function of enthalpy and entropy, like enthalpy and entropy, Gibbs energy of the universe is not conserved.

By the way, the negative of the Gibbs free energy is the amount of non*PV* work available in a completely reversible process, and we know that completely reversible processes are not quite possible in the real world. In other words, the actual amount of non*PV* work that we will get out of the system is always something less than $-\Delta G$.

If a reaction produces a positive change in enthalpy and a negative change in entropy, the reaction can never be spontaneous. Conversely, if a reaction produces a negative change in enthalpy and a positive change in entropy, it must be spontaneous. If the signs of both enthalpy and entropy are the same for a reaction, the spontaneity of the reaction will depend upon temperature. A higher temperature will favor the direction favored by entropy. Remember, these changes are changes in the system and not the surroundings.

To finish this lecture, let's summarize the laws of thermodynamics. It's not so important to memorize the laws, as it is to understand them and keep them in mind. The first and second laws are the important ones for the MCAT.

0th Law: Two bodies in thermal equilibrium with the same system are in thermal equilibrium with each other. (In other words, temperature exists and is a state function.)

1st Law: The energy of an isolated system is conserved for any reaction.

2nd Law: The entropy of the universe increases for any reaction.

3rd Law: A perfect crystal at zero kelvin is assigned an entropy value of zero. All other substances and all temperatures have a positive entropy value. (Zero kelvin is unattainable.)

Summary:
Think of heat and work as the only two ways to change the energy of a system. Together heat and work result in the change in internal energy of a system at rest. Think of temperature as thermal energy per mole. Think of pressure as thermal energy per volume. Think of enthalpy as $U + PV$, or think of change in enthalpy at constant pressure as the heat. Think of entropy as the spreading out of energy. Entropy increases with temperature, volume, and number. Think of Gibbs Energy change as the negative of the maximum amount of energy available to do non*PV* work such as electrical work in a cell.

3.15 Equation Summary

Equations	
Work $w = P\Delta V_{\text{(constant pressure)}}$	**The First Law of Thermodynamics** $\Delta E = q + w$

The Average Kinetic Energy of a Single Molecule

$$K.E._{\text{avg}} = \frac{3}{2}RT$$

Enthalpy: Under Constant Conditions, No Change in Pressure

$$\Delta H = \Delta U + P\Delta V \quad (\text{const. } P)$$

Enthalpy: No Change in Pressure, Closed System

$$\Delta H = q$$

Heat of Reaction

$$\Delta H^{\circ}_{reaction} = \Delta H^{\circ}_{f\ products} - \Delta H^{\circ}_{f\ reactants}$$

The Second Law of Thermodynamics, Entropy

$$\Delta S_{system} + \Delta S_{surroundings} = \Delta S_{universe} \geq 0$$

Gibbs free energy, G

$$\Delta G = \Delta H - T\Delta S$$

Terms	
Activation energy	*PV* work
Catalyst	Radiation
Conduction	Reference Form
Convection	Reversible
Endothermic	Standard Enthalpy of Formation
Enthalpy	Standard State
Entropy *S*	State Functions
Exothermic	Surroundings
Gibbs Free Energy *G*	System
Heat	Temperature
Heat of Reaction	The First Law of Thermodynamics
Hess' law	The Second Law of Thermodynamics
Internal Energy	The Third Law of Thermodynamics
Intermediates	Transition State
Irreversible	Work

Thought Provoker Answers

Answer from page 63:

White is better. In summer, your house is cooler than the environment and white reflects away the heat. In winter, your house is warmer than the environment and white radiates away less heat.

Answer from page 67:

The closet will warm up because q_h is greater than q_c.

Answer from page 70:

The potential and kinetic energies of the ball are transferred to the internal energy of the ball and the pavement as the molecules of both collide with each other causing the molecules of both to vibrate faster and slightly separate.

Answer from page 71:

An ideal gas is like a bunch of tiny, volumeless marbles bouncing off each other. There are no intermolecular attractions. The translational component of internal energy is the only part of internal energy that can change for an ideal gas. Therefore, any change in the internal energy of an ideal gas will result in a corresponding change in temperature. This is not necessarily true for real gasses, liquids, or solids because they can put energy into other parts of their internal energy.

Answer from page 74:

Yes, as long as no nonPV work is done, because the pressure is constant at about 1 atm.

65.   Which of the following describes a reaction that is always spontaneous?

    A. increasing enthalpy and increasing entropy
    B. decreasing enthalpy and decreasing entropy
    C. increasing enthalpy and decreasing entropy
    D. decreasing enthalpy and increasing entropy

66.   Which of the following statements about entropy is false?

    A. The entropy of a system will always increase in a spontaneous reaction.
    B. Entropy is a measure of disorder.
    C. The entropy change of a forward reaction is exactly opposite to the entropy of the reverse reaction.
    D. Entropy increases with temperature.

67.   Which of the following is a violation of the law of conservation of energy?

    A. Heat can be changed completely to work in cyclical process.
    B. A system undergoing a reaction with constant enthalpy experiences a temperature change.
    C. After sliding to a stop, a box with initial kinetic energy K has only thermal energy in an amount less than K.
    D. A bond is broken and energy is released.

68.   All of the following are examples of processes which increase system entropy EXCEPT:

    A. the expanding universe
    B. aerobic respiration
    C. melting ice
    D. building a bridge

69.   Which of the following statements is most likely true concerning the reaction:

$$2A(g) + B(g) \rightarrow 2C(g) + D(s)$$

    A. System entropy is decreasing.
    B. System entropy is increasing.
    C. The reaction is spontaneous.
    D. The reaction is nonspontaneous.

70.   The reaction below shows the condensation of water.

$$H_2O(g) \rightarrow H_2O(l)$$

Which of the following will be positive for the water at 25°C and 1 atm?

    A. ΔH
    B. ΔS
    C. ΔG
    D. None of the above.

71. $$AgCl(s) \rightarrow Ag^+(aq) + Cl^-(aq)$$

During the course of the reaction above, both entropy and enthalpy are increased. If the reaction is not spontaneous at a given temperature and pressure, what can be done to make the reaction occur spontaneously?

    A. Increase the temperature.
    B. Decrease the temperature.
    C. Increase the pressure.
    D. Decrease the pressure.

72.   The normal boiling point of benzene (C_6H_6) is 80.1°C. If the partial pressure of benzene gas is 1 atm, which of the following is true of the reaction shown below at 80.1°C?

$$C_6H_6(l) \rightarrow C_6H_6(g)$$

    A. ΔS is negative
    B. ΔS is zero
    C. ΔG is negative
    D. ΔG is zero

SOLUTIONS

LECTURE

4

4.1 Solutions

A **solution** is a homogeneous mixture of two or more compounds in a single phase, such as solid, liquid, or gas. The MCAT will probably test your knowledge of liquid solutions only. However, you should be aware that solutions are possible in other phases as well. Brass is an example of a solid solution of zinc and copper. Generally, in a solution with two compounds, the compound of which there is more is called the **solvent**, and the compound of which there is less is called the **solute**. Sometimes, when neither compound predominates, both compounds are referred to as solvents. Although a compound's behavior does depend upon the molecules around it, the label of 'solvent' or 'solute' does not indicate a particular behavior.

There are three types of solutions: *ideal solutions, ideally dilute solutions*, and *nonideal solutions*. Ideal solutions are solutions made from compounds that have similar properties. In other words, the compounds can be interchanged within the solution without changing the spatial arrangement of the molecules or the intermolecular attractions. Benzene in toluene is an example of a nearly ideal solution because both compounds have similar bonding properties and similar size. In an ideally dilute solution, the solute molecules are completely separated by solvent molecules so that they have no interaction with each other. Nonideal solutions violate both of these conditions. On the MCAT, you can assume that you are dealing with an ideally dilute solution unless otherwise indicated; however, you should not automatically assume that an MCAT solution is ideal.

> Solvent usually indicates the compound that predominates in a solution.

> The concepts of an ideal and an ideally dilute solution are not tested directly on the MCAT. They are mentioned here in order to deepen your understanding of solutions and to help explain some apparent paradoxes which result when they are not considered.

> In ideally dilute solutions, the mole fraction of the solvent is approximately equal to one.

4.2 Colloids

Particles larger than small molecules may form mixtures with solvents. If gravity does not cause these particles to settle out of the mixture over time, the mixture is called a *colloidal system*, or *colloid*. (The term 'colloid' can also refer to the colloidal particles.) Colloidal particles are larger than solute particles, and can even be single large molecules such as hemoglobin. A colloidal system can be any combination of phases (except gas in gas). Some examples of colloidal systems are an *aerosol* (liquid or solid particles in a gas like fog or smoke), a *foam* (gas particles in a liquid like whipped cream), an *emulsion* (liquid particles in a liquid or solid like milk or butter), or a *sol* (solid particles in a liquid like paint).

Unlike a true solution, colloidal suspensions will scatter light, a phenomenon known as the *Tyndall effect*. A beam of light in a smoke filled theatre is visible due to the Tyndall effect.

Colloidal particles may be attracted (*lyophilic*) or repelled (*lyophobic*) by their *dispersion medium*. (The dispersion medium in a colloid is analagous to the solvent in a solution.) Lyophobic colloids form when amphipathic or charged particles adsorb to the surface of the colloidal particles stabilizing them in the dispersion medium. Protein in water is an example of a lyophilic colloid; emulsified fat in water is an example of a lyophobic colloid.

Colloidal particles are usually too small to be extracted by filtration; however, heating a colloid or adding an electrolyte may cause the particles to *coagulate*. The larger particles produced by coagulation will settle out or can be extracted by filtration. Colloidal systems can also be separated by a semipermeable membrane, a process called *dialysis*.

> A colloid is like a solution, only the solute particles are larger. The colloid particles are usually too small to be extracted by filtration but usually large enough or charged enough to be separated by a semipermeable membrane.

A characteristic of a colloid is that it illuminates a beam of light passing through it. Here, laser light passing first through tap water (at left) is revealed as a single beam due to the impurities in the water. On passing through the cuvette of distilled water (middle), so little dispersion of light occurs that the beam can hardly be seen at all. At right the colloidal suspension of gelatin has caused total dispersion of the light, illuminating the cuvette.

4.3   More Solutions

When a solute is mixed with a solvent, it is said to dissolve. The general rule for dissolution is **'like dissolves like'**. This rule refers to the polarity of the solute and solvent. Highly polar molecules are held together by strong intermolecular bonds formed by the attraction between their partially charged ends. Nonpolar molecules are held together by weak intermolecular bonds resulting from instantaneous dipole moments. These forces are called **London dispersion forces**. A polar solute interacts strongly with a polar solvent by tearing the solvent-solvent bonds apart and forming solvent-solute bonds. A nonpolar solute does not have enough charge separation to interact effectively with a polar solvent, and thus cannot intersperse itself within the solvent. A nonpolar solute can, however, tear apart the weak bonds of a nonpolar solvent. The bonds of a polar solute are too strong to be broken by the weak forces of a nonpolar solvent.

Water is a poor conductor of electricity unless it contains electrolytes. Electrolytes are compounds that form ions in aqueous solution.

Nonpolar Nerd's Club   Nonpolar Salty   The Polar Muscle Club

Like dissolves like; polar solvents dissolve polar solutes; nonpolar solvents dissolve nonpolar solutes.

Figure 4.1   Hydration Shell

Ionic compounds are dissolved by polar substances. When ionic compounds dissolve, they break apart into their respective cations and anions and are surrounded by the oppositely charged ends of the polar solvent. This process is called **solvation**. Water acts as a good solvent for ionic substances. The water molecules surround the individual ions pointing their positive hydrogens at the anions and their negative oxygens toward the cations. When several water molecules attach to one side of an ionic compound, they are able to overcome the strong ionic bond, and break apart the compound. The molecules then surround the ion. In water this process is called **hydration**. Something that is hydrated is said to be in an **aqueous phase**. The number of water molecules needed to surround an ion varies according to the size and charge of the ion. This number is called the *hydration number*. The hydration number is commonly 4 or 6.

When ions form in aqueous solution, the solution is able to conduct electricity. A compound which forms ions in aqueous solution is called an **electrolyte**. Strong electrolytes create solutions which conduct electricity well and contain many ions. Weak electrolytes are compounds which form few ions in solution.

For the MCAT you should be aware of common names, formulae, and charges for the polyatomic ions listed in Table 4.1.

Table 4.1   Polyatomic Ions

Name	Formula
Nitrite	NO_2^-
Nitrate	NO_3^-
Sulfite	SO_3^{2-}
Sulfate	SO_4^{2-}
Hypochlorite	ClO^-
Chlorite	ClO_2^-
Chlorate	ClO_3^-
Perchlorate	ClO_4^-
Carbonate	CO_3^{2-}
Bicarbonate	HCO_3^-
Phosphate	PO_4^{3-}

While it is important to drink water, drinking too much water can result in reduced sodium levels, a condition known as hyponatremia. In hyponatremia, normal sodium levels of 135 to 145 mM, are reduced to 125mM or below by drinking too much water. A sodium level below 120mM can be critical, and even result in death.

There are several ways to measure the concentration of a solution, five of which you should know for the MCAT: molarity (M), molality (m), mole fraction (χ), mass percentage, and parts per million (ppm). **Molarity** is the moles of the compound divided by the volume of the solution. Molarity generally has units of mol/L. **Molality** is moles of solute divided by kilograms of solvent. Molality generally has units of mol/kg and is usually used in formulae for colligative properties. The **mole fraction** is the moles of a compound divided by the total moles of all species in solution. Since it is a ratio, mole fraction has no units. **Mass percentage** is 100 times the ratio of the mass of the solute to the total mass of the solution. **Parts per million** is 10^6 times the ratio of the mass of the solute to the total mass of the solution.

$$M = \frac{\text{moles of solute}}{\text{volume of solution}}$$

$$m = \frac{\text{moles of solute}}{\text{kilograms of solvent}}$$

$$\chi = \frac{\text{moles of solute}}{\text{total moles of all solutes and solvent}}$$

$$\text{mass \%} = \frac{\text{mass of solute}}{\text{total mass of solution}} \times 100$$

$$\text{ppm} = \frac{\text{mass of solute}}{\text{total mass of solution}} \times 10^6$$

> Notice that parts per million is NOT the number of solute molecules per million molecules. It is the mass of the solute per mass of solution times one million.

Remember that solution concentrations are always given in terms of the form of the solute before dissolution. For instance, when 1 mole of NaCl is added to 1 liter of water, it is approximately a 1 molar solution and NOT a 2 molar solution even though each NaCl dissociates into two ions.

Normality measures the number of *equivalents* per liter of solution. The definition of an equivalent will depend upon the type of reaction taking place in the solution. The only time normality is likely to appear on the MCAT is with an acid-base reaction. In an acid-base reaction an equivalent is defined as the mass of acid or base that can furnish or accept one mole of protons. For instance, a 1 molar solution of H_2SO_4 would be called a 2 normal solution because it can donate 2 protons for each H_2SO_4.

73. What is the approximate molarity of a NaCl solution with a specific gravity of 1.006?

    A. 0.05 M
    B. 0.06 M
    C. 0.1 M
    D. 0.2 M

74. Which of the following substances is least soluble in water?

    A. NH_3
    B. NaCl
    C. HSO_4^-
    D. CCl_4

75. Which of the following solutions is the most concentrated? (Assume 1 L of water has a mass of 1 kg.)

    A. 1 M NaCl
    B. 1 m NaCl
    C. A aqueous solution with a NaCl mole fraction of 0.01
    D. 55 grams of NaCl mixed with one liter of water

76. The air we breathe is approximately 21% O_2 and 79% N_2. If the partial pressure of nitrogen in air is 600 torr, then all of the following are true EXCEPT:

    A. The mole fraction of nitrogen in air is 0.79.
    B. The mass of nitrogen in a 22.4 L sample of air is 22.1 grams at $0°C$.
    C. The partial pressure of oxygen is approximately 160 torr.
    D. For every 21 grams of oxygen in an air sample, there are 79 grams of nitrogen.

77. A polar solute is poured into a container with a nonpolar solvent. Which of the following statements best explains the reaction?

    A. The strong dipoles of the polar molecules separate the weak bonds between the nonpolar molecules.
    B. The dipoles of the polar molecules are too weak to break the bonds between the nonpolar molecules.
    C. The instantaneous dipoles of the nonpolar molecules are too weak to separate the bonds between the polar molecules.
    D. The instantaneous dipoles of the nonpolar molecules separate the bonds between the polar molecules.

78. A solution contains 19 grams of $MgCl_2$ in 0.5 liters of distilled water. If $MgCl_2$ totally dissociates, what is the concentration of chloride ions in the solution?

    A. 0.1 M
    B. 0.2 M
    C. 0.4 M
    D. 0.8 M

79. A student has 0.8 liters of a 3 molar HCl solution. How many liters of distilled water must she mix with the 3 molar solution in order to create a 1 molar HCl solution?

    A 0.8 L
    B. 1.6 L
    C. 2.4 L
    D. 3.2 L

80. All of the following substances are strong electrolytes EXCEPT:

    A HNO_3
    B. CO_2
    C. NaCl
    D. KOH

Iron (II) sulphate solution

4.5 Solution Formation for Condensed Phases

The formation of a solution is a physical reaction. It involves three steps:

Step 1: the breaking of the intermolecular bonds between solute molecules;

Step 2: the breaking of the intermolecular bonds between solvent molecules;

Step 3: the formation of intermolecular bonds between the solvent and the solute molecules.

Energy is required in order to break a bond. Recall from Chemistry Lecture 3 that a closed system at constant pressure the enthalpy change of a reaction equals the heat: $\Delta H = q$, and that for condensed phases not at high pressure (for instance the formation of most solutions that will be on the MCAT) enthalpy change approximately equals internal energy change: $\Delta H \approx \Delta U$. For solution chemistry of condensed phases we shall use these approximations. Thus the **heat of solution (ΔH_{sol})** is given by:

$$\Delta H_{sol} = \Delta H_1 + \Delta H_2 + \Delta H_3$$

Since energy is required to break a bond, the first two steps in dissolution are endothermic while the third step is exothermic.

Figure 4.2   Solution Formation

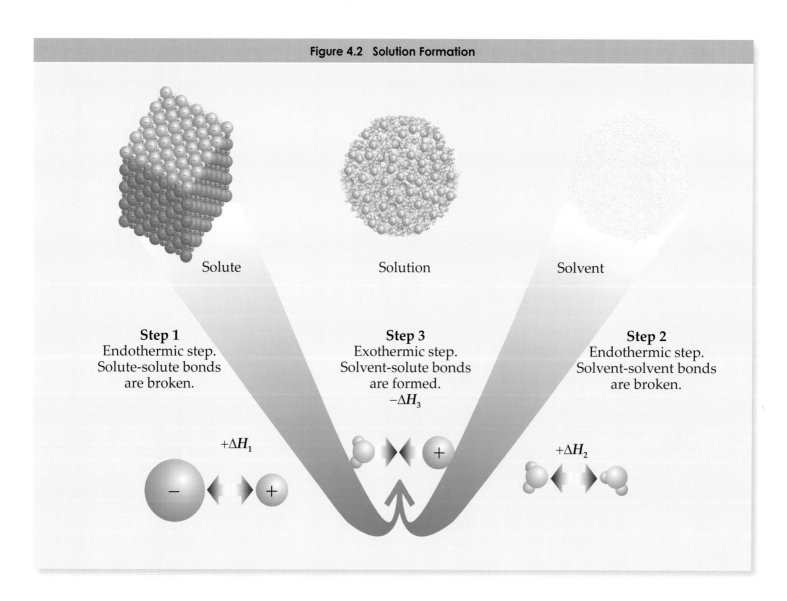

Solute

Solution

Solvent

Step 1
Endothermic step.
Solute-solute bonds
are broken.

$+\Delta H_1$

Step 3
Exothermic step.
Solvent-solute bonds
are formed.
$-\Delta H_3$

Step 2
Endothermic step.
Solvent-solvent bonds
are broken.

$+\Delta H_2$

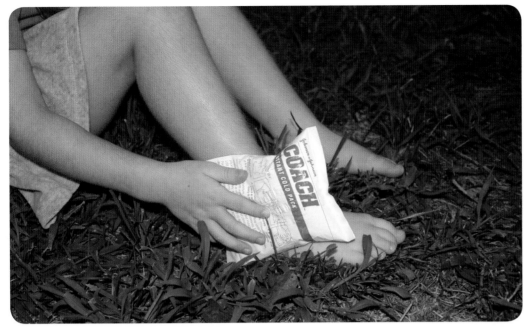

Instant cold pack placed on an injured ankle to reduce swelling. The cold pack contains ammonium nitrate and water, which when mixed together produce an endothermic reaction that feels cold.

Entropy usually increases for solid and liquids dissolving in liquids. Entropy usually decreases for gases dissolving in liquids.

If the overall reaction releases energy (is exothermic), the new intermolecular bonds are more stable than the old and, in general, the intermolecular attractions within the solution are stronger than the intermolecular attractions within the pure substances. Remember, less energy in the system usually means a more stable system. If the overall reaction absorbs energy (is endothermic), the reverse is true. Using the approximations mentioned above, the overall change in energy of the reaction is equal to the change in enthalpy and is called the heat of solution ΔH_{sol}. A negative heat of solution results in stronger intermolecular bonds, while a positive heat of solution results in weaker intermolecular bonds. Some books combine steps 2 and 3 of solution formation for aqueous solutions calling the sum of their enthalpy changes the *heat of hydration*.

Since the combined mixture is more disordered than the separated pure substances, the formation of a solution usually involves an increase in entropy. One exception to this rule is when a gas dissolves in a liquid or solid. When a gas dissolves in a liquid or solid, entropy change is usually negative. On the MCAT, for one condensed phase (liquid or solid) dissolving into another it is safe to assume an increase in entropy.

Breaking a bond always requires energy input. Since enthalpy and heat are equal at constant pressure, a solution with a negative enthalpy will give off heat when it forms. Thus, a solution that gives off heat when it forms is creating stronger bonds within the solution.

Recall that $\Delta G = \Delta H - T\Delta S$ and that a negative ΔG indicates a spontaneous reaction. When a liquid or solid dissolves in a liquid, ΔS is usually positive, therefore ΔS usually favors spontaneous solution formation for condensed phases. ΔH_{sol} can be negative or positive. If ΔH is negative, then, according to $\Delta G = \Delta H - T\Delta S$, ΔG must also be negative, and solution formation is spontaneous. Nearly all condensed phases with negative heats of solution will dissolve spontaneously. If ΔH_{sol} is positive (and ΔS is positive), temperature determines whether ΔG is positive or negative and whether a solution will form. Only some of the solutes with positive heats of solution will dissolve spontaneously.

4.6 Vapor Pressure

Imagine a pure liquid in a vacuum-sealed container. If we were to examine the space inside the container above the liquid, we would find that it is not really a vacuum. Instead it would contain vapor molecules from the liquid that have escaped. The liquid molecules are held in the liquid by intermolecular bonds. However, they contain a certain amount of kinetic energy, which depends upon the temperature. Some of the liquid molecules at the surface contain enough kinetic energy to break the intermolecular bonds that hold them in the liquid. These molecules launch themselves into the open space above the liquid. As the space above the liquid fills with molecules, some of the molecules crash back into the liquid. When the rate of molecules leaving the liquid equals the rate of molecules entering the liquid, equilibrium has been established. At this point, the pressure created by the molecules in the open space is called the **vapor pressure** of the liquid.

Figure 4.3 Vapor Pressure

Vapor Pressure

Pure liquid

> Equilibrium between the liquid and gas phases of a compound occurs when the molecules move from the liquid to the gas as quickly as they move from the gas to the liquid. The partial pressure of the compound necessary to create this equilibrium is called the vapor pressure of the compound.

> This equation is not important for MCAT, but it can help you remember that vapor pressure always increases as temperature increases.

Since vapor pressure is related to the kinetic energy of the molecules, vapor pressure is a function of temperature. A derivation of the Clausius-Clapeyron equation relates vapor pressure and temperature to the heat of vaporization:

$$\ln(P_v) = -\frac{\Delta H_{vap}}{R}\left(\frac{1}{T}\right) + C$$

where ΔH_{vap} is the heat of vaporization (always positive), and C is a constant specific to the compound. Vaporization is an endothermic process, so the equation indicates that vapor pressure increases with temperature.

> A compound evaporates when the vapor pressure of its liquid phase is greater than the partial pressure of its gaseous phase. It condenses when these conditions are reversed.

Imagine a puddle of water in the street on a still day. The puddle is exposed to the open air, so the gas above the puddle is made up of mostly oxygen and nitrogen. However, there is nearly always some moisture in the air. In other words, the air also contains water molecules. Recall from Chemistry Lecture 2.2 that there must be a partial pressure associated with these water molecules in the air. Imagine further that the temperature of the day is such that this partial pressure of water above the puddle happens to be equal to the vapor pressure of water. This means that water molecules are entering and leaving the puddle at the same rate. Now along comes a wind. Recall from Bernoulli's equation in Physics Lecture 5.8 that when a fluid moves, its pressure decreases, so the partial pressure of the water vapor decreases when the wind blows. Since the vapor pressure is a function of temperature, the vapor pressure doesn't change. (It is a number that we looked up in a reference book.) As a result, the partial pressure of the water vapor is lower than the vapor pressure of water at that temperature, and the number of water molecules leaving the puddle is greater than the number of water molecules entering the puddle; the water is **evaporating** from the puddle. If the reverse were true, and conditions made the air more moist so that the partial pressure of the water vapor were greater than the vapor pressure, then water would **condense** into the puddle. Of course the puddle doesn't have to be water. The same is true for any liquid.

When vapor pressure equals local atmospheric pressure, a compound boils. In our puddle example we compared vapor pressure and partial pressure. We can also compare vapor pressure and atmospheric pressure (in this case the total pressure applied to the liquid). Atmospheric pressure is the sum of all the partial pressures in the air above the puddle. A liquid boils when its vapor pressure equals the pressure applied to it. This can be done by raising the temperature, and thus raising the vapor pressure until it reaches the atmospheric pressure, or by lowering the atmospheric pressure until it equals the vapor pressure. Solids also have a vapor presssure. The melting point is the temperature at which the vapor pressures of the solid is equal to the vapor pressure of the liquid. Above the melting point the liquid vapor pressure is greater than that of the solid; below the melting point the liquid vapor pressure is less than that of the solid.

Boiling occurs when the vapor pressure of a liquid equals the atmospheric pressure. Melting occurs when the vapor pressure of the solid phase equals the vapor pressure of the liquid phase.

When a **nonvolatile solute** (a solute with no vapor pressure) is added to a liquid, some of those solute molecules will reach the surface of the solution, and reduce the amount of surface area available for the liquid molecules. Since the solute molecules don't break free of the solution but do take up surface area, the number of molecules breaking free from the liquid is decreased while the surface area of the solution and the volume of open space above the solution remain the same. From the ideal gas law, $PV = nRT$, we know that a decrease in n at constant volume and temperature is proportional to a decrease in P. The vapor pressure of the solution P_v is given by **Raoult's law**, and is proportional to the mole fraction of the liquid χ_a and the vapor pressure of the pure liquid P_a.

$$P_v = \chi_a P_a$$

If the solute is a **volatile solute** (a solute with a vapor pressure), the situation is a little more complicated. A volatile solute will also compete for the surface area of a liquid. However, some of the molecules of a volatile solute will escape from solution and contribute to the vapor pressure. If the solution is an ideal solution (solute and solvent have similar properties), the partial pressures contributed by the solvent and solute can be found by applying Raoult's law separately. The sum of the partial vapor pressures give the total vapor pressure of the solution, and we arrive at a modified form of Raoult's law:

$$P_v = \chi_a P_a + \chi_b P_b$$

where each χP term represents the partial vapor pressure contributed by the respective solvent, and P_v represents the total vapor pressure.

Figure 4.4 Nonvolitile Solute

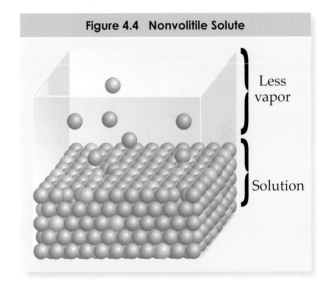

Less vapor

Solution

Figure 4.5 Volatile Solute

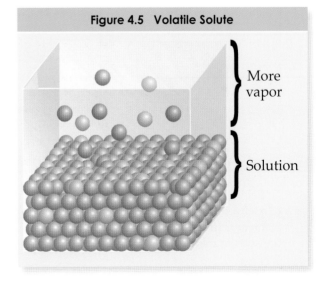

More vapor

Solution

Negative heats of solution form stronger bonds and lower vapor pressure; positive heats of solution form weaker bonds and raise vapor pressure.

But this is not the entire story. As we saw with heats of solution, if the solution is not ideal, the intermolecular forces between molecules will be changed. Either less energy or more energy will be required for molecules to break the intermolecular bonds and leave the surface of the solution. This means that the vapor pressure of a nonideal solution will deviate from the predictions made by Raoult's law. We can make a general prediction of the direction of the deviation based upon heats of solution. If the heat of solution is negative, stronger bonds are formed, fewer molecules are able to break free from the surface and there will be a negative deviation of the vapor pressure from Raoult's law. The opposite will occur for a positive heat of solution.

In order to really understand this section you must have a thorough understanding of many of the physics and chemistry concepts that we've studied so far (i.e. bond energy, thermodynamics, pressure, and solutions). I suggest that you re-read this section and be sure that you thoroughly understand the concepts.

The deviation of vapor pressure from Raoult's law can be represented graphically by comparing the mole fractions of solvents with their vapor pressures. Graph 1 below shows only the partial pressure of the solvent as its mole fraction increases. As predicted by Raoult's law, the relationship is linear. Graph 2 shows the vapor pressure of an ideal solution and the individual partial pressures of each solvent. Notice that the partial pressures add at every point to equal the total pressure. This must be true for any solution. Graph 3 and 4 show the deviations of nonideal solutions. The straight lines are the Raoult's law predictions and the curved lines are the actual pressures. Notice that the partial pressures still add at every point to equal the total pressure. Notice also that a positive heat of solution leads to an increase in vapor pressure, and a negative heat of solution, to a decrease in vapor pressure.

Figure 4.6 Graphs of Vapor Pressure

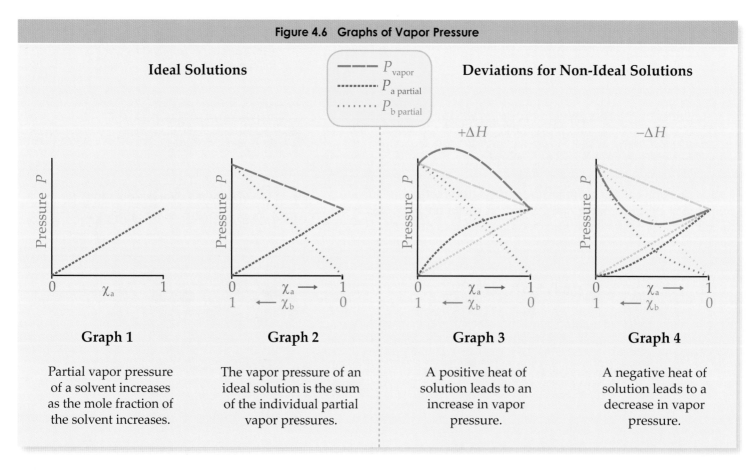

Graph 1	Graph 2	Graph 3	Graph 4
Partial vapor pressure of a solvent increases as the mole fraction of the solvent increases.	The vapor pressure of an ideal solution is the sum of the individual partial vapor pressures.	A positive heat of solution leads to an increase in vapor pressure.	A negative heat of solution leads to a decrease in vapor pressure.

81. NaCl dissolves spontaneously in water. Based upon the following reaction:

    $$NaCl(s) \rightarrow Na^+(g) + Cl^-(g) \quad \Delta H = 786 \text{ kJ/mol}$$

    the heat of hydration for NaCl must be:

    A. negative with a magnitude less than 786.
    B. negative with a magnitude greater than 786.
    C. positive with a magnitude greater than 786.
    D. Nothing can be determined about the heat of hydration without more information.

82. Which of the following indicates an exothermic heat of solution?

    A. Heat is evolved.
    B. The final solution is acidic.
    C. A precipitate is formed.
    D. The reaction is spontaneous.

83. When two pure liquids, *A* and *B*, are mixed, the temperature of the solution increases. All of the following must be true EXCEPT:

    A. The intermolecular bond strength in at least one of the liquids is less than the intermolecular bond strength between *A* and *B* in solution.
    B. The reaction is exothermic.
    C. The vapor pressure of the solution is less than both the vapor pressure of pure *A* and pure *B*.
    D. The rms velocity of the molecules increases when the solution is formed.

84. Which of the following will increase the vapor pressure of a liquid?

    A. increasing the surface area of the liquid by pouring it into a wider container
    B. increasing the kinetic energy of the molecules of the liquid
    C. decreasing the temperature of the liquid
    D. adding a nonvolatile solute

85. When two volatile solvents are mixed, the vapor pressure drops below the vapor pressure of either solvent in its pure form. What else can be predicted about the solution of these solvents?

    A. The solution is ideal.
    B. The mole fraction of the more volatile solvent is greater than the mole fraction of the less volatile solvent.
    C. The heat of solution is exothermic.
    D. The heat of solution is endothermic.

86. A solution composed of ethanol and methanol can be thought of as ideal. At room temperature, the vapor pressure of ethanol is 45 mmHg and the vapor pressure of methanol is 95 mmHg. Which of the following will be true regarding the vapor pressure of a solution containing only ethanol and methanol?

    A. It will be less than 45 mmHg.
    B. It will be greater than 45 mmHg and less than 95 mmHg.
    C. It will be greater than 95 mmHg and less than 140 mmHg.
    D. It will be greater than 140 mmHg.

87. Benzene and toluene combine to form an ideal solution. At 80°C, vapor pressure of pure benzene is 800 mmHg and the vapor pressure of pure toluene is 300 mmHg. If the vapor pressure of the solution is 400 mmHg, what are the mole fractions of benzene and toluene?

    A. 60% benzene and 40% toluene
    B. 50% benzene and 50% toluene
    C. 40% benzene and 60% toluene
    D. 20% benzene and 80% toluene

88. When solute *A* is added to solvent *B*, heat is released. Which of the following must be true of the solvation process?

    A. The bonds broken in solute *A* must be stronger than the bonds broken in solvent *B*.
    B. The bonds broken in solute A must be weaker than the bonds broken in solvent *B*.
    C. The bonds formed in the solution must be stronger than the bonds broken in solute *A* and solvent *B*.
    D. The bonds formed in the solution must be weaker than the bonds broken in solute *A* and solvent *B*.

4.7 Solubility

Solubility is a solute's tendency to dissolve in a solvent. On the MCAT, the solute will usually be a salt, and the solvent will most often be water. Dissolution of a salt is reversible on a molecular scale; dissolved molecules of the salt reattach to the surface of the salt crystal. For a dissolving salt, the reverse reaction, called **precipitation**, takes place initially at a slower rate than dissolution. As the salt dissolves and the concentration of dissolved salt builds, the rate of dissolution and precipitation equilibrate. When the rate of dissolution and precipitation are equal, the solution is said to be **saturated**; the concentration of dissolved salt has reached a maximum in a saturated solution. Just like any other reaction, the equilibrium established at the saturation point is dynamic; the concentrations of products and reactants remain constant, but the forward and reverse reactions continue at the same rate.

Salt cave formation along the coast of the Dead Sea in Jordan.

The equilibrium of a solvation reaction has its own equilibrium constant called the **solubility product** K_{sp}. Use K_{sp} the same way you would use any other equilibrium constant. Remember that solids and pure liquids have an approximate mole fraction of one and can be excluded from the equilibrium expression. Thus, solids are left out of the solubility product expression as in the example of the K_{sp} for barium hydroxide shown below.

$$Ba(OH)_2(s) \rightleftharpoons Ba^{2+}(aq) + 2OH^-(aq)$$

$$K_{sp} = [Ba^{2+}][OH^-]^2$$

> For most salts, crystallization is exothermic.

> Use K_{sp} like any other equilibrium constant to create an equilibrium expression. Set the K_{sp} equal to products over reactants raised to the power of their coefficients in the balanced equation. As always, leave out pure solids and liquids.

Solubility and the solubility product (K_{sp}) are not the same thing. The solubility of a substance in a given solvent is found from the solubility product. The solubility is the number of moles of solute per liter of a solution that can be dissolved in a given solvent. Solubility depends upon the common ions in the solution. The solubility product is independent of the common ions, and can be found in a reference book.

> Solubility and the solubility product are not the same thing. Solubility product or K_{sp} is a constant found in a book. Solubility is the maximum number of moles of the solute that can dissolve in solution.
>
> The solubility product changes only with temperature. The solubility depends upon the temperature and the ions in solution.

We can write an equation for the solvation of BaF_2 in water as follows:

$$BaF_2(s) \rightleftharpoons Ba^{2+}(aq) + 2F^-(aq)$$

The solubility product for BaF_2 is:

$$K_{sp} = [Ba^{2+}][F^-]^2$$

If we look in a book, we find that the K_{sp} for BaF_2 has a value of 2.4×10^{-5} at 25°C. Like any equilibrium constant, the K_{sp} is unitless. From the K_{sp} we can find the solubility of BaF_2 in any solution at 25°C. For instance, to find the solubility of BaF_2 in one liter of water, we simply saturate one liter of water with BaF_2. The solubility is the maximum number of moles per liter that can dissolve in the solution. We call the solubility 'x', since it is unknown. If x moles per liter of BaF_2 dissolve, then there will be x moles per liter of Ba^{2+} in solution and twice as many, or 2x moles per liter, of F^-. We plug these values into the K_{sp} equation and solve for x.

$$2.4 \times 10^{-5} = (x)(2x)^2$$

$$x \approx 1.8 \times 10^{-2}$$

1.8×10^{-2} mol/L is the solubility of BaF_2 in one liter of water at 25°C.

What would happen if we added 1 mole of F^- to our solution in the form of NaF? The solubility of BaF_2 would change. The NaF would completely dissociate forming 1 mole of F^- and 1 mole of Na^+. The Na^+ ions are not in the equilibrium expression and (ideally) would have no effect on the equilibrium. Because they have no effect, the Na^+ ions are called **spectator ions**. The F^- ions, however, do affect the equilibrium. Their disturbance of the equilibrium is called the **common ion effect** because it involves an ion common to an ion in the equilibrium expression. By Le Chatâlier's principle, the addition of a common ion will push the equilibrium in a direction which tends to reduce the concentration of that ion. In this case, the equilibrium will move to the left, and the solubility of BaF_2 will be reduced.

Figure 4.7 Common Ion Effect

To find out by exactly how much the solubility will be reduced, we go back to the equilibrium expression. One key to solving solubility problems is realizing that the order in which you mix the solution is irrelevant, so you should mix them in the order that is most convenient to you. In this case it is easiest to add the NaF first, since it completely dissociates. Now we add BaF_2 to a solution of 1 liter of water and 1 mole of F^-. Again, x moles will dissolve leaving x moles of Ba^{2+}. But this time, since there is already 1 mole of F^-, $2x + 1$ moles of F^- will be in solution at equilibrium.

$$2.4 \times 10^{-5} = (x)(2x + 1)^2$$

Now here's a trick to simplify the math. We know that the equilibrium is shifting to the left, so x will be smaller than our earlier calculations of 1.8×10^{-2}. Even 2x will be much smaller than 1. Thus, $2x + 1$ is going to be very close to 1. Therefore, we drop the 2x and solve:

$$2.4 \times 10^{-5} \approx (x)(1)^2$$

$$x \approx 2.4 \times 10^{-5}$$

> A common ion added to a saturated solution will shift the equilibrium increasing precipitate. It does NOT affect the K_{sp}.
>
> A common ion added to a solution that is not saturated will NOT shift the equilibrium, because in an unsaturated solution, there is no equilibrium to shift.

Just to be sure that we were correct in our estimation of 2x, we plug our estimated value of x into the term that we deleted (2x), and we see if it is truly much smaller than the term to which we added it (in this case 1).

$$2x = 4.8 \times 10^{-5} \ll 1$$

Our assumption was valid. Thus our new solubility of BaF_2 is 2.4×10^{-5} mol/L.

Oil and water don't mix.

4.8 Solubility Guidelines

Compounds with water solubilities of less than 0.01 mol L^{-1} are generally considered insoluble. MCAT will not require you to memorize the solubilities of different compounds. Nevertheless, here are a few solubility guidelines for compounds in water:

Nearly all ionic compounds containing nitrate (NO_3^-), ammonium (NH_4^+), and alkali metals (Li^+, Na^+, K^+...) are *soluble*.

Ionic compounds containing halogens (Cl^-, Br^-, I^-) are *soluble*, EXCEPT for silver, mercury, and lead compounds (Ag^+, Hg_2^{2+}, Pb^{2+}).

Sulfate compounds (SO_4^{2-}) are *soluble*, EXCEPT for mercury, lead, and the heavier alkaline metals (Hg_2^{2+}, Pb^{2+}, Ca^{2+}, Sr^{2+}, Ba^{2+}).

Compounds containing the heavier alkaline metals (Ca^{2+}, Sr^{2+}, Ba^{2+}) are *soluble* when paired with sulfides (S^{2-}) and hydroxides (OH^-).

Carbonates, phosphates, sulfides, and hydroxides (CO_3^{2-}, PO_4^{3-}, S^{2-}, OH^-) are generally *insoluble* other than in the cases mentioned above.

> It is very unlikely that an MCAT question would require that you know these solubilities. However, knowing them will make solution chemistry easier.

Notes:

4.9 Solubility Factors

Pressure and temperature affect solubilities. Pressure on liquids and solids has little effect, but pressure on a gas increases its solubility. For an ideally dilute solution, the increase in pressure of gas *a* over a solution is directly proportional to the solubility of gas *a*, if the gas does not react with, or dissociate in, the solvent. This relationship is given by *Henry's law*:

$$C = k_{a1}P_v$$

where C is the solubility of the gas *a* (typically in moles per liter), k_{a1} is Henry's law constant, which varies with each solute-solvent pair, and P_v is the vapor partial pressure of gas *a* above the solution. Strangely, Henry's law can also be written as:

$$P_v = \chi_a k_{a2}$$

where χ_a is the mole fraction of *a* in solution, P_v is the vapor partial pressure of gas *a*, and k_{a2} is Henry's law constant. Although both equations show that the concentration of a gas in solution is proportional to the vapor partial pressure of the gas above the solution, the Henry's law constant in the second equation has a different value than the Henry's law constant in the first equation. If we compare the second equation with Raoult's law $(P_v = \chi_a P_a)$, they appear to conflict unless P_a has the same value as k_{a2}. In fact, they do NOT agree. Both are approximations. Raoult's law is most accurate when looking at the vapor partial pressure of a solvent with high concentration. Henry's law is more accurate when looking at the vapor partial pressure of a volatile solute where the solute has a low concentration. ***In other words, in an ideally dilute solution, the solvent obeys Raoult's law and the solute obeys Henry's law.*** One way to remember this is when the solvent concentration is high, each solvent molecule is surrounded by other solvent molecules, so it behaves more like a pure solvent. Thus the solvent vapor partial pressure is proportional to its vapor pressure as a pure liquid; Raoult's law. When the volatile solute concentration is low, each molecule is surrounded by solvent molecules creating a deviation from the behavior of the pure volatile solute. Thus its vapor partial pressure is not proportional to its pressure as a pure substance (Raoult's law doesn't work in this case), but is proportional to some constant; Henry's law.

> The most important thing to remember about Henry's law is that it demonstrates that the solubility of a gas is proportional to its vapor partial pressure. We can remember this by thinking of a can of soda. When we open the can and release the pressure, the solubility of the gas decreases causing some gas to rise out of the solution and create the familiar hiss and foam.

As shown by Raoult's law and Henry's law, the partial vapor pressure of a solution component is always proportional to its mole fraction. If the component predominates as the solvent, Raoult's law says that the partial vapor pressure is proportional to the pure vapor pressure. If the component represents a tiny amount of solution, Henry's law says that the vapor partial pressure is proportional to Henry's law constant.

Raoult's law

- ● Volatile solvent particles
- ● Nonvolatile solute particles

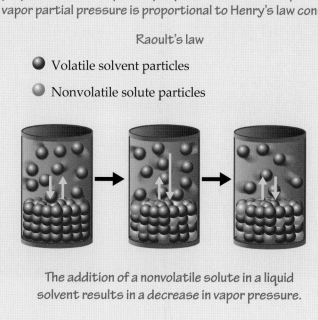

The addition of a nonvolatile solute in a liquid solvent results in a decrease in vapor pressure.

Henry's law

Pressure on gas increases its solubility.

Equilibrium   Increased pressure   Equilibrium
causes more
molecules to dissolve

Le Chatâlier's principle, when applied to solutions, should be used with caution. Because heat energy is a product of a reaction with a negative heat of solution, Le Chatâlier's principle predicts that a temperature increase will push such a reaction to the left decreasing the solubility of the solute. However, entropy increase can be large in solution formation. From the equation $\Delta G = \Delta H - T\Delta S$, we see that a temperature increase emphasizes the ΔS term tending to result in a more negative ΔG and thus a more spontaneous reaction. Due to the large increase in entropy, the water solubility of many solids increases with increasing temperature regardless of the enthalpy change. To be absolutely certain, the change in solubility due to temperature must be found by experiment, but the solubility of most salts increases with temperature.

On the other hand, the entropy change when a gas dissolves into a liquid is usually negative. Thus the solubility of gases usually decreases with increasing temperature. You can remember this by understanding why hot waste water from factories that is dumped into streams is hazardous to aquatic life. The hot water has a double effect. First, it holds less oxygen than cold water. Second, it floats on the cold water and seals it off from the oxygen in the air above.

Other factors that affect the solubility of a gas are its size, and reactivity with the solvent. Heavier, larger gases experience greater van der Waals forces and tend to be more soluble. Gases that chemically react with a solvent have greater solubility.

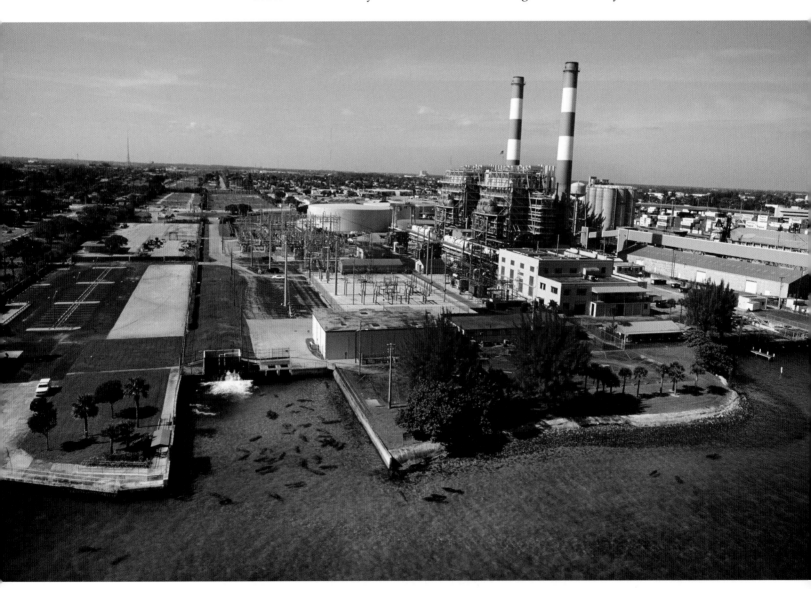

West Indian Manatees attracted to the warm water effluent of power plants.

4.10 Equation Summary

Units of Concentration

$$M = \frac{\text{moles of solute}}{\text{volume of solution}} \qquad m = \frac{\text{moles of solute}}{\text{kilograms of solvent}}$$

$$\chi = \frac{\text{moles of solute}}{\text{total moles of all solutes and solvent}}$$

$$\text{mass \%} = \frac{\text{mass of solute}}{\text{total mass of solution}} \times 100$$

$$\text{ppm} = \frac{\text{mass of solute}}{\text{total mass of solution}} \times 10^6$$

Raoult's Law

$$P_v = \chi_a + P_a \qquad P_v = \chi_a P_a + \chi_b P_b$$

4.11 Terms You Need To Know

Terms

'Like Dissolves Like'	Parts Per Million
Aqueous Phase	Precipitation
Common Ion Effect	Raoult's Law
Electrolyte	Saturated
Heat Of Solution (ΔH_{sol})	Solubility
Hydration	Solubility Product (K_{sp})
London Dispersion Forces	Solute
Mass Percentage	Solution
Molality	Solvation
Molarity	Solvent
Mole	Spectator Ions
Mole Fraction	Vapor Pressure
Nonvolatile Solute	Volatile Solute

94. Which of the following expressions represents the solubility product for $Cu(OH)_2$?

A. $K_{sp} = [Cu^{2+}][OH^-]^2$
B. $K_{sp} = [Cu^{2+}]2[OH^-]$
C. $K_{sp} = [Cu^{2+}]2[OH^-]^2$
D. $K_{sp} = [Cu^{2+}][OH^-]$

89. When a solution is saturated:

A. the solvent changes to solute, and the solute changes to solvent at an equal rate.
B. the vapor pressure of the solution is equal to atmospheric pressure.
C. the concentration of solvent is at a maximum.
D. the concentration of solvent is at a minimum.

95. If the solubility of $PbCl_2$ is equal to x, which of the following expressions will be equal to the solubility product for $PbCl_2$?

A. $4x^3$
B. $2x^3$
C. x^3
D. x^2

90. The addition of a strong base to a saturated solution of $Ca(OH)_2$ would:

A. decrease the number of OH^- ions in solution.
B. increase the number of Ca^{2+} ions in solution.
C. cause $Ca(OH)_2$ to precipitate.
D. decrease the pH.

96. A beaker contains a saturated solution of CaF_2 ($K_{sp} = 4 \times 10^{-11}$). There are some Na^+ ions in the solution. If NaF is added to the beaker, which of the following will occur?

A. The concentration of Na^+ will decrease.
B. The concentration of Ca^{2+} will decrease.
C. The concentration of F^- will decrease.
D. All concentrations will remain constant.

91. Na_2SO_4 dissociates completely in water. From the information given in the table below, if Na_2SO_4 were added to a solution containing equal concentrations of aqueous Ca^{2+}, Ag^+, Pb^{2+}, and Ba^{2+} ions, which of the following solids would precipitate first?

Compound	K_{sp}
$CaSO_4$	6.1×10^{-5}
Ag_2SO_4	1.2×10^{-5}
$PbSO_4$	1.3×10^{-8}
$BaSO_4$	1.5×10^{-9}

A. $CaSO_4$
B. Ag_2SO_4
C. $PbSO_4$
D. $BaSO_4$

92. A sealed container holds gaseous oxygen and liquid water. Which of the following would increase the amount of oxygen dissolved in the water?

A. expanding the size of the container
B. adding an inert gas to the container
C. decreasing the temperature of the container
D. shaking the container

93. The K_{sp} of $BaCO_3$ is 1.6×10^{-9}. How many moles of barium carbonate can be dissolved in 3 liters of water?

A. 4×10^{-5} moles
B. 6.9×10^{-5} moles
C. 1.2×10^{-4} moles
D. 2.1×10^{-4} moles

HEAT CAPACITY, PHASE CHANGE AND COLLIGATIVE PROPERTIES

5.1   Phases

If all the intensive macroscopic properties of a system are constant, that system is said to be *homogeneous*. Any part of a system that is homogeneous is called a **phase**. A phase is uniform throughout with respect to chemical composition and physical state. Some examples of different phases are crystalline solid, amorphous solid, aqueous solution, pure liquid, and gas. A system may have a number of solid and liquid phases, but it will usually have only one gaseous phase. Pure substances have only one gaseous phase and usually have only one liquid phase.

> Most of the time, you can think of phases as solid, liquid, and gas. Just be aware that this is not the technical definition. And when we discuss things like solutions, remember that pure water is a different phase than an aqueous solution containing Na^+ ions. Another common example is rhombic sulfur and monoclinic sulfur; these are two different solid phases of the same element.

5.2 Heat Capacity

Phase changes arise through changes in the manner in which internal energy is distributed over molecules and space. In other words, a phase change may result when the energy of each molecule is decreased or increased, or when the space around each molecule is reduced or enlarged. Such changes are accomplished via heat or work. In order to understand phase changes then, we must understand how substances react to heat and *PV* work.

The **heat capacity** of a substance is the added energy required to increase the temperature of that substance by one degree. The heat capacity (*C*) is defined as:

$$C = \frac{q}{\Delta T}$$

Don't let the name 'heat capacity' fool you. Recall that heat is a process of energy transfer, and cannot be stored. Heat capacity was given its name before heat was fully understood. 'Internal energy capacity' would be a better, but not perfect, name. Not perfect because we can change the temperature of a substance at constant internal energy by changing only the volume. Likewise, in an isothermal expansion of a gas, we can expand a gas at constant temperature by adding heat during the expansion.

If, while being heated, no PV work is done by a system at rest, nearly all the heat energy goes into increasing the temperature. When the system is allowed to expand at constant pressure, some energy leaves the system as work and the temperature increase is diminished. Thus constant pressure heat capacities are greater than constant volume heat capacities.

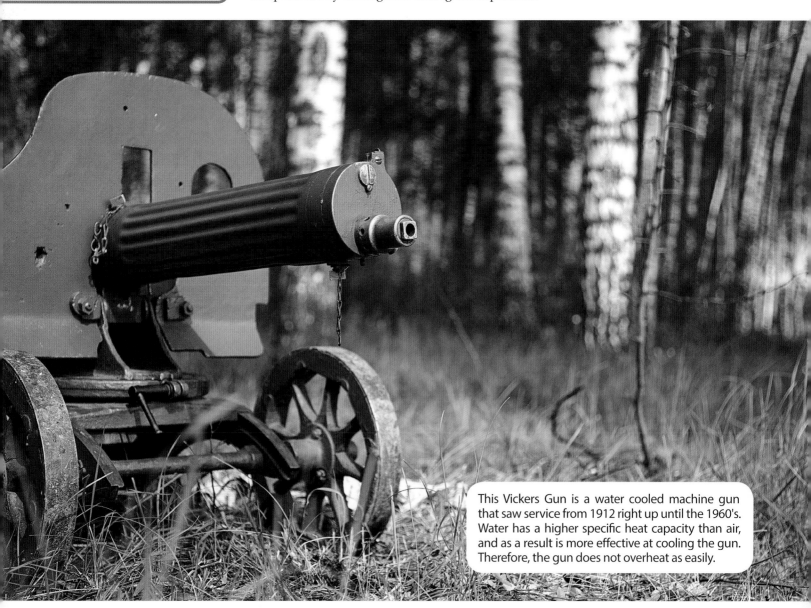

This Vickers Gun is a water cooled machine gun that saw service from 1912 right up until the 1960's. Water has a higher specific heat capacity than air, and as a result is more effective at cooling the gun. Therefore, the gun does not overheat as easily.

There are two heat capacities for any substance: a constant volume heat capacity C_V and a constant pressure heat capacity C_P. If we recall the first law of thermodynamics for a system at rest, $\Delta U = q + w$, and remember the relationship between temperature and internal energy, we can understand why the same substance can have different responses to the same amount of energy change. For instance, if the volume of a system is held constant, then the system can do no PV work; all energy change must be in the form of heat. This means that none of the energy going into the system can escape as work done by the system. Most of the energy must contribute to a temperature change. On the other hand, when pressure is held constant and the substance is allowed to expand, some of the energy can leave the system as PV work done on the surroundings as the volume changes. Thus, at constant pressure, a substance can absorb energy with less change in temperature by expelling some of the energy to the surroundings as work. C_P is greater than C_V.

$$C_V = \frac{q}{\Delta T_{\text{constant volume}}}$$

$$C_P = \frac{q}{\Delta T_{\text{constant pressure}}}$$

Notes:

Just think about the heat capacity of a substance as the amount of energy a substance can absorb per unit of temperature change. Don't worry too much about the difference between constant pressure and constant volume heat capacities. The MCAT might even ignore this fact completely.

A large amount of energy is required to change the state of water. For the sweat to evaporate, a large amount of heat energy is required, some of which is taken from our bodies. Because some heat is taken from our bodies, we begin to feel cooler when sweat evaporates

Finally, a compound can also absorb energy at either constant pressure or constant volume by stretching its bonds. This means that the more bonds a molecule has the more energy it can channel into bond stretching rather than into raising its temperature. Bond stretching, where possible, can account for a large amount of energy absorption, so, for a compound with lots of bonds, the value of C_p approaches the value of C_v. The ratio of the heat capacities C_p/C_v is called either the *isentropic expansion factor* or the *adiabatic index*, and is represented by γ (or mechanical engineers use the symbol κ). This is the same gamma that appears in equations for sound waves (See Physics Lecture 6.1). When we examine γ for various gases, we see that there is a general trend for γ to approach 1 as the number of molecular bonds increases (See Table 5.1).

Table 5.1   Adiabatic Index in Relation to Bonds

Gas	Number of β bonds per molecule	Adiabatic Index $\gamma = C_p/C_v$
Helium	0	1.67
Argon	0	1.67
Hydrogen	1	1.40
Nitrogen	1	1.40
Water vapor	2	1.33
Methane	4	1.30
Ethylene	5	1.24
Ethane	7	1.19

For a solid or a liquid, both of which experience very little change in volume, there is a more important reason why constant volume and pressure heat capacities differ. The intermolecular forces of a solid or liquid are much stronger than those of a gas. Small changes in the intermolecular distances of noncompressible phases result in large changes in intermolecular potential energy. Intermolecular potential energy does not affect temperature, and thus heat is absorbed at constant pressure with less change in temperature than when heat is absorbed at constant volume. Again: C_P is greater than C_V.

> Notice that something with a greater heat capacity can absorb more heat with less temperature change.

Although a negative heat capacity is theoretically possible under extremely unusual circumstances and has even been demonstrated by experiment, heat capacity on the MCAT will always be positive; the temperature will always increase when energy is added to a substance at constant volume or pressure. In the real world, heat capacity also changes with temperature; the amount of energy that a substance can absorb per change in temperature varies with the temperature. However, unless otherwise indicated, for the MCAT, assume that heat capacity does not change with temperature.

Thought Provoker

On a hot summer day, a bucket of sand will be hotter than a bucket of water. If they both absorbed the same amount of heat, how can this be?

Answer: See page 120

Sometimes the MCAT will give you the heat capacity of an entire system. For instance, a thermometer may be made from several substances each with its own heat capacity. The thermometer may be immersed in a bath of oil. The oil has its own heat capacity. On the MCAT, the heat capacity of the thermometer-oil system may be precalculated and given in units of energy divided by units of temperature: i.e. J/K or cal/°C. For such a situation, we would use the following equation:

$$q = C\Delta T$$

Sometimes the MCAT will give a specific heat capacity c. *Specific* means divided by mass, so the **specific heat capacity** is simply the heat capacity per unit mass. A specific heat usually has units of J kg^{-1} K^{-1} or cal g^{-1} °C^{-1}. When a specific heat is given, use the following equation:

The specific heat of cooking oil is about half the specific heat of water. About half as much energy is required to raise the temperature of an equal amount of oil.

$$q = mc\Delta T$$

The '*m*' in this equation is for mass, not molality. This equation is easy to remember because it looks like q = MCAT. Notice that the symbol for specific heat is usually a lower case '*c*' while the symbol for heat capacity is usually an upper case '*C*'.

> Use units to help you solve heat capacity problems. For instance, if a heat capacity is given in cal g^{-1} °C^{-1}, then you know that to find the heat (measured in calories) you simply multiply by grams and degrees Celsius. This gives you the equation $q = mc\Delta T$. Most of the time you don't have to know the formula, if you look at the units. Also with heat capacity problems, follow the energy flow, remembering that energy is always conserved: $\Delta E = q + w$.

> By the way, don't be surprised if you see molar heat capacity or something similar. Heat capacities can be given per mole, per volume, per gram, or per whatever. Just use the equation $q = mc\Delta T$ and rely on the units of c to find the units of m. For instance, if c is given as the molar heat capacity, m would be in moles.

For the MCAT you must know that water has a specific heat of 1 cal g^{-1} °C^{-1}. This was once the definition of a calorie.

$$c_{water} = 1 \ cal \ g^{-1} \ °C^{-1}$$

Thought Provoker

When eating a piece of pizza it can be either a pleasant or painful experience. No, we're not talking about the quality of pizza, but rather where you bite. If you eat the crust right out of the oven, there usually isn't a problem. But if you bite into the hot cheese from right out of the oven, you could burn your mouth. Why does where you bite make such a difference?

Answer: See page 112

5.3 Calorimeters

A calorimeter is a device which measures energy change. There are both constant pressure and constant volume calorimeters. A **coffee cup calorimeter** is an example of a constant pressure calorimeter because it measures energy change at atmospheric pressure. In a coffee cup calorimeter, two coffee cups are used to insulate the solution. A stirrer maintains equal distribution of energy throughout, and a thermometer measures the change in temperature. Obviously, a coffee cup calorimeter cannot contain expanding gases. Reactions that take place inside a coffee cup calorimeter occur at the constant pressure of the local atmosphere. A coffee cup calorimeter is used to measure **heats of reaction**. (Recall that at constant pressure $q = \Delta H$.) For instance, if we mix HCl and NaOH in a coffee cup calorimeter, the net ionic reaction is:

$$H^+ + OH^- \rightarrow H_2O$$

Using the specific heat of water, the mass of water, and the measured change in temperature, we can solve for q in the equation: $q = mc\Delta T$. Since $q = \Delta H$ at constant pressure, we have the heat of reaction.

A **bomb calorimeter** measures energy change at constant volume. A bomb calorimeter tells us the internal energy change in a reaction. (Recall that at constant volume $q = \Delta U$.) In a bomb calorimeter, a steel container full of reactants is placed inside another rigid, thermally insulated container. When the reaction occurs, heat is transferred to the surrounding water (shown in the diagram). Using the known heat capacity of the container and the equation: $q = C\Delta T$, we can deduce the heat of the reaction, and thus the internal energy change in the reaction.

A bomb calorimeter

Figure 5.1 Calorimeters

Thermometer

Stirrer
Insulating container
Water

Steel bomb

Reactants

Coffee cup calorimeter

Bomb calorimeter

97. 20 grams of NaCl is poured into a coffee cup calorimeter containing 250 ml of water. If the temperature inside the calorimeter drops 1°C by the time the NaCl is totally dissolved, what is the heat of solution for NaCl and water? (specific heat of water is 4.18 J/g °C.)

- **A.** −3 kJ/mol
- **B.** −1 kJ/mol
- **C.** 1 kJ/mol
- **D.** 3 kJ/mol

98. Using a bomb calorimeter, the change in energy for the combustion of one mole of octane is calculated to be -5.5×10^3 kJ. Which of the following is true concerning this process?

- **A.** Since no work is done, the change in energy is equal to the heat.
- **B.** Since there is no work, the change in energy is equal to the enthalpy.
- **C.** Since work is done, the change in energy is equal to the heat.
- **D.** The work done can be added to the change in energy to find the enthalpy.

99. Which of the following are true statements?

- **I.** The heat capacity of a substance is the amount of heat that substance can hold per unit of temperature.
- **II.** The specific heat for a single substance is the same for all phases of that substance.
- **III.** When heat is added to a fluid, its temperature will change less if it is allowed to expand.

- **A.** I only
- **B.** III only
- **C.** I and III only
- **D.** I, II, and III

100. Substance *A* has a greater heat capacity than substance *B*. Which of the following is most likely true concerning substances *A* and *B*?

- **A.** Substance *A* has larger molecules than substance *B*.
- **B.** Substance *B* has a lower boiling point than substance *A*.
- **C.** At the same temperature, the molecules of substance *B* move faster than those of substance *A*.
- **D.** Substance *A* has more methods of absorbing energy than substance *B*.

101. In a free adiabatic expansion, a real gas is allowed to spread to twice its original volume with no energy transfer from the surroundings. All of the following are true concerning this process EXCEPT:

- **A.** No work is done.
- **B.** Increased potential energy between molecules results in decreased kinetic energy and the gas cools.
- **C.** Entropy increases.
- **D.** The gas loses heat.

Metal	Specific Heat c (J/g-°C)
Fe	0.44
Au	0.13
Al	0.90
Cu	0.39

102. If samples of equal mass of all of the metals listed are subjected to the same heat source, which metal would be expected to show the LEAST change in temperature?

- **A.** Iron
- **B.** Gold
- **C.** Aluminum
- **D.** Copper

103. In an experiment, it was found that 6 kJ of heat were required to raise the temperature of a sample of copper by 15°C. If the experiment was repeated with a gold sample of the same mass, how much heat would be required achieve the same temperature change?

- **A.** 2 kJ
- **B.** 4 kJ
- **C.** 12 kJ
- **D.** 18 kJ

104. When a sample of aluminum of unknown mass was subjected to 1.8 kJ of heat, the temperature of the aluminum sample increased from 26°C to 31°C. What was the mass of the sample?

- **A.** 200 g
- **B.** 400 g
- **C.** 600 g
- **D.** 800 g

5.4 Phase Changes

Recall from Chemistry Lecture 5.1 that a phase is any part of a system that is homogeneous. For MCAT purposes, we will consider only a pure substance changing from solid to liquid to gas. We shall examine H_2O at constant pressure of 1 atm. If we start with ice at –10°C and begin heating uniformly at a constant rate, initially, the energy going into the ice increases the vibration of its molecules and raises its temperature. When the ice reaches 0°C, the temperature stops increasing. Energy now goes into breaking and weakening hydrogen bonds. This results in a phase change; the ice becomes liquid water. When all of the ice has changed to water, the temperature begins to rise again; the heat goes into increased movement of the molecules. When the water reaches 100°C, the temperature stops rising. The energy once again goes into breaking hydrogen bonds. This process results in a second phase change: liquid water to steam. Once all the hydrogen bonds are broken, the heat increases the speed of the molecules and the temperature rises again. This simplified explanation of phase change is diagrammed below in a heating curve.

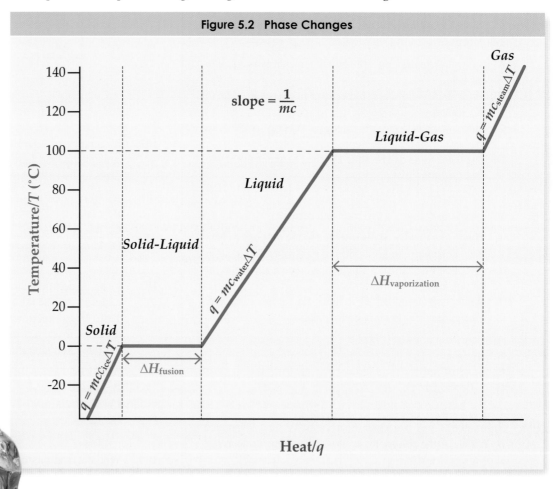

Figure 5.2 Phase Changes

Notice that at 0°C and 100°C the heat stops changing the temperature until the phase change is complete. At these temperatures, the heat capacity is infinite. These points are called the **normal melting point** and **normal boiling point** for water. The word 'normal' indicates a constant pressure of 1 atm. Since the pressure is constant, heat equals the enthalpy change ($q = \Delta H$). The enthalpy change associated with melting is called the **heat of fusion**; the enthalpy change associated with boiling, the **heat of vaporization**. Since enthalpy change is a state function, exactly the same amount of heat absorbed during melting is released during freezing. This is also true for vaporization and condensation, and sublimation and deposition.

The slope of the heating curve, where not zero, is proportional to the inverse of the specific heat. Since the mass of a substance does not change with phase change, the slope is dependent on the specific heat. Notice that each phase of a substance has a unique slope, and therefore a unique specific heat.

Each phase of a substance has its own specific heat.

Figure 5.3 Phase Changes

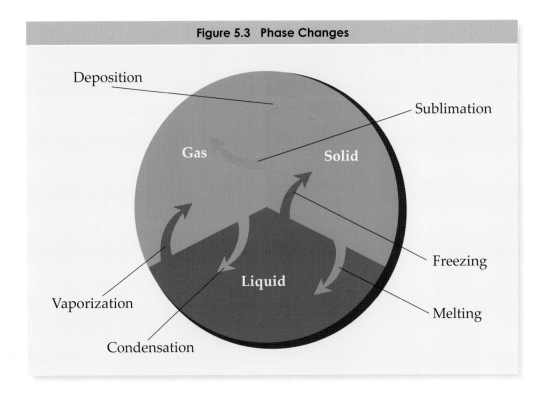

You need to know the names of the types of phase changes:

solid to liquid = melting
liquid to solid = freezing

liquid to gas = vaporization
gas to liquid = condensation

solid to gas = sublimation
gas to solid = deposition

The heating curve shows that melting and boiling are endothermic processes; heat is added. This is also true for sublimation. You should also know that melting, boiling, and sublimation normally increase volume and molecular motion and therefore result in increased system entropy. This means that entropy and enthalpy have the same sign for a phase change; both entropy and enthalpy are positive for melting, vaporization, and sublimation. Thus entropy and enthalpy must be negative for freezing, condensation, and deposition. From the equation $\Delta G = \Delta H - T\Delta S$, recall from Chemistry Lecture 3.14 when enthalpy and entropy have the same sign for a process, temperature dictates the direction of that process. Higher temperatures push such a process toward an increase in entropy and a decrease in enthalpy, and lower temperatures push the same process towards a decrease in entropy and an increase in enthalpy. So phase changes at constant pressure are governed by temperature.

Evaporation occurs when the partial pressure above a liquid is less than the liquid's vapor pressure, but the atmospheric pressure is greater than the vapor pressure. Under these conditions, the liquid evaporates rather than boils. So ice, water, and steam all have different specific heats.

Sublimation of dry ice

5.5 Phase Diagrams

Pressure and temperature are two important intensive properties that help determine the phase of a substance. A **phase diagram** indicates the phases of a substance at different pressures and temperatures. Each section of a phase diagram represents a different phase. The lines marking the boundaries of each section represent temperatures and pressures where the corresponding phases are in equilibrium with each other. Like other equilibriums in chemistry, this equilibrium is a dynamic equilibrium. For instance, when water and steam are in equilibrium, water molecules are escaping from the liquid phase at the same rate that they are returning. Notice that there is only one point where a substance can exist in equilibrium as a solid, liquid, and gas. This point is called the **triple point**.

There is also a temperature above which a substance cannot be liquefied regardless of the pressure applied. This temperature is called the **critical temperature**. The pressure required to produce liquefaction while the substance is at the critical temperature is called the **critical pressure**. Together, the critical temperature and critical pressure define the **critical point**. Fluid beyond the critical point has characteristics of both gas and liquid, and is called *supercritical fluid*.

Most solids are more dense than their liquid counterparts, but ice is less dense than water. The glass on the right shows ice floating on water. In the glass on the left is ice made from deuterium. Deuterium is a heavier than normal hydrogen isotope.

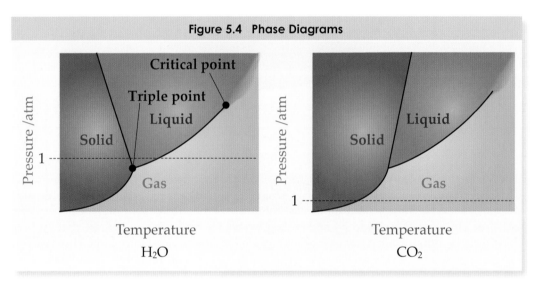

Figure 5.4 Phase Diagrams

For phase changes you must know where the energy goes. It enters the substance as heat or *PV* work, but what then? During a phase change, it breaks bonds and doesn't change the temperature. When the phase is NOT changing, energy increases molecular movement, which increases the temperature.

Think about this: for a single sample of a substance, *P*, *V*, *n*, and *T* are interrelated in such a way that if you know three of them, you can derive the other. This means that a phase diagram can also be given as a comparison between volume and pressure, or volume and temperature. What would that look like? See question 109 on the next page for the answer.

Comparing the phase diagrams for water and carbon dioxide, we notice some interesting things. Even if it were not labeled, we could approximate the location of the 1 atm mark for either diagram. We know that at atmospheric pressure, water exists in all three phases at different temperatures. Thus, we know that the 1 atmosphere mark must be above the triple point. Since carbon dioxide (dry ice) sublimes (changes from solid to gas) at one atmosphere, we know that the triple point must be above the 1 atm mark.

Compare the equilibrium line separating the liquid and solid phases on each diagram shown. For water, the line has a negative slope; for carbon dioxide, a positive slope. Most phase diagrams resemble carbon dioxide in this respect. The negative slope of water explains why ice floats. Since volume decreases with increasing pressure, as we move upward on the phase diagram from ice to liquid water, the volume occupied by H_2O must be decreasing and thus the water must be increasing in density. Therefore, water must be denser than ice. The reason for this is that the crystal structure formed by ice requires more space than the random arrangement of water molecules.

105. What is the total heat needed to change 1 gram of water from –10°C to 110°C at 1 atm? (ΔH_{fusion} = 80 cal/g, $\Delta H_{\text{vaporization}}$ = 540 cal/g, specific heat of ice and steam are 0.5 cal/g °C)

A. –730 cal
B. –630 cal
C. 630 cal
D. 730 cal

106. When heat energy is added evenly throughout a block of ice at 0°C and 1 atm, all of the following are true EXCEPT:

A. The temperature remains constant until all the ice is melted.
B. The added energy increases the kinetic energy of the molecules.
C. Entropy increases.
D. Hydrogen bonds are broken.

107. Below is a phase diagram for carbon dioxide.

What is the critical temperature for carbon dioxide?

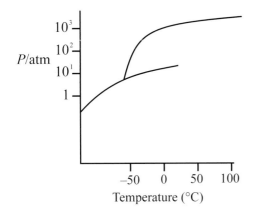

A. –57°C
B. 0°C
C. 31°C
D. 103°C

108. The diagram below compares the density of water in the liquid phase with its vapor phase.

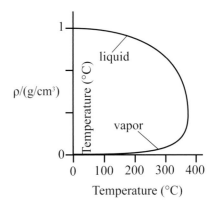

What is the critical temperature of water?

A. 0°C
B. 135°C
C. 374°C
D. 506°C

109. In graph (*a*) below, isotherms for water are plotted against pressure and volume. Graph (*b*) is a phase diagram of water with pressure vs. temperature.

(*a*)

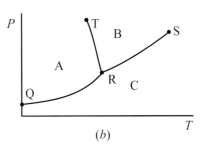

(*b*)

The area inside the dashed line on graph (*a*) is represented on graph (*b*) by:

A. the line between points R and S.
B. the area B.
C. the area C.
D. parts of both area B and C.

110. A solid 78 gram sample of benzene (C_6H_6) was gradually heated until it was melted completely. The heating curve for the sample is shown below.

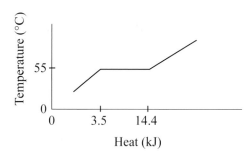

What is the heat of fusion of benzene?

A. 3.5 kJ/mole
B. 10.9 kJ/mole
C. 14.4 kJ/mole
D. 17.9 kJ/mole

111. At atmospheric pressure, the temperature of a pot of boiling water remains at 100°C, when heat is added. The best explanation as to why the added energy does not raise the temperature is that:

A. at the boiling point, the large heat capacity of water allows water to absorb the added energy.
B. the hydrogen bonds of water are strong enough to absorb the added energy without breaking.
C. as the water becomes steam, the added energy becomes kinetic energy of the gas molecules.
D. the added energy is used to break bonds between water molecules.

112. A student has a block of an unknown solid in the laboratory. Which of the following will most likely melt the block?

  I. Heating the solid at constant pressure
 II. Compressing the solid at constant temperature
III. Accelerating the solid to high speeds to increase its kinetic energy.

A. I only
B. I and II only
C. I and III only
D. I, II, and III

5.6 Colligative Properties

Some properties in chemistry depend solely on the number of particles, irrespective of the type of particle. Such properties are called **colligative**. There are four colligative properties of solutions: vapor pressure, boiling point, freezing point, and osmotic pressure.

Colligative properties depend upon number, not kind.

In Chemistry Lecture 4.6, we saw that the addition of a nonvolatile solute will lower the vapor pressure of the solution in direct proportion to the number of particles added, as per Raoult's law. The vapor pressure has an important relationship to the normal boiling point. When the vapor pressure of a solution rises to equal the pressure applied to the solution (typically local atmospheric pressure), the solution begins to boil. Thus, the boiling point of a substance is also changed by the addition of a solute. The addition of a nonvolatile solute lowers the the vapor pressure and elevates the boiling point. The equation for the **boiling point elevation** of an ideally dilute solution due to the addition of a nonvolatile solute is:

A substance boils when its vapor pressure equals the local atmospheric pressure.

$$\Delta T = k_b m i$$

where k_b is a specific constant of the substance being boiled, m is the molality of the solution, and i, called the **van't Hoff factor**, is the number of particles into which a single solute particle will dissociate when added to solution.

When using the nonvolatile solute equations, be sure to consider the number of particles after dissociation.

The van't Hoff factor has two possible values: the expected value and the observed value. For an ionic compound, the *expected value* of the van't Hoff factor is the number of ions created upon complete dissociation. For instance, the expected value of i for NaCl is 2, and for $MgCl_2$ is 3. These values are for an ideally dilute solution. It turns out that, in a nonideal solution consisting of ions, there is *ion pairing*. Ion pairing is the momentary aggregation of two or more ions into a single particle. Ion pairing is not the solute incompletely dissolving; ion pairs are still in the aqueous phase. Ion pairs occur due to the strong attraction between positive and negative ions. The *observed value* of the van't Hoff factor will take into account ion pairing. Ion pairing increases with solution concentration, and decreases with increasing temperature. In a dilute solution, the observed value will be only slightly less than the expected value. On the MCAT, use the expected value unless otherwise instructed.

For boiling point and freezing point calculations molality is used instead of molarity because molarity doesn't change with temperature while molarity does.

You cannot apply the boiling point elevation equation to volatile solutes. As shown in Chemistry Lecture 4.6, a volatile solute can actually decrease the boiling point by increasing the vapor pressure. If you know the heat of solution, you can make qualitative predictions about the boiling point change when a volatile solute is added. For instance, since you know that an endothermic heat of solution indicates weaker bonds, which lead to higher vapor pressure, you can predict that the boiling point will go down.

Figure 5.5
ΔT for Boiling and Freezing Points

Melting point also changes when a solute is added, but it is not related to the vapor pressure. Instead, it is a factor of crystallization. Impurities (the solute) interrupt the crystal lattice and lower the freezing point. **Freezing point depression** for an ideally dilute solution is given by the equation:

$$\Delta T = k_f m i$$

Again, the constant k_f is specific for the substance being frozen.

In other words, if you add water to milk, at first you get watery milk. However, if you continue to add water you have something that looks more like milky water than watery milk. If you add enough water, you no longer even realize there is any milk. So when you add pure liquid B to pure liquid A, at first you are polluting liquid A and your freezing point drops below that of pure liquid A. At some point, however, if you continue to add pure liquid B, the freezing point of your solution begins to rise toward the freezing point of pure liquid B.

Be careful with freezing point depression. If you add a liquid solute, the impurities will initially lower the melting point; however, as the mole fraction of the solute increases, you will come to a point where the solvent becomes the impurity preventing the solute from freezing. At this point, additional solute acts to reduce the impurities creating a more pure solute, and the freezing point of the solution will rise as solute is added.

The fourth colligative property is **osmotic pressure**. Osmotic pressure is a measure of the tendency of water (or some other solvent) to move into a solution via osmosis. To demonstrate osmotic pressure, we divide a pure liquid by a membrane that is permeable to the liquid but not to the solute. We then add solute to one side. Due to entropy, nature wants to make both sides equally dilute. Since the solute cannot pass through the barrier to equalize the concentrations, the pure liquid begins to move to the solution side. As it does so, the solution level rises and the pressure increases. Eventually a balance between the forces of entropy and pressure is achieved. The extra pressure on the solution side is called osmotic pressure. Osmotic pressure Π is given by:

$$\Pi = iMRT$$

where M is the molarity of the solution.

Related to osmotic pressure is *osmotic potential*. Osmotic potential is a partial measure of a system's free energy. Pure water is arbitrarily assigned an osmotic potential of zero. When a solute is added, the osmotic potential becomes negative. At constant temperature and pressure, water flows from higher osmotic potential to lower osmotic potential. *Water potential*, another related term, is similar to osmotic potential but takes into account temperature and pressure. Water potential is essentially the same as free energy. When water and the solution in the diagram below have come to equilibrium, points A and B have the same water potential, but the osmotic potential of point B is less than that of point A.

Albumin (shown here in solution in yellow) is a blood protein. Albumin plays a vital role in osmotic pressure regulation.

Figure 5.6 Osmotic Pressure

Selectively permeable membrane

Water A •

Solution B •

h_B

h_A

$$\Pi_B = iM_B RT$$

and

$$P_A = \rho g h_A \qquad P_B = \rho g h_B$$

$$\Pi_B = P_B - P_A$$

$$\Pi_B = \rho g h_B - \rho g h_A$$

Water molecules are small enough to move through the pores in the membrane.

Solute particles are too large to move through the pores in the membrane

Students often think about osmotic pressure as the pressure pulling into a solution, and hydrostatic pressure as the pressure pushing out of a solution. Although this is technically incorrect because pressure is a scalar and has no direction, thinking about osmotic pressure in this way may give you some intuition about it.

Equations
Heat Capacity
$$q = C\Delta T$$
Specific Heat Capacity
$$q = mc\Delta T$$
Calorie/ Specific Heat of Water
$$c_{water} = 1 \ cal \ g^{-1} \ {}^{\circ}C^{-1}$$
Boiling Point Elevation
$$\Delta T = k_b mi$$
Freezing point depression
$$\Delta T = k_f mi$$
Osmotic Pressure
$$\Pi = iMRT$$

Terms	
Boiling Point Elevation	Heats of reaction
Bomb calorimeter	Heats of vaporization
Coffee cup calorimeter	Normal boiling point
Colligative Properties	Normal melting point
Critical point	Osmotic pressure
Critical pressure	Phase
Critical temperature	Phase diagram
Freezing point depression	Point elevation
Heat capacity C	Triple point
Heats of fusion	Van't Hoff factor

Thought Provoker

Answer from page 108:

The answer lies in the differences in specific heat. Sand has a very low specific heat of 0.48 J/(g · K). This means that it takes 0.48 J of energy to raise 1 gram of sand by 1 degree Celsius. Water, on the other hand, has a very high heat capacity at 4.18 J/(g · K). This means that it must absorb much more energy in order to raise 1g of water by 1 degree Celsius.

Answer from page 109:

Be careful here, the key in this question is to realize that both the cheese and the crust are at the same temperature. Looking at our equation, if ΔT is the same, the heat (q) is going to be the only difference. A higher specific heat will result in a greater q, thereby burning your mouth. Cheese must have a higher specific heat. Also, cheese conducts heat and transfers heat better than the crust.

113. Which of the following aqueous solutions will have the lowest boiling point?

    A. 0.5 M glucose
    B. 1 M glucose
    C. 0.5 M NaCl
    D. 0.6 M NaCl

114. An object experiences a greater buoyant force in seawater than in fresh water. The most likely reason for this is:

    A. Seawater has greater osmotic pressure making the pressure difference greater at different depths.
    B. Fresh water has greater osmotic pressure making the pressure difference greater at different depths.
    C. Seawater has greater density.
    D. Fresh water has greater density.

115. Glycol ($C_2H_6O_2$) is the main component in antifreeze. What mass of glycol must be added to 10 liters of water to prevent freezing down to –18.6°C? (The molal freezing point depression constant for water is 1.86°C kg/mol.)

    A. 3.1 kg
    B. 6.2 kg
    C. 10 kg
    D. 12.4 kg

116. A student holds a beaker of pure liquid A in one hand and pure liquid B in the other. Liquid A has a higher boiling point than liquid B. When the student pours a small amount of liquid B into liquid A, the temperature of the solution increases. Which of the following statements is true?

    A. The boiling point of the solution is lower than either pure liquid A or B.
    B. The boiling point of the solution is higher than either pure liquid A or B.
    C. The freezing point of the solution is higher than either pure liquid A or B.
    D. The vapor pressure of the solution is higher than pure liquid B.

117. 500 ml of an aqueous solution having a mass of 503 grams and containing 20 grams of an unknown protein was placed into a bulb and lowered into pure water as shown. A membrane permeable to water but not to the solute separated the solution from the water.

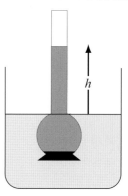

The height of the column of solution was found to be 'h'. Which of the following statements is true concerning this procedure?

    A. A large value for h indicates a low osmotic pressure in the solution.
    B. A large value for h indicates a high osmotic pressure in the pure water.
    C. A large value for h indicates that the protein has a low molecular weight.
    D. A large value for h indicates that the protein has a high molecular weight.

118. Calcium chloride is sometimes sprinkled on winter sidewalks to melt snow and ice. If 333 grams of calcium chloride is dissolved completely in 1.00 kg of water, what will be the freezing point of the solution? (The molal freezing point depression constant for water is 1.86°C kg/mol.)

    A. –5.58°C
    B. –9.30°C
    C. –11.7°C
    D. –16.7°C

119. A popular experiment uses freezing point depression to find the molar mass of an unknown solute. If a known mass of an unknown non-polar solute is placed into a known mass of a known non-polar solvent and the freezing point depression is measured, which of the following expressions will be equal to the molar mass of the unknown solute?

A. $$\dfrac{(k_f)(\text{grams of solute})}{(\Delta T)(\text{kg of solvent})}$$

B. $$\dfrac{(k_f)(\text{kg of solvent})}{(\Delta T)(\text{grams of solute})}$$

C. $$\dfrac{(\Delta T)(\text{grams of solute})}{(k_f)(\text{kg of solvent})}$$

D. $$\dfrac{(\Delta T)(\text{kg of solvent})}{(k_f)(\text{grams of solute})}$$

120. A student prepared two solutions in separate flasks. Solution A consisted of 0.1 mole of sodium fluoride in 1 liter of water. Solution B consisted of 0.1 mole of potassium chloride in 1 liter of water. The student then heated both flasks and measured the boiling point of each solution. Which of the solutions would be expected to have the higher boiling point?

A. Solution A, because sodium fluoride has a lower molar mass than potassium chloride.
B. Solution B, because potassium chloride is less volatile than sodium fluoride.
C. Solution A, because potassium chloride will not dissociate completely in water.
D. Both solutions will have the same boiling point.

ACIDS AND BASES

6.1 Definitions

There are three definitions of an acid that you must know for the MCAT: Arrhenius, Brønsted-Lowry, and Lewis. These definitions are given here in the order in which they were created. An **Arrhenius acid** is anything that produces hydrogen ions in aqueous solution, and an Arrhenius base is anything that produces hydroxide ions in aqueous solution. This definition covers only aqueous solutions. **Brønsted and Lowry** redefined acids as anything that donates a proton, and bases as anything that accepts a proton. Finally, the **Lewis** definition is the most general, defining an acid as anything that accepts a pair of electrons, and a base as anything that donates a pair of electrons. The Lewis definition includes all the acids and bases in the Brønsted-Lowry and more. Lewis acids include molecules that have an incomplete octet of electrons around the central atom, like $AlCl_3$ and BF_3. They also include all simple cations except the alkali and the heavier alkaline earth metal cations. The smaller the cation and the higher the charge, the stronger the acid strength. Fe^{3+} is a common example of a Lewis acid. Molecules that are acidic only in the Lewis sense are not generally called acids unless they are referred to explicitly as Lewis acids.

Lewis Acids

Brønsted-Lowry Acids

Arrhenius Acids

Notice that in the Bronsted definition, the acid 'donates', and in the Lewis definition the acid 'accepts'.

Acids taste sour or tart; bases taste bitter. Bases are slippery when wet.

Beware of Acid Rain

Relief work on the facade of St. Bartholomews Church in midtown Manhattan damaged from years of acid rain.

Although you must memorize the definitions, it is usually convenient to think of an acid as H^+ and a base as OH^-. In fact, aqueous solutions always contain both H^+ and OH^-. An aqueous solution containing a greater concentration of H^+ than OH^- is acidic, while an aqueous solution containing a greater concentration of OH^- than H^+ is basic. An aqueous solution with equal amounts of H^+ and OH^- is neutral.

$$H^+$$
acid

$$OH^-$$
base

> Many reactions in living cells involve the transfer of a proton. The rate of such reactions depends upon the concentration of H^+ ions or the pH.

One measure of the hydrogen ion concentration is called the pH, where $p(x)$ is a function in which, given any x, $p(x) = -\log(x)$. If we measure the hydrogen ion concentration in moles per liter ($[H+]$ the brackets always indicate concentration), pH is given by:

$$pH = -\log[H^+]$$

The scale for pH generally runs from 0 to 14, but since any H^+ concentration is possible, any pH value is possible. At 25°C, a pH of 7 is neutral; a lower pH is acidic and a higher pH is basic. Each point on the pH scale corresponds to a tenfold difference in hydrogen ion concentration. An acid with a pH of 2 produces 10 times as many hydrogen ions as an acid with a pH of 3, and 100 times as many hydrogen ions as an acid with a pH of 4.

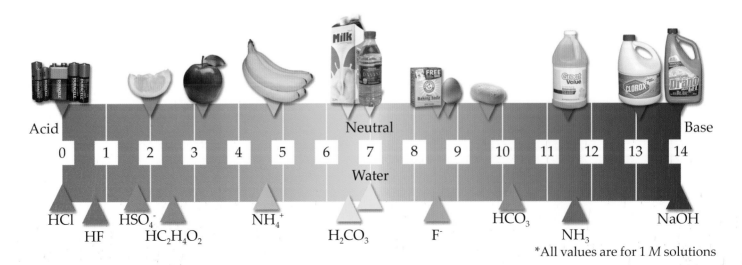

*All values are for 1 M solutions

You must understand some very basic ideas about logarithms for the MCAT. pH uses the base 10 logarithm. The base 10 logarithm is used to solve a problem like:

$$10^x = 3.16$$

The answer is: $x = \log(3.16)$. Luckily on the MCAT we don't have to do calculations; instead we estimate. Since 10^0 equals 1, and 10^1 equals 10, in the problem above x must be between 0 and 1. The answer is: $x = 0.5$. Applying this to acids, if we have a hydrogen ion concentration of 10^{-3}, the log of 10^{-3} is -3, and the negative log of 10^{-3} is positive 3. Thus the pH is 3. If we have a hydrogen ion concentration of a little more than 10^{-3}, say 4×10^{-3}, then the solution is a little more acidic and the pH is slightly lower than 3: say 2.4. Notice that 4×10^{-3} is not as large a number as 10^{-2}, so the pH is lower than 3 but not quite 2. On the MCAT you **must** be able to estimate pH values as shown in this paragraph.

$$\log(10^1) = \log(10) = 1$$
$$\uparrow \qquad \uparrow$$
$$\log(3.16) = .5$$
$$\uparrow \qquad \uparrow$$
$$\log(10^0) = \log(1) = 0$$

The second and last thing you should know about logarithms is:

$$\log(AB) = \log(A) + \log(B)$$

This is easily verifiable:

$$\log(10^2) = 2; \; \log(10^3) = 3;$$

$$\log(10^2 \times 10^3) = 5.$$

From the definitions of an acid, it must be clear that, if there is an acid in a reaction, there must also be a base; you can't have a proton donated without something to accept it. We can write a hypothetical acid-base reaction in aqueous solution as follows:

$$\textbf{HA} + \textbf{H}_2\textbf{O} \rightleftharpoons \textbf{H}_3\textbf{O}^+ + \textbf{A}^-$$

Here, HA is the acid, and, since water accepts the proton, water is the base. If we look at the reverse reaction, the hydronium ion donates a proton to A^-, making the hydronium ion the acid and A^- the base. To avoid confusion, we refer to the reactants as the acid and base, and the products as the conjugate acid and conjugate base. Thus, in every reaction the acid has its conjugate base, and the base has its conjugate acid. Deciding which form is the conjugate simply depends upon in which direction you happen to be viewing the reaction.

> You should recognize a hydronium ion H_3O^+. The hydronium ion is simply a hydrated proton. For MCAT acid and base reactions, a hydronium ion and a proton are the same thing.

Acid donates proton — Base accepts proton — Conjugate acid — Conjugate base

In other words, it is correct to say either: "HA is the conjugate acid of base A⁻"; or "A⁻ is the conjugate base of acid HA." You must be able to identify conjugates on the MCAT.

You should also know that the stronger the acid, the weaker its conjugate base, and the stronger the base, the weaker its conjugate acid. **Warning:** Many students and even some prep books translate this into "Strong acids have weak conjugate bases, and weak acids have strong conjugate bases." The second part of this statement is incorrect! Acid strength is on the logarithmic scale and a weak acid may have a strong or weak conjugate base.

$K_w = K_a K_b$

Some substances act as either an acid or a base, depending upon their environment. They are called **amphoteric**. Water is a good example. In the reaction $HA + H_2O \rightarrow A^- + H_3O^+$, water acts as a base accepting a proton. Water can also act like an acid by donating a proton $A^- + H_2O \rightarrow HA + OH^-$.

For the MCAT, you need to recognize the strong acids and bases in Table 6.1.

By the way, when we say "strong acid" in inorganic chemistry, we mean an acid that is stronger than H_3O^+. A strong base is stronger than OH^-. With bases, we often call something as strong as OH^-, like NaOH, a strong base. For MCAT purposes, we assume that a strong acid or base completely dissociates in water.

Table 6.1 Strong Acids and Bases			
Strong Acids		*Strong Bases*	
Hydroiodic acid	HI	Sodium hydroxide	NaOH
Hydrobromic acid	HBr	Potassuim hydroxide	KOH
Hydrochloric acid	HCl	Amide ion	NH_2^-
Nitric acid	HNO_3	Hydride ion	H^-
Perchloric acid	$HClO_4$	Calcium hydroxide	$Ca(OH)_2$
Chloric acid	$HClO_3$	Sodium oxide	Na_2O
Sulfuric acid	H_2SO_4	Calcium oxide	CaO

Figure 6.1   Common Household Acids and Bases

Acids

Bases

Some acids can donate more than one proton. These acids are called **polyprotic acids**. An acid that can donate just two protons can be called a **diprotic acid** as well as a polyprotic acid. The second proton donated by a polyprotic acid is usually so weak that its effect on the pH is negligible. On the MCAT the second proton can almost always be ignored. (The rule of thumb is that if the K_a values differ by more than 10^3, the second proton can be ignored.) For instance, the second proton from H_2SO_4 is a strong acid; yet, except with dilute concentrations (concentrations less than $1\ M$), it has a negligible effect on the pH of H_2SO_4 solution. This is because H_2SO_4 is so much stronger than HSO_4^-. Notice here that the percent dissociation of an acid decreases with acidity. This means that acids dissociate less in more concentrated solutions. It does not mean that concentrated solutions are less acidic.

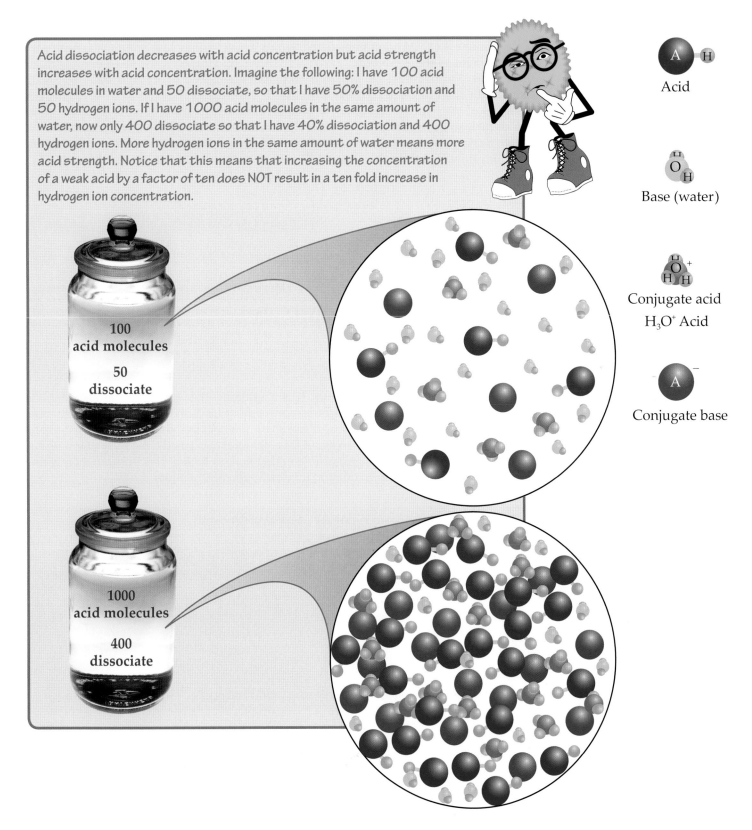

Acid dissociation decreases with acid concentration but acid strength increases with acid concentration. Imagine the following: I have 100 acid molecules in water and 50 dissociate, so that I have 50% dissociation and 50 hydrogen ions. If I have 1000 acid molecules in the same amount of water, now only 400 dissociate so that I have 40% dissociation and 400 hydrogen ions. More hydrogen ions in the same amount of water means more acid strength. Notice that this means that increasing the concentration of a weak acid by a factor of ten does NOT result in a ten fold increase in hydrogen ion concentration.

100 acid molecules
50 dissociate

1000 acid molecules
400 dissociate

A—H
Acid

Base (water)

Conjugate acid
H_3O^+ Acid

A⁻
Conjugate base

6.2 How Molecular Structure Affects Acid Strength

There are three factors in molecular structure that determine whether or not a molecule containing a hydrogen will release its hydrogen into solution, and thus act as an acid:

1) The strength of the bond holding the hydrogen to the molecule;

2) The polarity of the bond; and

3) The stability of the conjugate base

If we examine the C–H bond in methane, which has extremely low acidity, it is nearly the same strength as the H–Cl bond in hydrochloric acid. However, the H–Cl bond is much more polar, and therefore the proton is more easily removed in aqueous solution. HCl is more acidic than methane. On the other hand, a comparison of the bond strengths and polarities of the hydrogen halides shows that, although the H–F bond is the most polar, it is also the strongest bond. In addition, the small size of the fluorine ion concentrates the negative charge and adds to its instability. In this case, the bond strength and conjugate instability outweigh the polarity, and HF is the weakest of the hydrogen halide acids.

Figure 6.2 Comparision of CH₄ and HCl

Figure 6.3 Comparision of Hydrogen Halides

> In a series of oxyacids, more oxygens means a stronger acid.

Keeping conjugate stability in mind, if we examine the oxyacids, we see that the electronegative oxygens draw electrons to one side of the bond, increasing polarity. The oxygens in the conjugate of an oxyacid can share the negative charge spreading it over a larger area and stabilizing the conjugate base. In similar oxyacids, the molecule with the most oxygens makes the strongest acid. Another way to look at this phenomenon is that the acidity increases with the oxidation number of the central atom.

Figure 6.4 Acidity of Oxyacids

6.3 Hydrides

Binary compounds (compounds with only two elements) containing hydrogen are called hydrides. Hydrides can be basic, acidic, or neutral. On the periodic table, the basic hydrides are to the left, and the acidic hydrides are to the right. For instance, NaH is basic; H_2S is acidic. Following this trend, metal hydrides are either basic or neutral, while nonmetal hydrides are acidic or neutral. (Ammonia, NH_3, is an exception to this rule.) The acidity of nonmetal hydrides tends to increase going down the periodic table. $H_2O < H_2S < H_2Se < H_2Te$

Calcium hydride (CaH_2) reacting with water, releasing hydrogen gas (H_2).

Table 6.2 Non-metal Hydrides

	Group			
	4A	5A	6A	6A
Period 2	CH_4 Neither acidic nor basic	NH_3 Weakly basic	H_2O --------	HF Weakly acidic
Period 3	SiH_4 Neither acidic nor basic	PH_3 Weakly basic	H_2S Weakly acidic	HCl Strongly acidic

Increasing Acidity

Increasing Acidity

Notes:

121. Ammonia reacts with water to form the ammonium ion and hydroxide ion.

$$NH_3 + H_2O \rightarrow NH_4^+ + OH^-$$

According to the Brønsted-Lowry definition of acids and bases, what is the conjugate acid of ammonia?

- **A.** NH_3
- **B.** NH_4^+
- **C.** OH^-
- **D.** H^+

122. By definition, a Lewis base:

- **A.** donates a proton.
- **B.** accepts a proton.
- **C.** donates a pair of electrons.
- **D.** accepts a pair of electrons.

123. Which of the following is the strongest base in aqueous solution?

- **A.** Cl^-
- **B.** NH_4^+
- **C.** F^-
- **D.** Br^-

124. Which of the following is amphoteric?

- **A.** an amino acid
- **B.** H_2SO_4
- **C.** NaOH
- **D.** HF

125. The addition of an electron withdrawing group to the alpha carbon of a carboxylic acid will:

- **A.** increase the acidity of the proton by making the O–H bond more polar.
- **B.** increase the acidity of the proton by making the O–H bond stronger.
- **C.** decrease the acidity of the proton by making the O–H bond more polar.
- **D.** decrease the acidity of the proton by stabilizing the conjugate base.

126. A student prepared two acid solutions. Solution A has a hydrogen ion concentration of 6.0×10^{-5} mole L^{-1}. Solution B has a hydrogen ion concentration of 1×10^{-7} mole L^{-1}. The pH of solution A differs from that of solution B by:

- **A.** 1.3
- **B.** 2.8
- **C.** 3.7
- **D.** 5.0

127. In the reaction below, ammonia and boron trifluoride combine when a coordinate covalent bond is formed between nitrogen and boron. In this reaction, ammonia acts as a:

$$NH_3 + BF_3 \rightarrow H_3NBF_3$$

- **A.** Lewis acid
- **B.** Lewis base
- **C.** Brønsted-Lowry acid
- **D.** Brøndted-Lowry base

128. Two chemical reactions involving water are shown below.

$$NH_4^+ + H_2O \rightarrow NH_3 + H_3O^+$$
Reaction 1

$$NaH + H_2O \rightarrow Na^+ + OH^- + H_2$$
Reaction 2

Which of the following is true?

- **A.** Water acts as a base in Reaction 1 and an acid in Reaction 2.
- **B.** Water acts as an acid in Reaction 1 and a base in Reaction 2.
- **C.** Water acts as a base in both reactions.
- **D.** Water acts as neither an acid nor a base.

6.4 Equilibrium Constants for Acid-Base Reactions

Pure water reacts with itself to form hydronium and hydroxide ions as follows:

$$H_2O + H_2O \rightarrow H_3O^+ + OH^-$$

This is called the **autoionization of water**. K_w is the equilibrium constant for this reaction.

$$K_w = [H^+][OH^-]$$

(For convenience, we have substituted H^+ for H_3O^+.) At 25°C the equilibrium of this reaction lies far to the left:

$$K_w = 10^{-14}$$

Figure 6.5   Autoionization of Water

In a neutral aqueous solutions at 25°C, the H^+ concentration and the OH^- concentration are equal at 10^{-7} mol L^{-1}. The pH of the solution is found by taking the negative log of the hydrogen ion concentration, which is: $-\log[10^{-7}] = 7$. An acid or base added to an aqueous solution will change the concentrations of both H^+ and OH^-, but K_w will remain 10^{-14} at 25°C. For example, in a solution with a pH of 2, the ion concentrations will be: $[H^+] = 10^{-2}$ mol L^{-1} and $[OH^-] = 10^{-12}$ mol L^{-1}. Using the p(x) function and the rule: $\log(AB) = \log(A) + \log(B)$, we can put this relationship into a simple equation:

$$pH + pOH = pK_w \qquad\qquad pH + pOH = 14$$
$$\text{(For an aqueous solution at 25°C)}$$

An acid will have its own equilibrium constant in water, called the **acid dissociation constant** K_a. If we use our hypothetical acid-base reaction: $HA + H_2O \rightarrow H_3O^+ + A^-$, then the acid dissociation constant for the acid HA is:

$$K_a = \frac{[H^+][A^-]}{[HA]}$$

Corresponding to every K_a, there is a K_b. The K_b is the equilibrium constant for the reaction of the conjugate base with water. For the conjugate base A^-, the reaction is:

$$A^- + H_2O \rightarrow OH^- + HA$$

and the K_b is:

$$K_b = \frac{[OH^-][HA]}{[A^-]}$$

Notice that the reaction for K_b is the reaction of the conjugate base and water, and it is not the reverse of the reaction for K_a. Notice also that the product of the two constants is K_w.

$$K_a K_b = \frac{[H^+]\cancel{[A^-]}}{\cancel{[HA]}} \times \frac{[OH^-]\cancel{[HA]}}{\cancel{[A^-]}} = [H^+][OH^-] = K_w$$

$$K_a K_b = K_w$$

Using the p(x) function and the rule: $\log(AB) = \log(A) + \log(B)$, this formula can also be written as:

$$pK_a + pK_b = pK_w \qquad\qquad pK_a + pK_b = 14$$
$$\text{(At 25°C)}$$

It may seem like there are a lot of equations to memorize here, but it is really very simple.

First, all equilibrium constants are derived from the law of mass action. They are all products over reactants, where pure solids and liquids are given a concentration of one. Once you know how to find one K, you should know how to find any K. The subscript on the constant is supposed to make things less complicated, not more complicated.

Second, memorize that: $K_w = 10^{-14}$ at 25°C.

Third, remember the log rule, $\log(AB) = \log(A) + \log(B)$, and you can derive any of the equations.

Notice that the larger the K_a and the smaller the pK_a, the stronger the acid. A K_a greater than 1 or a pK_a less than zero indicates a strong acid. The same is true of the K_b and pK_b of a base.

The pH of urine is affected by various chemicals in the blood.

Finding the pH

Very strong acids and bases will dissociate almost completely. This means that the HA or BOH concentration (for the acid and base respectively) will be nearly zero. Since division by zero is impossible, for such acids and bases, there is no K_a or K_b. Surprisingly, this fact makes it easier to find the pH of strong acid and strong base solutions. Since the entire concentration of acid or base is assumed to dissociate, the concentration of H^+ or OH^- is the same as the original concentration of acid or base. For instance, a 0.01 molar solution of HCl will have 0.01 mol L^{-1} of H^+ ions. Since $0.01 = 10^{-2}$, and $-\log(10^{-2}) = 2$, the pH of the solution will be 2. Likewise, in a 0.01 molar solution of NaOH, we will have 0.01 mol L^{-1} of OH^- ions. (Be careful here!) The pOH will equal 2 so the pH will equal 12. You can avoid a mistake here by remembering that an acid has a pH below 7 and a base has a pH above 7.

Weak acids and bases can be a little trickier. Doing a sample problem is the best way to learn. For example, in order to find the pH of a 0.01 molar solution of HCN, we do the following:

1. Set up the equilibrium equation:

$$K_a = \frac{[H^+][CN^-]}{[HCN]} = 6.2 \times 10^{-10}$$

2. If we add 0.01 moles of HCN to one liter of pure water, then 'x' amount of that HCN will dissociate. Thus, we will have 'x' mol L^{-1} of H^+ ions and 'x' mol L^{-1} of CN^- ions. The concentration of undissociated HCN will be whatever is left, or '$0.01 - x$'. Plugging these values into the equation above, we have:

$$\frac{[x][x]}{[0.01 - x]} = 6.2 \times 10^{-10}$$

3. If we solve for x, we have a quadratic equation. Forget it! You don't need this for the MCAT. We make an assumption that x is less than 5% of 0.01, and we will check it when we are done. Throwing out the x in the denominator, we have:

$$\frac{[x][x]}{[0.01]} \approx 6.2 \times 10^{-10}$$

Thus, x is approximately 2.5×10^{-6}. This is much smaller than 0.01, so our assumption was valid. 'x' is the concentration of H^+ ions. The pH of the solution is between 5 and 6. This is close enough for the MCAT. Calculating the actual number gives us $-\log(2.5 \times 10^{-6}) = 5.6$. Just to make sure, we ask ourselves, "Is 5.6 a reasonable pH for a dilute weak acid?" The answer is yes.

For a weak base, the process is the same, except that we use K_b, and we arrive at the pOH. Subtract the pOH from 14 to find the pH. This step is often forgotten. If we ask ourselves, "Is this pH reasonable for a weak base?", we won't forget this step.

So notice that 0.01 M of weak acid yielded significantly less than 0.01 M H+ in solution, since weak acids do not dissociate completely. You should also appreciate that if we increase the concentration of the weak acid by a factor of 10, the pH will drop, but it will not drop down by a whole pH point. Again, this is because the extra added acid does not dissociate completely.

6.6 | *Salts*

Salts are ionic compounds that dissociate in water. Often, when salts dissociate, they create acidic or basic conditions. The pH of a salt solution can be predicted qualitatively by comparing the conjugates of the respective ions. Find the conjugate of the salt cation by removing a proton from it. If the salt cation has no protons, then add OH to it to find the conjugate. Find the conjugate of the salt anion by adding a proton to it. Then compare the strength of the conjugates you've made. If the conjugates are both strong, then the salt solution is neutral. If one of the conjugates is strong and the other is weak, then the pH of the salt solution favors the strong conjugate. Here are some examples:

Na^+ and Cl^- are the conjugates of NaOH and HCl respectively, so, as a salt, NaCl produces a neutral solution. NH_4NO_3 is composed of the conjugates of the base NH_3 and the strong acid HNO_3 respectively. Thus, NH_4^+ is acidic and NO_3^- is neutral. As a salt, NH_4NO_3 is weakly acidic.

> When considering salts, remember, all cations, except those of the alkali metals and the heavier alkaline Earth metals (Ca^{2+}, Sr^{2+}, and Ba^{2+}), act as weak Lewis acids in aqueous solutions.

Himalayan rock salt
(sodium chloride)

Kala Namak (India)
(sodium chloride)

Alaea red salt (Hawaii)
(sodium chloride)

Black pearl salt (Hawaii)
(sodium chloride)

Maldon salt
(sodium chloride)

Himalayan salt
(sodium chloride)

Common salt
(sodium chloride)

Gerand salt
(sodium chloride)

Herb salt
(sodium chloride & herbs)

Atlantic sea salt
(sodium chloride)

Various types of salts are shown above. Salts vary in transparency, opacity, and color.
The size of the individual crystals is a major determinant in the transparency of a salt.

129. Which of the following is the K_b for the conjugate base of carbonic acid?

A. $\dfrac{[H_2CO_3]}{[H^+][HCO_3^-]}$

B. $\dfrac{[OH^-][HCO_3^-]}{[H_2CO_3]}$

C. $\dfrac{[H^+][H_2CO_3]}{[HCO_3^-]}$

D. $\dfrac{[OH^-][H_2CO_3]}{[HCO_3^-]}$

130. An aqueous solution of $0.1\ M$ HBr has a pH of:

A. 0
B. 1
C. 2
D. 14

131. Carbonic acid has a K_a of 4.3×10^{-7}. What is the pH when 1 mole of $NaHCO_3$ is dissolved in 1 liter of water?

A. 3.2
B. 3.8
C. 10.2
D. 12.5

132. Stomach acid has a pH of approximately 2. Sour milk has a pH of 6. Stomach acid is:

A. 3 times as acidic as sour milk.
B. 4 times as acidic as sour milk.
C. 100 times as acidic as sour milk.
D. 10,000 times as acidic as sour milk.

133. Which of the following salts is the most basic?

A. $NaClO_3$
B. NH_4Cl
C. KBr
D. NaCN

134. The acid dissociation constant for HBrO is 2×10^{-9}. What is the base dissociation constant for BrO^-?

A. 5×10^{-5}
B. 5×10^{-6}
C. 5×10^{-7}
D. 5×10^{-8}

135. A solution of soapy water has a pH of 10. What is the hydroxide ion concentration?

A. $10^{-10}\ M$
B. $10^{-7}\ M$
C. $10^{-4}\ M$
D. $10^{-1}\ M$

136. When solid sodium acetate, $NaC_2H_3O_2$ is added to pure water, the pH of the solution will:

A. decrease because Na^+ acts as an acid.
B. increase because Na^+ acts as a base.
C. decrease because $C_2H_3O_2^-$ acts as an acid.
D. increase because $C_2H_3O_2^-$ acts as a base.

6.7 | *Titrations*

A **titration** is the drop-by-drop mixing of an acid and a base. Titrations are performed in order to find the concentration of some unknown by comparing it with the concentration of the **titrant**. The changing pH of the unknown as the acidic or basic titrant is added is represented graphically as a sigmoidal curve. Figure 6.6 is the **titration curve** of a strong acid titrated by a strong base.

Notice the portion of the graph that most nearly approximates a vertical line. The midpoint of this line is called the **equivalence point** or the **stoichiometric point**. The equivalence point for a monoprotic acid is the point in the titration when there are equal equivalents of acid and base in solution. (An *equivalent* is the mass of acid or base necessary to produce or consume one mole of protons.) For instance, since there is a one to one correspondence between HCl with NaOH, the equivalence point for a titration of HCl with NaOH will be reached when the same number of moles of HCl and NaOH exist in solution. This is not necessarily when they are at equal volumes. If the concentrations differ (and they probably will) the equivalence point will not be where the volumes are equal.

For equally strong acid-base titrations, the equivalence point will usually be at pH 7. (**Warning!** For a diprotic acid whose conjugate base is a strong acid, like H_2SO_4, this is not the case.)

The graph to the right is for the titration of a strong acid with a strong base. In other words, we are slowly adding base to an acid. This is clear because we start with a very low pH and finish with a very high pH. For a titration of a strong base with a strong acid, we would simply invert the graph.

A titration of an acid in aqueous solution with a base.

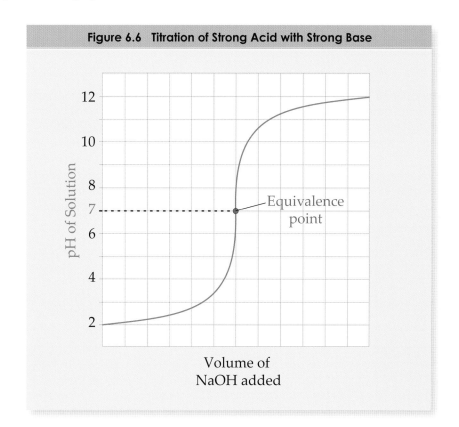

The titration of a weak acid with a strong base looks slightly different than the curve in Figure 6.6, and is shown below. The equivalence point is also not as predictable. Of course, if the base is stronger than the acid, the equivalence point will be above 7, and if the acid is stronger than the base, the equivalence point will be below 7.

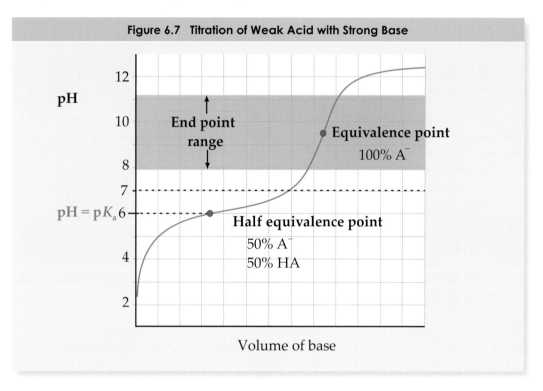

Figure 6.7 Titration of Weak Acid with Strong Base

> Before a titration of a weak acid with a strong base begins you have 100% HA. At the half equivalence point the base has stripped the protons off of exactly half the molecules of acid, so at the half equivalence point HA = A⁻. At the equivalence point the base has stripped all the protons from all the acid molecules, and you have 100% A⁻.

Notice the half equivalence point. This is probably more likely be tested by the MCAT than the equivalence point. The **half equivalence point** is the point where exactly one half of the acid has been neutralized by the base. In other words, the concentration of the acid is equal to the concentration of its conjugate base. Notice that the half equivalence point occurs at the midpoint of the section of the graph that most represents a horizontal line. This is the spot where we could add the largest amount of base or acid with the least amount of change in pH. Such a solution is considered to be **buffered**. The half equivalence point shows the point in the titration where the solution is the most well buffered.

> The Henderson-Hasselbalch equation is simply a form of the equilibrium expression for K_a:
>
> $$K_a = \frac{[H^+][A^-]}{[HA]}$$
>
> $$K_a = [H^+]\frac{[A^-]}{[HA]}$$
>
> using the log rule: $$-\log(K_a) = -\log[H^+] - \log\frac{[A^-]}{[HA]}$$
>
> $$pK_a = pH - \log\frac{[A^-]}{[HA]}$$
>
> There is no need to memorize it, since it is so easy and so quick to derive it.

Notice also that, at the half equivalence point, the pH of the solution is equal to the pK_a of the acid. This is predicted by the **Henderson-Hasselbalch equation**:

$$pH = pK_a + \log\frac{[A^-]}{[HA]}$$

Recall that $\log(1) = 0$; thus when $[A^-] = [HA]$, $pH = pK_a$.

If we were to make a buffer solution, we would start with an acid whose pK_a is closest to the pH at which we want to buffer our solution. Next we would mix equal amounts of that acid with its conjugate base. We would want the concentration of our buffer solution to greatly exceed the concentration of outside acid or base affecting our solution. So, a buffer solution is made from equal and copious amounts of a weak acid and its conjugate base.

It appears from the Henderson-Hasselbalch equation that we could add an infinite amount of water to a buffered solution with no change in pH. Of course, this is ridiculous. Will adding Lake Tahoe to a beaker of buffered solution change the pH of that solution? The Henderson-Hasselbalch equation in the form above does not allow for *ion pairing*. (Ion pairing is when oppositely charged ions in solution bond momentarily to form a single particle.) Water will generally act like a base in acidic solution and an acid in basic solution. If you add a base or water to an acidic, buffered solution, it is clear from the titration curve that the pH will increase. It just won't increase as rapidly as other solutions less well buffered. However, a question on the MCAT is more likely to consider the ideal circumstance where adding a *small* amount of water to an ideally dilute, buffered solution will have no effect on the pH.

Warning! You cannot typically use the Henderson-Hasselbalch equation to find the pH at the equivalence point. Instead, you must use the pK_b of the conjugate base. You can find the K_b from the pK_a and the K_w. The concentration of the conjugate base at the equivalence point is equal to the number of moles of acid divided by the volume of acid plus the volume of base used to titrate. Don't forget to consider the volume of base used to titrate. Unless the base has no volume, the concentration of the conjugate at the equivalence point will not be equal to the original concentration of the acid. The pH at the equivalence point involves much more calculation than the pH at the half equivalence point. For this reason, it is more likely that the MCAT will ask about the pH at the half equivalence point.

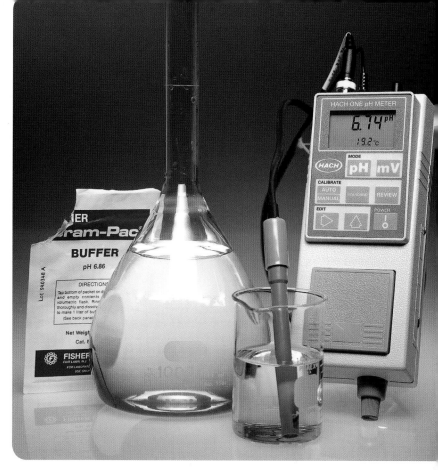

The pH of a buffer remains constant regardless of the volume of the solution.

Finding the pH at the equivalence point is a good exercise, but you won't have to do it on the MCAT. Here are the steps:

Use K_a and K_w to find the K_b

$$K_b = \frac{K_w}{K_a}$$

Set up the K_b equilibrium expression.

$$K_b = \frac{[OH^-][HA]}{[A^-]}$$

Solve for the OH⁻ concentration, and find the pOH.

Subtract the pOH from 14 to find the pH.

$$14 - pOH = pH$$

Acid-base reaction with indicator. A reaction of lemon juice, baking powder, and a universal indicator.

You don't need to memorize this stuff about indicators, but it's useful to understand.

By the way, you can remember that the indicator changes color at the end point by spelling indicator as:

Endicator

6.9 | Indicators and the End Point

To find the equivalence point, a chemical called an **indicator** is used. (A pH meter can also be used.) The indicator is usually a weak acid whose conjugate base is a different color. We can designate an indicator as HIn, where In⁻ represents the conjugate base. In order for the human eye to detect a color change, the new form of the indicator must reach ⅒ the concentration of the original form. For example, if we titrate an acid with a base, we add a small amount of indicator to our acid. (We add only a small amount because we don't want the indicator to affect the pH.) At the initial low pH, the HIn form of the indicator predominates. As we titrate, and the pH increases, the In⁻ form of the indicator also increases. When the In⁻ concentration reaches ⅒ of the HIn concentration, a color change can be detected by the human eye. If we titrate a base with an acid, the process works in reverse. Thus, the pH of the color change depends upon the direction of the titration. The pH values of the two points of color change give the **range** of an indicator. An indicator's range can be predicted by using the Henderson-Hasselbalch equation as follows:

$$pH = pK_a + \log \frac{[In^-]}{[HIn]}$$

$$\text{lower range of color change} \Rightarrow \quad pH = pK_a + \log \frac{1}{10} \Rightarrow pH = pK_a - 1$$

$$\text{upper range of color change} \Rightarrow \quad pH = pK_a + \log \frac{10}{1} \Rightarrow pH = pK_a + 1$$

The point where the indicator changes color is called the **endpoint**. Do not confuse the equivalence point with the end point. We usually choose an indicator whose range will cover the equivalence point.

You can also monitor the pH with a pH meter. A pH meter is a concentration cell comparing the voltage difference between different concentrations of H⁺. (See Chemistry Lecture 7 for concentration cells.)

Since we established that the Henderson-Hasselbalch equation is not useful to find the pH of the equivalence point, how can it be useful to find an indicator range that will include the equivalence point?

The answer is that we are using the indicator concentrations in the Henderson-Hasselbalch equation, and the indicator never reaches its equivalence point in the titration. The indicator ions do not approach zero concentration near the color change range.

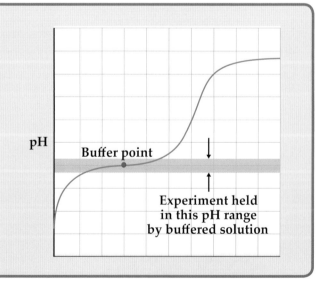

If the MCAT asks you which indicator to use for a titration, you should choose an indicator with a pK_a as close as possible to the pH of the titrations equivalence point.

6.10 Polyprotic Titrations

Titrations of polyprotic acids will have more than one equivalence point and more than one half equivalence point. For the MCAT, assume that the first proton completely dissociates before the second proton begins to dissociate. (This assumption is only acceptable if the second proton is a much weaker acid than the first, which is usually the case.) Thus we have a titration curve like the one shown below.

A digital pH meter measures the pH of a solution by comparing the electrical potential of the solution to the electrical potential of a standard solution inside the meter.

Figure 6.8   Polyprotic Titration

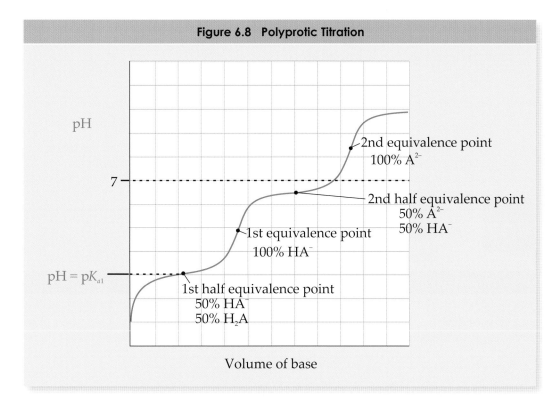

Notes:

6.11 Equation Summary

Equations		
Acid	**Base**	**pH**
H^+	OH^-	$pH = -\log[H^+]$

Henderson-Hasselbalch equation

$$pH = pK_a + \log \frac{[A^-]}{[HA]}$$

6.12 Terms You Need to Know

Terms	
Amphoteric	Hydronium Ion H_3O^+
Arrhenius Acid	Indicator
Arrhenius Base	K_a
Autoionization of Water	K_b
Brønsted-Lowry Acid	Lewis Acid
Brønsted-Lowry Base	Lewis Base
Buffered	Polyprotic
Conjugate Acid	Range
Conjugate Base	Salts
Diprotic	Stoichiometric Point
Endpoint	Titrant
Equivalence Point	Titration
Half Equivalence Point	Titration Curve
Henderson-Hasselbalch Equation	

137. The titration curve below represents the titration of:

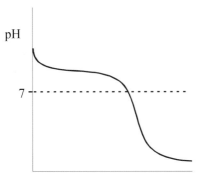

A. a strong acid with a weak base.
B. a strong base with a weak acid.
C. a weak acid with a strong base.
D. a weak base with a strong acid.

138. The following is a list of acid dissociation constants for 4 acids.

	K_a
Acid 1	1.2×10^{-7}
Acid 2	8.3×10^{-7}
Acid 3	3.3×10^{-6}
Acid 4	6.1×10^{-5}

Which acid should be used to manufacture a buffer at a pH of 6.1?

A. Acid 1
B. Acid 2
C. Acid 3
D. Acid 4

139. If the expected equivalence point for a titration is at a pH of 8.2, which of the following would be the best indicator for the titration?

Indicator	K_a
phenolphthalein	1.0×10^{-8}
bromthymol blue	7.9×10^{-8}
methyl orange	3.2×10^{-4}
methyl violet	1.4×10^{-3}

A. phenolphthalein
B. bromthymol blue
C. methyl orange
D. methyl violet

140. On the titration curve of the H_2CO_3 pictured below, at which of the following points is the concentration of HCO_3^- the greatest?

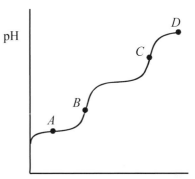

A. point A
B. point B
C. point C
D. point D

141. Which of the following is the equivalence point when the weak acid, acetic acid, is titrated with NaOH?

A. 4.3
B. 7
C. 8.7
D. 14

142. A buffered solution has a pH that cannot readily be changed. A buffered solution will be produced by mixing equal volumes of:

A. 1 M HCl and 1 M NaC$_2$H$_3$O$_2$
B. 1 M HCl and 1 M NaOH
C. 1 M HC$_2$H$_3$O$_2$ and 1 M NaC$_2$H$_3$O$_2$
D. 1 M HC$_2$H$_3$O$_2$ and 1 M NaOH

143. All of the following statements regarding HCO$_3^-$ are true EXCEPT:

A. HCO$_3^-$ can act as a Brønsted Lowry acid.
B. HCO$_3^-$ can act as a Lewis base.
C. HCO$_3^-$ is amphoteric.
D. HCO$_3^-$ is a polyprotic acid.

144. The acid dissociation constant for HC$_6$H$_7$O$_6$ is 8.0×10^{-5}. If a solution contains equal concentrations of HC$_6$H$_7$O$_6$ and C$_6$H$_7$O$_6^-$, what will be the pH of the solution?

A. 3.0
B. 4.1
C. 5.3
D. 9.0

ELECTROCHEMISTRY

7.1 Oxidation-Reduction

In an oxidation-reduction reaction (called a redox reaction for short), electrons are transferred from one atom to another. The atom that loses electrons is oxidized; the atom that gains electrons is reduced.

7.2 Oxidation States

In order to keep track of the electrons in a redox reaction, you must memorize the oxidation states of certain atoms. Oxidation states are the possible charge values that an atom may hold within a molecule. In many cases, these charges don't truly exist; it is simply a system to follow the electrons of a redox reaction. Even though they do not represent actual charges, the oxidation states must add up to the charge on the molecule or ion. For instance, the sum of the oxidation states of the atoms in a neutral molecule must equal zero. The oxidation states that you must memorize for the MCAT are given in Table 7.1. When a conflict arises, the rule occupying the higher position on the table is given priority.

Table 7.1 General Oxidation State Rules

Oxidation State	Atom
0	Atoms in their elemental form
-1	Fluorine
+1	Hydrogen (except when bonded to a metal, like NaH: then -1.)
-2	Oxygen (except when it is in a peroxide, like H_2O_2: then -1.)

In general, when in a compound, elements in the following groups have the oxidation states listed in the table below. It is helpful to know Table 7.2 but not crucial for the MCAT.

For the MCAT, you probably won't need to memorize any other oxidation states than those in Table 7.1.

Table 7.2 Group Oxidation States	
Oxidation State	*Group on Periodic Table*
+1	Group 1 elements (alkali metals)
+2	Group 2 elements (alkaline earth metals)
-3	Group 15 elements (nitrogen family)
-2	Group 16 elements (oxygen family)
-1	Group 17 elements (halogens)

The idea is simple; a general guideline for oxidation states is the atom's variance from a noble gas configuration. However, if all atoms had permanent oxidation states, no redox reactions could take place. The oxidation states in Table 7.2 are to be used only as a general guideline. When the two tables conflict, the first table is given priority. For example, the oxidation state of nitrogen in NO_3^- is +5 because the –2 on the oxygens have priority and dictate the oxidation state on nitrogen. (Don't forget that the oxidation states for NO_3^- must add up to the 1– charge on the molecule.) The transition metals change oxidation states according to the atoms with which they are bonded. Although each transition metal has only certain oxidation states that it can attain, the MCAT will not require that you memorize these.

The following is an example of a redox reaction:

$$2H_2 + O_2 \rightarrow 2H_2O$$

Here oxygen and hydrogen begin in their elemental form, and thus have an oxidation state of zero. Once the water molecule is formed, hydrogen's oxidation state is +1, and oxygen's is –2. In this case, we say that hydrogen has been **oxidized**; hydrogen has lost electrons; its oxidation state has increased from 0 to +1. Oxygen, on the other hand, has been reduced; it has gained electrons; its oxidation state has been reduced from 0 to –2. Whenever there is oxidation, there must also be reduction.

Since in any redox reaction one atom is oxidized and another atom is reduced, there is a **reducing agent** (also called the **reductant**) and an **oxidizing agent** (also called the **oxidant**). Because the reducing agent is giving electrons to an atom, an atom in the reducing agent must be giving up some of its own electrons. Since an atom in the reducing agent gives up electrons, an atom in the reducing agent is oxidized. The reverse is true for the oxidizing agent. Thus, the reducing agent is the compound containing the atom being oxidized, and the oxidizing agent is the compound containing the atom being reduced. For example, in the following reaction, methane is the reducing agent and dioxygen is the oxidizing agent.

To help keep oxidation and reduction straight, just remember:

Lose
Electrons   the Lion says...
Oxidation

Gain
Electrons
Reduction

Carbon goes from –4 to +4.

$$CH_4 + 2O_2 \rightarrow CO_2 + 2H_2O$$

Oxygen goes from 0 to –2.

Notice that the reducing agents and oxidizing agents are compounds, not atoms. In a redox reaction, the atom is oxidized or reduced; the compound is the oxidant or reductant. In the reaction:

$$Cd(s) + NiO_2(s) + 2H_2O(l) \rightarrow Cd(OH)_2(s) + Ni(OH)_2(s)$$

Ni is reduced. NiO_2 is the oxidizing agent.

> The oxidizing agent gets reduced; the reducing agent gets oxidized.

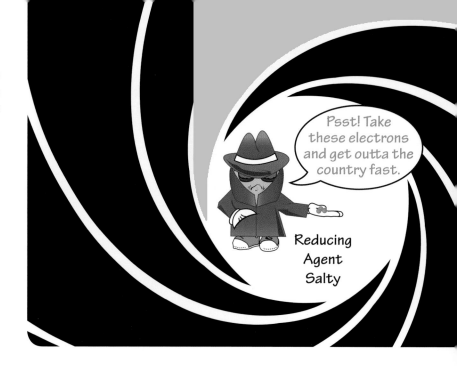

7.3 Oxidation-Reduction Titrations

In a redox titration we want to find the molarity of a reducing agent. To do this, we titrate with a strong oxidizing agent. Instead of pH on the *y*-axis of our graph, we will have a voltage. Recall from Physics Lecture 7.1 that voltage is a potential <u>difference</u>, so, in order to even have a voltage, our solution must be <u>different</u> from another solution. We call that other solution a *standard solution*. When *referenced* to a standard solution, our solution with the reducing agent has a potential difference or voltage. As we add strong oxidizing agent to our solution, the voltage increases, at first gradually and then quite suddenly. Just like in an acid/base titration there is a half equivalence point near the middle of the gradual increase and an equivalence point when the voltage suddenly shoots up. Like an acid/base titration, we choose an indicator that changes color as close as possible to the expected equivalence point, or we simply monitor the voltage with a voltmeter.

> Knowledge of oxidation-reduction titrations is not required for the MCAT. However, it is possible that there will be a passage which explains them. They are included here just so you won't be shocked if you see one in a passage.

The equivalence point occurs when all the moles of reducing agent in our solution have been completely oxidized. Unlike an acid/base titration where the number of moles of base required to reach the equivalence points is equal to the number of moles of acid in the solution being titrated, in a redox titration the number of moles of oxidizing agent required to reach the equivalence point will be <u>either</u> equal <u>or</u> some multiple of the number of moles of the reducing agent in the solution being titrated. This is because one molecule of the oxidizing agent may accept a different number of electrons than one molecule of the reducing agent gives up.

Figure 7.1 Redox Titration Curve

Electrode potential, V vs. Volume of 0.1M Ce^{4+}, mL

$Fe^{2+} + Ce^{4+} \rightleftharpoons Fe^{3+} + Ce^{3+}$

Equivalence point, Fe^{2+}

For example, imagine we have 100 mL of a solution with an unknown concentration of Sn^{2+} ions. To discover the concentration, we titrate with a 5 mM solution of the strong oxidizing agent Ce^{4+}. In this reaction, Sn^{2+} will be oxidized to Sn^{4+}, while Ce^{4+} will be reduced to Ce^{3+}.

$$Sn^{2+} \rightarrow Sn^{4+} + 2e^-$$
$$Ce^{4+} + e^- \rightarrow Ce^{3+}$$

Since each atom of Sn^{2+} is giving up two electrons, and each atom of Ce^{4+} is accepting only one electron, two Ce^{4+} atoms will be required for each Sn^{2+} atom. If 2 mL of Ce^{4+} solution are required to reach the equivalence point, we find the molarity of the original Sn^{2+} solution as follows:

$$2 \text{ mL}_{Ce^{4+} \text{ solution}} \times \frac{5 \text{ mmol}}{L} \times \frac{1L}{1000 \text{ mL}} = 0.01 \text{ mmoles of } Ce^{4+}$$

Since we need two atoms of Ce^{4+} to oxidize only one atom of Sn^{2+}, 0.01 mmoles of Ce^{4+} are required to oxidize 0.005 mmoles of Sn^{2+}.

$$\frac{0.005 \text{ mmoles of } Sn^{2+}}{100 \text{ mL}_{Unknown Sn^{2+} \text{ solution}}} \times \frac{1000 \text{ mL}}{L} = 0.05 \text{ mM}_{Sn^{2+} \text{ solution}}$$

Figure 7.2 Redox Titration Apparatus

pH meter with millivolt scale

Indicator electrode

Reference electrode

Magnetic stirrer

145. What is the oxidation state of sulfur in HSO_4^-?

  A. −2
  B. +3
  C. +6
  D. +7

146. Which of the following statements is true concerning the reaction:

$$2Al_2O_3 + 3C \rightarrow 4Al + 3CO_2$$

  A. Both aluminum and carbon are reduced.
  B. Both aluminum and carbon are oxidized.
  C. Aluminum is reduced and carbon is oxidized.
  D. Carbon is reduced and aluminum is oxidized.

147. What is the reducing agent in the following reaction:

$$2HCl + Zn \rightarrow ZnCl_2 + H_2$$

  A. Zn
  B. Zn^{2+}
  C. H^+
  D. Cl^-

148. The first step in producing pure lead from galena (PbS) is as follows:

$$2PbS(s) + 3O_2(g) \rightarrow 2PbO(s) + 2SO_2(g)$$

All of the following are true concerning this reaction EXCEPT:

  A. Both lead and sulfur are oxidized.
  B. Oxygen is the oxidizing agent.
  C. Lead sulfide is the reducing agent.
  D. Lead is neither oxidized nor reduced.

149. All of the following are always true concerning oxidation-reduction reactions EXCEPT:

  A. An atom in the reducing agent is always oxidized.
  B. If reduction takes place, so must oxidation.
  C. An atom in the oxidizing agent gains electrons.
  D. If an atom of the reductant loses two electrons, an atom of the oxidant gains two electrons.

150. The process below takes place in acidic solution.

$$NO_2^-(aq) \rightarrow NO_3^-(aq)$$

In this process, the oxidation state of nitrogen is:

  A. reduced from +2 to +3.
  B. oxidized from +2 to +3.
  C. reduced from +3 to +5.
  D. oxidized from +3 to +5.

151. Which of the following statements is true about the reaction below?

$$HNO_3 + NaHCO_3 \rightarrow NaNO_3 + H_2CO_3$$

  A. Nitrogen is reduced and oxygen is oxidized.
  B. Oxygen is reduced and carbon is oxidized.
  C. Hydrogen is reduced and sodium is oxidized.
  D. No oxidation or reduction takes place.

152.
$$Cl_2 + 2Br^- \rightarrow Br_2 + 2Cl^-$$

In the reaction shown above,

  A. Cl_2 is the oxidizing agent and Br^- is oxidized.
  B. Cl_2 is the oxidizing agent and Br^- is reduced.
  C. Cl_2 is the reducing agent and Br^- is oxidized.
  D. Cl_2 is the reducing agent and Br^- is reduced.

_____

Standard hydrogen electrodes are devices constructed to provide a standard baseline against which to measure oxidation-reduction potentials.

7.4 Potentials

Since in a redox reaction electrons are transferred, and since electrons have charge, there is an **electric potential (*E*)** associated with any redox reaction. The potentials for the oxidation component and reduction component of a reaction can be approximated separately based upon a *standard hydrogen electrode* (SHE) discussed later in this lecture. Each component is called a **half reaction**. Of course, no half reaction will occur by itself; any reduction half reaction must be accompanied by an oxidation half reaction. There is only one possible potential for any given half reaction. Since the reverse of a reduction half reaction is an oxidation half reaction, it would be redundant to list potentials for both the oxidation and reduction half reactions. Therefore, half reaction potentials are usually listed as **reduction potentials**. To find the oxidation potential for the reverse half reaction, the sign of the reduction potential is reversed. Table 7.3 is a list of some common reduction potentials.

Notice that, except for nickel, the metals used to make coins have negative oxidation potentials. In other words, unlike most metals, platinum, gold, silver, mercury, and copper do not oxidize (or dissolve) spontaneously under standard conditions in the presence of aqueous H^+.

Also notice that Table 7.3 gives us the reduction potential for $Ag^{2+}(aq)$ and the oxidation potential for $Ag(s)$. (Warning: The table does not give us the oxidation potential for Ag^{2+}.) The strongest oxidizing agent is shown on the upper left hand side of a reduction table. The strongest reducing agent is shown on the lower right hand side of a reduction table. Notice that water is both a poor oxidizing agent and a poor reducing agent.

Finally, notice that the second half reaction in Table 7.3 is part of the final reaction in aerobic respiration where oxygen accepts electrons to form water. Predictably, this reaction has a high positive potential.

Table 7.3 Standard Reduction Potentials at 25° C	
Half Reaction	*Potential E°*
$Au^{3+}(aq) + 3e^- \rightarrow Au(s)$	1.50
$O_2(g) + 4H^+(aq) + 4e^- \rightarrow H_2O(l)$	1.23
$Pt^{2+}(aq) + 2e^- \rightarrow Pt(s)$	1.2
$Ag^{2+}(aq) + 2e^- \rightarrow Ag(s)$	0.80
$Hg^{2+}(aq) + 2e^- \rightarrow Hg(l)$	0.80
$Cu^+(aq) + e^- \rightarrow Cu(s)$	0.52
$Cu^{2+}(aq) + 2e^- \rightarrow Cu(s)$	0.34
$2H^+(aq) + 2e^- \rightarrow H_2(g)$	0.00
$Fe^{3+}(aq) + 3e^- \rightarrow Fe(s)$	-0.036
$Ni^{2+}(aq) + 2e^- \rightarrow Ni(s)$	-0.23
$Fe^{2+}(aq) + 2e^- \rightarrow Fe(s)$	-0.44
$Zn^{2+}(aq) + 2e^- \rightarrow Zn(s)$	-0.76
$H_2O(l) + 2e^- \rightarrow H_2(g) + 2OH^-(aq)$	-0.83

Reactants in this direction are stronger oxidizing agents and more easily reduced.

Products in this direction are stronger reducing agents and more easily oxidized.

Recall from physics that electric potential has no absolute value. Thus the values in the table above are assigned based upon the arbitrary assignment of a zero value to the half reaction that occurs at a standard hydrogen electrode:

$$2H^+ + 2e^- \rightarrow H_2 \qquad E° = 0.00 \text{ V}$$

This is the only reduction potential that you need to memorize.

An example of an oxidation potential taken from the table above would be:

$$Ag(s) \rightarrow Ag^{2+}(aq) + 2e^- \qquad E° = -0.80 \text{ V}$$

If we wish to find the potential of the following ionic reaction:

$$2Au^{3+} + 3Cu \rightarrow 3Cu^{2+} + 2Au$$

we can separate the reaction into its two half reactions and add the half reaction potentials:

$$
\begin{array}{ll}
2(Au^{3+} + 3e^- \rightarrow Au) & E° = 1.50 \text{ V} \\
3(Cu \rightarrow Cu^{2+} + 2e^-) & \underline{E° = -0.34 \text{ V}} \\
& = 1.16 \text{ V}
\end{array}
$$

Warning: Since reduction potentials are intensive properties, we do not multiply the half reaction potential by the number of times it occurs.

A platinum-hydrogen electrode is the standard used to measure redox (reduction-oxidation) potentials of ions. In this case the iron (III) to iron (II) redox potential is +0.77 volts.

7.5 Balancing Redox Reactions

Balancing redox reactions can be tricky. When you have trouble, follow the steps below to balance a redox reaction that occurs in acidic solution.

1. Divide the reaction into its corresponding half reactions.

2. Balance the elements other than H and O.

3. Add H_2O to one side until the O atoms are balanced.

4. Add H^+ to one side until the H atoms are balanced.

5. Add e^- to one side until the charge is balanced.

6. Multiply each half reaction by an integer so that an equal number of electrons are transferred in each reaction.

7. Add the two half reactions and simplify.

For redox reactions occurring in basic solution, follow the same steps, then neutralize the H^+ ions by adding the same number of OH^- ions to both sides of the reaction.

> All this effort to balance a redox reaction will get you, at most, one point on the MCAT. MCAT just doesn't require the balancing of redox reactions very often, so spend your time accordingly.

Notes:

The Galvanic Cell

If two distinct electrically conducting chemical phases are placed in contact, and one charged species from one phase cannot freely flow to the other phase, a tiny amount of charge difference may result. This tiny charge difference creates an electric potential between the phases (typically one or two volts). By offering an alternative path for electron flow, a **galvanic cell** (also called a **voltaic cell**) uses the electric potential between such phases to generate a current of electrons from one phase to another in a conversion of chemical energy to electrical energy.

A galvanic cell is made of a multiphase series of components with no component occurring in more than one phase. All phases must conduct electricity, but at least one phase must be impermeable to electrons. Otherwise, electrons would move freely throughout the circuit and come to a quick equilibrium. The phase that is impermeable to electrons is an ionic conductor carrying the current in the form of ions. The ionic conducting phase is usually an electrolyte solution in the form of a **salt bridge**. The components of a simple galvanic cell can be symbolized by the letters T-E-I-E'-T', where T represents the **terminals** (electronic conductors such as metal wires), E represents the electrodes (also electronic conductors), and I the ionic conductor (often the salt bridge). When the cell is formed, the emf is the electric potential difference between T and T'.

A simple galvanic cell has two **electrodes**: the **anode** and the **cathode**. The anode is marked with a negative sign and the cathode is marked with a positive sign. The oxidation half reaction takes place at the anode, and the reduction half reaction takes place at the cathode. Depending upon the text, electrodes may refer to only a strip of metal or both a strip of metal and the electrolyte solution in which it is submerged. The strip of metal and solution together may also be called a *half cell*.

Only potential differences between chemically identical forms of matter are easily measurable, so the two terminals of a galvanic cell must be made of the same material. The **cell potential (E)**, also called the **electromotive force (emf)**, is the potential difference between the terminals when they are not connected. Connecting the terminals reduces the potential difference due to internal resistance within the galvanic cell. The drop in the emf increases as the current increases. The current from one terminal to the other through the *load* (or resistance) flows in the direction opposite the electron flow. Since electrons in the anode have higher potential energy than those in the cathode, electrons flow through the load from the anode to the cathode.

Alternatively, you can remember that reduction occurs at the cathode, and reduction is the adding of electrons, so electrons flow to the cathode. Or else, since the anode is negative and the cathode is positive, you can think of this as electrons being repelled by the negative charge on the anode and attracted to the positive charge on the cathode. Recall that electron flow is in the opposite direction of current flow, so current flows from the cathode to the anode.

A voltaic cell may be made by inserting zinc and copper electrodes into a watermelon. In this example a potential of over 0.9 V is obtained.

The standard state cell potential is simply the sum of the standard state potentials of the corresponding half reactions. The cell potential for a galvanic cell is always positive; a galvanic cell always has chemical energy that can be converted to work. The real cell potential depends upon the half reactions, the concentrations of the reactants and products, and the temperature.

Below is an example of a simple galvanic cell with the standard hydrogen electrode (SHE). Hydrogen gas is bubbled over the platinum plate. The platinum acts as a catalyst in the production of H^+ ions. The half reaction is shown. The platinum plate carries an electron through the wire to the silver strip. Ag^+ accepts the electron converting the Ag^+ ion to solid silver and allowing a chloride ion to solvate into the aqueous solution.

Electrons are negatively charged, so they are attracted to the positive cathode and repelled by the negative anode in a galvanic cell.

A voltmeter (orange) measures a voltage (potential difference) of 1.1 volts for a zinc-copper battery cell.

Since, by convention, the oxidation potential of hydrogen is zero, the cell potential of any electrode used in conjunction with the SHE will be exactly equal to the reduction potential of the half reaction occurring at the other electrode. Thus, some half reaction reduction potentials can be measured using the SHE.

Notice that there is no salt bridge in the SHE Galvanic Cell. Both electrodes are in contact with the same solution so no salt bridge is necessary. When a cell contains two different solutions, a liquid junction is required to separate the solutions. Because ions can move across a liquid junction, any liquid junction creates an additional small potential difference that affects the potential of the galvanic cell. A **salt bridge** is a type of liquid junction that minimizes this potential difference. Typically a salt bridge is made from an aqueous solution of KCl. The salt bridge allows ionic conduction between solutions without creating a strong extra potential within the galvanic cell. It is able to minimize the potential because the K^+ ions move toward the cathode at about the same rate that the Cl^- move toward the anode. Below is an example of a simple galvanic cell that requires a salt bridge. Without the salt bridge, the solutions in the cell below would mix providing a low resistance path for electrons to move from $Zn(s)$ to $Cu^{2+}(aq)$ effectively short circuiting the cell, and leaving it with a cell potential of zero.

You should sketch a couple of your own galvanic cells so that you know how they are made. Notice that the concentrations are 1 M. This represents standard conditions and allows the use of the values from the reduction half reaction table to calculate the cell potential.

To find the cell potential when the concentrations are not 1 M, see Chemistry Lecture 7.9 The Nernst Equation.

Here is exactly what's going on in the galvanic cell diagram in Figure 7.5. The solid zinc atoms would like to get rid of their electrons, but they need a place to put them. The Cu^{2+} ions in solution are happy to take them. This creates a potential difference. The question is how to transfer electrons without building up a charge difference. Remember that separating charges is energy expensive. The "sea of electrons" in the copper wire allow the electrons a path of low resistance, but the electrons won't flow if they are building up a charge difference. The salt bridge allows ions to move (negative ions toward the anode and positive ions toward the cathode), and carry away any charge build up. As electrons leave the solid zinc strip, Zn^{2+} ions are formed dissolving into solution. At the cathode Cu^{2+} ions catch the electrons coming through the wire and form solid Cu.

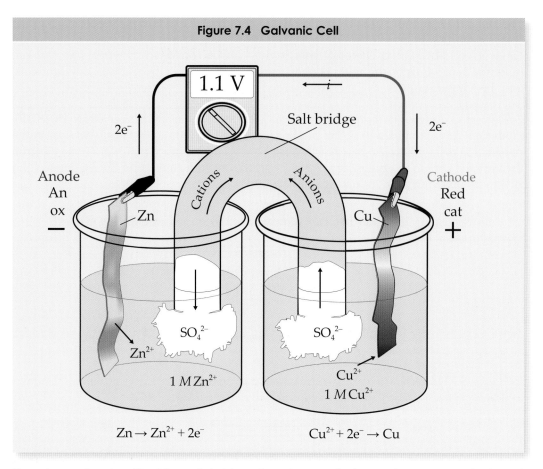

Figure 7.4 Galvanic Cell

$$Zn \rightarrow Zn^{2+} + 2e^- \qquad Cu^{2+} + 2e^- \rightarrow Cu$$

Even in a galvanic cell with a salt bridge, there is some leakage of ions across the liquid junction, which causes the battery to lose its chemical potential over time. Commercial cells use an insoluble salt to prevent this from happening.

For the cell diagram in Figure 7.5 we can refer to Table 7.3 and solve for the standard emf as follows:

$$Cu^{2+}(aq) + 2e^- \rightarrow Cu(s) \qquad E° = 0.34 \text{ V}$$
$$Zn^{2+}(aq) + 2e^- \rightarrow Zn(s) \qquad \underline{-[E° = -0.76 \text{ V}]}$$
$$\text{emf} = 1.1 \text{ V}$$

Again, remember that this is the potential when the concentrations are at standard state and 25° C; this means 1 molar concentrations.

7.7 IUPAC Conventions

Galvanic cells can be represented by a *cell diagram*. Each phase is listed from left to right beginning with the terminal attached to the anode and ending with the terminal attached to the cathode. The terminals are often omitted because they are always the same material and do not take part in the reaction. A vertical line is placed between phases. A double vertical line is used to indicate a salt bridge. A dotted vertical line indicates a boundary between two miscible liquids, and species in the same phase are separated by a comma.

$Pt'(s) \mid Zn(s) \mid Zn^{2+}(aq) \| Cu^{2+}(aq) \mid Cu(s) \mid Pt(s)$

Cell Diagram

The standard state emf can be found from the cell diagram by subtracting the potential of the reduction half reaction on the left (the reaction at the anode) from the potential of the reduction half reaction on the right (the reaction at the cathode).

It is unlikely that MCAT will require that you know the IUPAC conventions for a galvanic cell diagram. You can remember that the cathode is on the right because reduction and right both begin with an 'r'. Don't spend too much time here.

7.8 Free Energy and Chemical Energy

A positive cell potential indicates a spontaneous reaction as shown by the following equation:

$$\Delta G = -nFE_{max}$$

where n is the number of moles of electrons that are transferred in the balanced redox reaction, and F is Faraday's constant, which is the charge on one mole of electrons (96,486 C mol^{-1}). This equation says that the free energy represents the product of the total charge nF times the voltage E. Recall from Physics Lecture 7 that the product of charge and voltage equals work ($w = qV$). Since this is electrical work, it is not the result of a change in pressure or volume, so it represents nonPV work. Recall from Chemistry Lecture 3 that the change in Gibbs free energy represents the maximum amount of nonPV work available from a reaction at constant temperature and pressure. A negative ΔG indicates that the work is being done <u>by</u> the system and not <u>on</u> the system.

Michael Faraday (1791-1867), British chemist and physicist, suggested the concepts of electric and magnetic fields.

Since F is a positive constant and n can only be positive, E_{max} must be positive when ΔG is negative. Thus a positive E_{max} indicates a spontaneous reaction in a galvanic cell.

When all the conditions are standard, we can write the equation above using the '°' symbol as follows (the 'max' is part of the definition of ΔG and is assumed):

$$\Delta G^{\circ} = -nFE^{\circ}$$

ΔG° can be found in books, but what about ΔG for non-standard state conditions? There are an infinite number of possible combinations of concentrations of reactants and products and temperatures with which we could start a reaction. How can we predict the maximum available work from these combinations? In order to make predictions about reactions that do not occur at standard state, we must use the following equation, which relates ΔG with ΔG°:

$$\Delta G = \Delta G^{\circ} + RT \ln(Q)$$

where Q is the reaction quotient discussed in Chemistry Lecture 2, and 'ln( )' is the natural logarithm. You may see this equation written using a base 10 logarithm as:

$$\Delta G = \Delta G^{\circ} + 2.3RT \log(Q)$$

This is based upon the crude approximation: $2.3\log(x) \approx \ln(x)$.

There is no need to confuse ΔG and ΔG°. ΔG° is a specific ΔG only one molar concentrations for Q, then $Q = 1$, and $RT\ln(Q) = 0$, leaving us with $\Delta G = \Delta G^{\circ}$. This is what we would expect for a reaction at standard conditions. (Remember, standard conditions don't actually indicate a particular temperature; you can have standard conditions at any temperature. Standard conditions are usually assumed to be 298 K.)

Recall from Chemistry Lecture 3 that at equilibrium, there is no available free energy with which to do work; $\Delta G = 0$ by definition. Thus, if we have equilibrium conditions, we can plug in a value of 0 for ΔG, and rewrite "$\Delta G = \Delta G^{\circ} + RT \ln(Q)$" as:

$$\Delta G^{\circ} = -RT \ln(K)$$

> Memorizing this equation isn't nearly as important as understanding what it says about the relationship between ΔG, ΔG°, Q and K.

> Remember that ln(1) = 0.

In this equation, both K and $\Delta G°$ vary with temperature. Whenever you specify a new temperature, you must look up a new $\Delta G°$ for that temperature. Notice that since this equation uses the natural log of the equilibrium constant, a value of 1 for K will result in a value of 0 for $\Delta G°$. For the MCAT you should understand the relationship between K and $\Delta G°$.

$$\text{if} \quad K = 1 \quad \text{then} \quad \Delta G° = 0$$
$$\text{if} \quad K > 1 \quad \text{then} \quad \Delta G° < 0$$
$$\text{if} \quad K < 1 \quad \text{then} \quad \Delta G° > 0$$

Warning: This relationship does NOT say that if a reaction has an equilibrium constant that is greater than one, then the reaction is always spontaneous. That doesn't make any sense, since the spontaneity of a reaction depends upon starting concentrations of products and reactants. It does say that if a reaction has an equilibrium constant that is greater than one, the reaction is spontaneous at standard state (starting molar concentrations of exactly 1 M) and the particular temperature used to derive that particular equilibrium constant.

7.9 The Nernst Equation

The galvanic cell pictured below is drawn with standard conditions of 1 M concentrations. That's great for the instant that the concentrations are all one molar, but what about for the rest of the time? How can we find the potential when the concentrations aren't one molar? If we take the equation:

$$\Delta G = \Delta G° + RT \ln(Q)$$

and substitute $-nFE$ for ΔG, and $-nFE°$ for $\Delta G°$, and then divide by $-nF$, we get:

$$E = E° - \frac{RT}{nF} \ln(Q)$$

This is the *Nernst equation*. At 298 K, and in base 10 logarithm form, the Nernst equation is:

$$E = E° - \frac{0.06}{n} \log(Q)$$

The Nernst equation allows us to plug in nonstandard concentrations to create Q and find the cell potential.

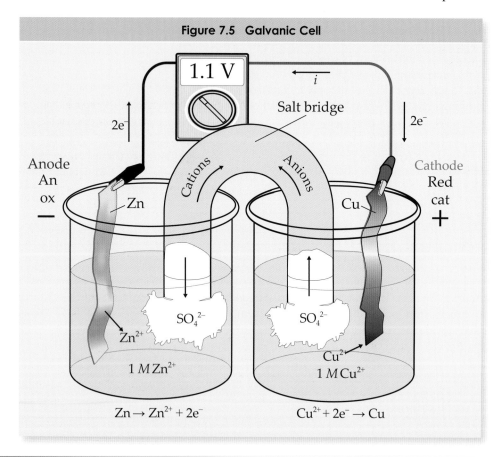

Figure 7.5 Galvanic Cell

1.1 V

i

Salt bridge

$2e^-$ $2e^-$

Cations   Anions

Anode
An
ox
−

Zn   Cu

Cathode
Red
cat
+

SO_4^{2-} SO_4^{2-}

Zn^{2+}

Cu^{2+}

1 M Zn^{2+} 1 M Cu^{2+}

$Zn \rightarrow Zn^{2+} + 2e^-$ $Cu^{2+} + 2e^- \rightarrow Cu$

Questions 153 through 160 are **NOT** based on a descriptive passage.

153. Which of the following statements about a galvanic cell is false?

   A. If $E° = 0$, a reaction may still be spontaneous depending upon the chemical concentrations.
   B. A galvanic cell with a positive potential can perform work.
   C. Reduction takes place at the cathode.
   D. A salt bridge balances the charge by allowing positive ions to move to the anode.

154. The values of all of the following are reversed when a reaction is reversed EXCEPT:

   A. enthalpy
   B. Gibbs energy
   C. the rate constant
   D. reaction potential

155. Which of the following is true for a reaction, if $\Delta G°_{298} = 0$? (The 298 subscript indicates a temperature of 298 K.)

   A. The reaction is at equilibrium.
   B. At 298 K and 1 M concentrations of products and reactants the equilibrium constant equals one.
   C. ΔG is also zero.
   D. The reaction is spontaneous at temperatures greater than 298 K.

156. The following is a table of half reactions:

Half Reaction	$E°$ (V)
$Ag^{2+} + e^- \rightarrow Ag^+$	1.99
$Fe^{3+} + e^- \rightarrow Fe^{2+}$	0.77
$Cu^{2+} + 2e^- \rightarrow Cu$	0.34
$2H^+ + 2e^- \rightarrow H_2$	0.00
$Fe^{2+} + 2e^- \rightarrow Fe$	−0.44
$Zn^{2+} + 2e^- \rightarrow Zn$	−0.76

The strongest reducing agent shown in the table is:

   A. Zn
   B. Zn^{2+}
   C. Ag^+
   D. Ag^{2+}

157. A negative cell potential indicates which of the following:

   A. Both half reactions are nonspontaneous.
   B. The reduction half reaction potential is greater than the oxidation half reaction potential.
   C. The oxidation half reaction potential is greater than the reduction half reaction potential.
   D. The cell is electrolytic.

Questions 158 through 160 are based on the information below.

A galvanic cell uses the reaction between solid tin and aqueous copper ions to produce electrical power.

$$Sn(s) + 2Cu^{2+}(aq) \rightarrow Sn^{2+}(aq) + 2Cu(s)$$

$Sn^{2+}(aq) + 2e^- \rightarrow Sn(s)$ $E° = -0.14$ V
$2Cu^{2+}(aq) + 2e^- \rightarrow Cu(s)$ $E° = 0.15$ V

158. The standard state cell potential for this reaction is:

   A. 0.01 V
   B. 0.16 V
   C. 0.29 V
   D. 0.44 V

159. The reaction in the cell is allowed to proceed. As the reaction in the cell progresses, the cell potential will:

   A. decrease as the concentration of Sn^{2+} increases.
   B. decrease as the concentration of Sn^{2+} decreases.
   C. increase as the concentration of Sn^{2+} increases.
   D. increase as the concentration of Sn^{2+} decreases.

160. Which of the following is true of the tin/copper cell reaction?

   A. $K > 1$ and $\Delta G° > 0$
   B. $K > 1$ and $\Delta G° < 0$
   C. $K < 1$ and $\Delta G° > 0$
   D. $K < 1$ and $\Delta G° < 0$

7.10 More Cells

A **concentration cell** is a limited form of a galvanic cell with a reduction half reaction taking place in one half cell and the exact reverse of that half reaction taking place in the other half cell.

Figure 7.6 Concentration Cell

Contractions of the heart are controlled by a combination of electrochemistry and semipermeable membranes. Cell membranes have variable permeability with respect to ions Na^+, K^+, and Ca^{2+}. The difference in concentrations of K^+ ions between the intracellular fluid, or ICF and extracellular fluid, or ECF generates a concentration cell. Changes in the relative concentrations in the ICF and ECF lead to changes in the emf of the voltaic cell.

Of course, when we add the two half reactions we get: $E° = 0$. If the concentrations were equal on both sides, the concentration cell potential would be zero. You can use the Nernst equation to find the potential for a concentration cell. (If you need the Nernst equation, the MCAT will give it to you.) It is much more likely that the MCAT will ask you a qualitative question like "In which direction will current flow in the concentration cell?" In this case, we must think about nature's tendency for balance; nature wants to create the greatest entropy. The more concentrated side will try to become less concentrated, and electrons will flow accordingly.

To use the Nernst equation to find the potential of a concentration cell at 25°C, we must realize that Fe^{2+} is both a product and a reactant. Thus, we simply substitute for Q the ratio of the Fe^{2+} concentrations on either side. For the case above we have:

$$E = E° - \frac{0.06}{2} \log\left(\frac{0.01}{0.1}\right)$$

$n = 2$ because 2 electrons are used each time the reaction occurs, and $E°$ equals zero. Concentration cells tend to have small potentials.

If we hook up a power source across the resistance of a galvanic cell, and force the cell to run backwards, we have created another type of cell, the **electrolytic cell**. Any electrolytic cell on the MCAT will have a negative emf. In the electrolytic cell, the cathode is marked negative and the anode is marked positive. Reduction still takes place at the cathode and oxidation at the anode.

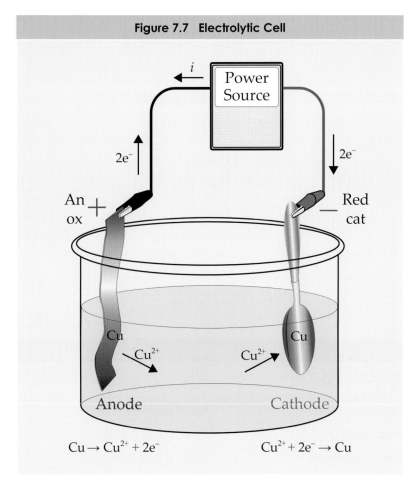

Figure 7.7   Electrolytic Cell

$$Cu \rightarrow Cu^{2+} + 2e^-$$ $$Cu^{2+} + 2e^- \rightarrow Cu$$

In a copper refinery plant large electrolytic cells (brown) are used to purify impure copper by passing an electric current through it while it is molten. The impurities collect at one electrode, and the pure copper can be run off to be collected for processing.

Electrolytic cells are used in industry for metal plating, and for purifying metals. For instance, pure sodium can be collected through electrolysis of sodium chloride solution in a *Downs cell*. The half reactions are as follows:

$$Na^+ + e^- \rightarrow Na \qquad E° = -2.71 \text{ V}$$
$$2Cl^- \rightarrow 2e^- + Cl_2 \qquad E° = -1.36 \text{ V}$$

Notice that this reaction will not run in aqueous solution because, from Table 7.3, we see that water has a less negative reduction potential than sodium. In fact, this indicates that solid sodium will oxidize spontaneously in water.

The assignment of positive and negative to electrodes in galvanic and electrolytic cells is based upon perspective. Galvanic cells are used to provide energy to an external load, so the electrodes are labeled so that negative electrons will flow toward the positive electrode. Electrons flow from the load to the cathode, so the cathode is labeled positive in the galvanic cell. The focus of electrolytic cells is within the cell itself. For instance, electrophoresis uses an electrolytic cell. It is important that negatively charged amino acids within the electrolytic cell flow toward the positive electrode, so the anode is labeled positive in the electrolytic cell.

For cells, you should learn to diagram a galvanic cell by yourself. Once you can do that, the other cells can be created from the galvanic cell. Remember that galvanic cells have a positive cell potential; electrolytic cells have a negative potential. Galvanic cells are spontaneous; electrolytic are forced by an outside power source.

'Electrochemical' cell can mean either 'galvanic' or 'electrolytic' cell.

For any and all cells, remember 'Red Cat, An Ox'. This translates to Reduction at the Cathode, and Oxidation at the Anode.

7.11 Equation Summary

Equations
$2H^+ + 2e^- \rightarrow H_2 \qquad E° = 0.00 \text{ V}$
$\Delta G = -nFE_{max}$ $\Delta G = \Delta G° + RT \ln(Q)$ $\Delta G° = -RT \ln(K)$
if $K = 1$ then $\Delta G° = 0$ if $K > 1$ then $\Delta G° < 0$ if $K < 1$ then $\Delta G° > 0$

7.12 Terms You Need To Know

Terms	
Anode	Oxidation States
Cathode	Oxidized
Cell Potential (E)	Oxidizing Agent
Concentration Cell	Redox Reaction
Electric Potential (E)	Reduced
Electrodes	Reducing Agent
Electrolytic Cell	Reductant
Electromotive Force (Emf)	Reduction Potentials
Galvanic Cell	Salt Bridge
Half Reaction	Terminals
Oxidant	Voltaic Cell

161. A galvanic cell is prepared with solutions of Mg^{2+} and Al^{3+} ions separated by a salt bridge. A potentiometer reads the difference across the electrodes to be 1.05 Volts. The following standard reduction potentials at 25°C apply:

Half Reaction	$E°$ (V)
$Al^{3+} + 3e^- \rightarrow Al$	-1.66
$Mg^{2+} + 2e^- \rightarrow Mg$	-2.37

Which of the following statements is true concerning the galvanic cell at 25°C?

A. Magnesium is reduced at the cathode.
B. The concentrations of ions are 1 M.
C. The reaction is spontaneous.
D. For every aluminum atom reduced, an equal number of magnesium atoms are oxidized.

162. Which of the following is true for an electrolytic cell?

A. Reduction takes place at the anode.
B. The reaction is spontaneous.
C. electrons flow to the cathode.
D. An electrolytic cell requires a salt bridge.

163. A concentration cell contains 0.5 M aqueous Ag^+ on one side and 0.1 M aqueous Ag^+ on the other. All of the following are true EXCEPT:

A. Electrons will move from the less concentrated side to the more concentrated side.
B. Electrons will move from the anode to the cathode.
C. As the cell potential moves toward zero, the concentrations of both sides will tend to even out.
D. $\Delta G > 0$

164. According to the Nernst equation:

$$E = E° - \frac{0.06}{n} \log\left(\frac{x}{y}\right)$$

if a concentration cell has a potential of 0.12 V, and a concentration of 0.1 M Ag^+ at the anode, what is the concentration of Ag^+ at the cathode?

A. $10^{-3}\ M$
B. $10^{-1}\ M$
C. $1\ M$
D. $10\ M$

165. A spoon is plated with silver in an electrolytic process where the half reaction at the cathode is:

$$Ag^+(aq) + e^- \rightarrow Ag(s) \quad E° = 0.8\ V$$

If the current i is held constant for t seconds, which of the following expressions gives the mass of silver deposited on the spoon? (F is Faraday's constant.)

A. $107.8\ itF$

B. $107.8\dfrac{it}{F}$

C. $107.8\dfrac{i}{tF}$

D. $107.8\dfrac{iF}{t}$

166. The charge on 1 mole of electrons is given by Faraday's constant, 96,500 C/mol. A galvanic cell was operated continuously for 5 minutes and 0.01 moles of electrons were passed through the wire. If the voltage remained constant for the entire time, what is the current generated by the cell?

A. 3 A
B. 5 A
C. 6 A
D. 9 A

167. The reduction potential for two half reactions are given below.

$$2H_2O(l) + 2e^- \rightarrow H_2(g) + 2OH^-(aq) \quad E^\circ = -0.8 \text{ V}$$

$$Na^+(aq) + e^- \rightarrow Na(s) \quad E^\circ = -2.7 \text{ V}$$

Aqueous sodium cannot be reduced to solid sodium in an electrolytic cell because:

A. aqueous sodium will combine with aqueous hydroxide to form solid sodium hydroxide.
B. liquid water is more easily reduced than aqueous sodium.
C. aqueous sodium must be oxidized to form solid sodium.
D. hydrogen gas is more easily oxidized than solid sodium.

168. The reaction above takes place in a galvanic cell. Which of the following is true?

$$2Ag^{2+} + Fe \rightarrow 2Ag^+ + Fe^{2+} \quad E^\circ = 2.4 \text{ V}$$

A. Ag^{2+} is reduced at the anode.
B. Ag^{2+} is oxidized at the anode.
C. Ag^{2+} is reduced at the cathode.
D. Ag^{2+} is oxidized at the cathode.

STOP!

DO NOT LOOK AT THESE EXAMS UNTIL CLASS.

30-MINUTE IN-CLASS EXAM FOR LECTURE 1

Passage I (Questions 1-7)

There are five types of interactions within and between molecules. Intramolecular interactions include covalent and ionic bonds. Intermolecular interactions include van der Waals's forces, dipole-dipole, and hydrogen bonds. Table 1 lists the typical energies for these interactions.

Interaction	Typical Energy kJ mol^{-1}
Van der Waals's	0.1 – 5
Dipole-dipole	5 – 20
Hydrogen bond	5 – 50
Ionic bond	400 – 500
Covalent bond	150 – 900

Table 1 Energies of interactions

The boiling point of a substance increases with the strength of its intermolecular bonds. Figure 1 shows the boiling points of hydrides for some main-group elements and of the noble gases.

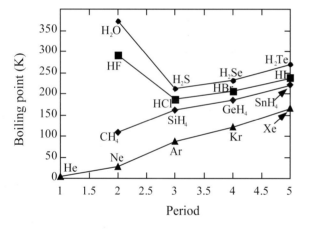

Figure 1 Boiling points of some main-group hydrides and the noble gases.

1. Why does the boiling point of H_2O and HF deviate from the trend in Figure 1?

   A. F and O both occur in the second period.
   B. The size of H_2O and HF are small relative to the other molecules
   C. H_2O and HF are less polarizable.
   D. H_2O and HF can hydrogen bond.

2. What type of bonding holds together the compound $MgCl_2$?

   A. covalent
   B. ionic
   C. hydrogen
   D. van der Waals's

3. Why do the boiling points of the noble gases increase as the period increases?

   A. The bonds are stronger because larger atoms are more polarizable as period increases.
   B. The bonds are weaker because larger atoms are more polarizable as period increases.
   C. The bonds are stronger because larger atoms are less polarizable as period increases.
   D. The bonds are weaker because larger atoms are less polarizable as period increases.

4. The atomic radius of Ne is:

   A. greater than Ar
   B. less than Ar
   C. the same as Ar
   D. cannot be determined

5. Why are boiling points a better indication of intermolecular bonding than melting points?

   A. Vaporization requires more energy than melting.
   B. Vaporization requires less energy than melting.
   C. Transition from solid to liquid involves other factors such as crystalline lattice structures.
   D. Vaporization is easier to measure.

6. What type of intermolecular bonding occurs in gaseous CH_4?

   A. covalent
   B. ionic
   C. hydrogen
   D. van der Waals's

7. Why is a dipole-dipole interaction stronger than a van der Waals's interaction?

   A. Dipole-dipole is an electrostatic interaction.
   B. Van der Waals's interactions rely on temporarily induced dipoles.
   C. Van der Waals's interactions require a large surface area.
   D. Dipole-dipole interactions only occur with ionically bonded compounds.

Figure 1 shows atomic radius as a function of atomic number for the first three periods of the periodic table. Within a period the atomic radius decreases as the atomic number increases, but the atomic radius increases as the period increases.

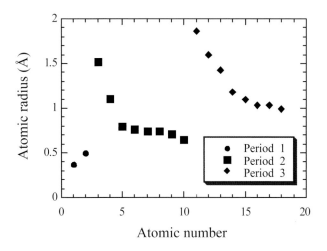

Figure 1 Atomic radius as a function of atomic number

Electronegativity of an atom also follows a trend in the periodic table. Electronegativity for any element (X) is based upon the difference (Δ) between the actual bond energy of a bond between element X and hydrogen and the expected bond energy of the same bond:

$$\Delta = (H—X)_{\text{actual bond energy}} - (H—X)_{\text{expected bond energy}}$$

where the expected bond energy is given by:

$$H—X_{\text{exp bond energy}} = \frac{H—H_{\text{bond energy}} + X—X_{\text{bond energy}}}{2}$$

Pauling electronegativity values are assigned to each element based upon its Δ value with respect to fluorine. Flourine is arbitrarily given a value of 4.0. The electronegativity of elements may be used to predict the type of bonding found in a molecule. Large differences in electronegativities of atoms in a bond result in an ionic bond.

8. If Se has an atomic radius of 1.16 Å, what is the predicted atomic radius of As?

    A. 1.05 Å
    B. 1.15 Å
    C. 1.25 Å
    D. 1.97 Å

9. Which of the following elements is the most chemically similar to Na?

    A. H
    B. Mg
    C. C
    D. Cs

10. Which element has the largest atomic radius?

    A. Li
    B. Ne
    C. Rb
    D. Br

11. Why is the electronegativity scale adjusted to fluorine?

    A. The researcher who discovered electronegativity was working with fluorine.
    B. Fluorine has the smallest atomic radius.
    C. Fluorine has the smallest electronegativity.
    D. Fluorine has the greatest electronegativity.

12. How does electron affinity change with atomic number?

    A. Electron affinity becomes more exothermic as atomic number increases in a period and a group.
    B. Electron affinity becomes less exothermic as atomic number increases in a period and a group.
    C. Electron affinity becomes more exothermic as atomic number increases in a period and less exothermic as atomic number increases in a group.
    D. Electron affinity becomes less exothermic as atomic number increases in a period and more exothermic as atomic number increases in a group.

13. Why does the atomic radius follow the trends observed in Figure 1?

    A. As the atomic number increases, the nuclear charge increases.
    B. As the atomic number increases, the nuclear charge decreases.
    C. As the atomic number increases, the nuclear charge increases and as the period increases the number of electron shells increases.
    D. As the atomic number increases, the nuclear charge increases and as the period increases the number of electron shells decreases.

GO ON TO THE NEXT PAGE.

14. Hydrogen has a Pauling electronegativity of 2.1. What is the value of Δ for hydrogen?

    A. 0
    B. 1.0
    C. 2.1
    D. 4.0

15. What type of intramolecular bonding is found in a CO molecule?

    A. covalent
    B. ionic
    C. hydrogen
    D. van der Waals's

Passage III (Questions 16-21)

The empirical formula of a hydrocarbon can be determined using an instrument similar to the one shown in Figure 1. A sample hydrocarbon is combusted. The absorption chambers absorb all the water and carbon dioxide from the reaction. $CaCl_2$ can absorb both water and CO_2. The masses of the chambers before and after the reaction are compared to find the moles of carbon and hydrogen in the sample.

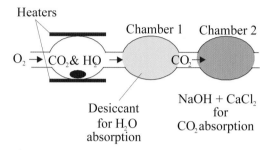

Figure 1 A combustion train

For example: propane can be combusted in the apparatus as follows:

$$C_3H_8 + 5O_2 \rightarrow 4H_2O + 3CO_2$$

In an experiment using the combustion train, a gaseous fuel used in welding (containing only C and H) is reacted with O_2. The mass of the absorbers in Chamber 1 increases by 0.9 grams and the mass of the absorbers in Chamber 2 increases by 4.4 grams.

The density of the welding gas is 1.1 g L^{-1} at 25°C and atmospheric pressure. At the same conditions, O_2 has a density of 1.3 g L^{-1}.

16. What is the empirical formula of the welding gas?

    A. CHO
    B. CH
    C. C_2H_2
    D. C_3H_8

17. What is the molecular weight of the gas?

    A. 13 g/mol
    B. 26 g/mol
    C. 32 g/mol
    D. 60 g/mol

18. A compound has an empirical formula of CH_2O. Using osmotic pressure, the molecular weight is determined to be 120 g/mol. What is the molecular formula for this compound?

A. CH_2O
B. $C_4H_4O_3$
C. $C_3H_6O_3$
D. $C_4H_8O_4$

19. If 1 mole of C_3H_8 is reacted with 2.5 moles of O_2, how many moles of H_2O will be produced?

A. 1 mole of H_2O
B. 2 moles of H_2O
C. 3 moles of H_2O
D. 4 moles of H_2O

20. What would happen if the order of the chambers in the combustion train were reversed?

A. The amount of CO_2 calculated would be higher than the actual amount produced.
B. The amount of CO_2 calculated would be lower than the actual amount produced.
C. The amount of H_2O calculated would be higher than the actual amount produced.
D. Nothing, the experiment would still give the same results.

21. Why is it necessary to react the O_2 in excess when using a combustion train?

A. In addition to the combustion reaction, the O_2 is used as a carrier gas.
B. In addition to the combustion reaction, the O_2 is used as a source of energy to propel the non-spontaneous reaction.
C. O_2 needs to be the limiting reagent in order for the calculations to be correct.
D. The sample needs to be the limiting reagent in order for the calculations to be correct.

Questions 22 through 23 are **NOT** based on a descriptive passage.

22. What is the electron configuration of a chloride ion?

A. [Ne] $3s^2\, 3p^5$
B. [Ne] $3s^2\, 3p^6$
C. [Ne] $3s^2\, 3d^{10}\, 3p^5$
D. [Ar] $3s^2\, 3p^6$

23. According to the Heisenberg uncertainty principle, which of the following pairs of properties of an electron cannot be known with certainty at the same time?

A. charge and velocity
B. spin and subshell
C. average radius and energy
D. momentum and position

STOP. IF YOU FINISH BEFORE TIME IS CALLED, CHECK YOUR WORK. YOU MAY GO BACK TO ANY QUESTION IN THIS TEST BOOKLET.

STOP.

30-MINUTE IN-CLASS EXAM FOR LECTURE 2

Over the years, many attempts have been made to find an equation which represents the behavior of non-ideal gases. Although none of the equations are completely accurate, they do allow an investigation of some of the macroscopic properties of real gases. The most commonly used of these is the *Van der Waals equation:*

$$\left(P + a\frac{n^2}{v^2}\right)(V - nb) = nRT$$

where P is the absolute pressure, n is the number of moles, V is the volume, T is the absolute temperature, R is the gas constant (0.08206 L atm/mol K), and a and b are constants determined experimentally for each gas studied. Table 1 gives the values of a and b for some common gases:

Gas	a (atm L^2/mol)	b (L/mol)
Ar	1.4	0.032
HCl	3.7	0.041
Cl$_2$	6.4	0.054
H$_2$	0.25	0.027
NH$_3$	4.3	0.037
O$_2$	4.3	0.032

Table 1 Van der Waals constants for various gases

To help quantify the deviation of a real gas from ideality, a *compression factor Z* has been defined by $Z = PV/nRT$. Figure 1 shows how the compression factor for ammonia depends on pressure at several different temperatures.

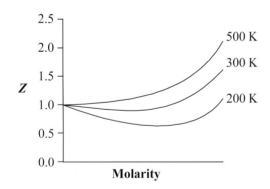

Figure 1 Compression factors for ammonia

24. For an ideal gas, which of the following is most likely the correct graph?

A.

B.

C.

D.

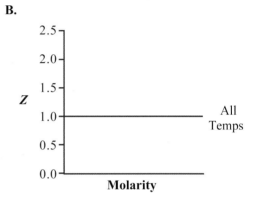

25. For an ideal gas, what can be said about the constants *a* and *b*?

A. They are both zero.
B. They are both positive and equal to each other.
C. They depend on the temperature of the gas.
D. They must be determined experimentally.

26. Based on the information in the passage, under which of the following conditions does ammonia behave most ideally?

A. Low temperatures and low pressures
B. Low temperatures and high pressures
C. High temperatures and low pressures
D. High temperatures and high pressures

27. Which of the following statements is NOT true for an ideal gas?

A. The average kinetic energy of the molecules depends only on the temperature of the gas.
B. At constant volume in a sealed container, the pressure of the gas is directly proportional to its temperature.
C. At constant temperature in a sealed container, the volume of the gas is directly proportional to its pressure.
D. The intermolecular attractions between the gas molecules are negligible.

28. Which of the following demonstrates nonideal behavior of a gas?

A. Some of the molecules move more rapidly than others.
B. Condensation occurs at low temperatures.
C. The gas exerts a force on the walls of its container.
D. The average speed of the molecules in the gas is proportional to the square root of the absolute temperature.

29. Why must absolute temperature be used in the Van der Waals equation?

A. Because the Van der Waals equation is a nonrelativistic equation.
B. Because it is impossible to have a negative absolute temperature.
C. Because ratios of temperatures on other scales, such as the Celsius scale, are meaningless.
D. Because international convention requires it.

Passage II (Questions 30-37)

In 1889, Svante Arrhenius proposed that the rate constant for a given reaction is given by the formula:

$$k = Ae^{-\frac{E_a}{RT}}$$

where E_a is the *activation energy* for the reaction, R is the gas constant (8.314 J/mol K), T is the absolute temperature, and A is a factor, which depends on factors such as molecular size. *Catalysts* change the reaction pathway, which may result in a change in E_a, A, or both.

In *heterogeneous catalysis*, the catalyst is in a different phase from the reactants and products. For example, a solid may catalyze a fluid-phase reaction. Such a catalysis involves the following steps:

1. A reactant molecule diffuses through the liquid to the surface of the catalyst.

2. The reactant molecule bonds to the catalyst (*adsorption*).

3. Adsorbed molecules bond with each other or with a molecule which collides with the adsorbed molecules.

4. The product leaves the catalyst.

In *homogeneous catalysis*, the catalyst is in the same phase as the reactants and products. Acids often act by this mechanism.

30. Which of the following is true of a catalyzed reaction?

A. A catalyst may be the limiting reagent.
B. At equilibrium, more products are produced when a catalyst is present.
C. The catalyzed reaction pathway has a lower energy of activation than the uncatalyzed reacton pathway.
D. The rate of the reverse reacton will be slower for the catalyzed reaction.

31. Consider the following mechanism:

$$Cl + O_3 \rightarrow ClO + O_2$$
$$ClO + O \rightarrow Cl + O_2$$

In this mechanism, what is the catalyst?

A. Cl
B. O_3
C. ClO
D. O_2

GO ON TO THE NEXT PAGE.

32. As the temperature of a reaction increases, which of the following always occurs?

- **A.** The rate constant increases.
- **B.** The rate constant decreases.
- **C.** The activation energy increases.
- **D.** The activation energy decreases.

33. Consider a reversible reaction. If the activation energy for the forward reaction is lowered by a catalyst, what can be said about the activation energy for the reverse reaction?

- **A.** It is also lowered.
- **B.** It is raised.
- **C.** It is unaffected by the catalyst.
- **D.** The effect of the catalyst on the reverse reaction cannot be predicted without more information.

34. Suppose a reaction is acid-catalyzed by a solution of pH 3.0. What can be said about the pH of the resulting solution?

- **A.** It will be greater than 3.0 because the acid is consumed.
- **B.** It will be equal to 3.0 because the acid is regenerated.
- **C.** It will be equal to 3.0 because catalysts have no effect on equilibrium.
- **D.** It cannot be predicted without information on the acidity of the reactants and products.

35. The rate of a reaction may depend on which of the following?

- **I.** Concentrations of the reactants
- **II.** Concentration of a catalyst
- **III.** Surface area of a heterogeneous catalyst
- **IV.** Temperature

- **A.** I only
- **B.** IV only
- **C.** I and IV only
- **D.** I, II, III, and IV

36. H_2 can be added to ethylene in the presence of a heterogeneous catalyst such as solid platinum. What might account for the initial attraction between the hydrogen molecules and the solid platinum?

- **A.** hydrogen bonding
- **B.** metallic bonding
- **C.** van der Waals attraction
- **D.** the plasma continuum effect

37. If the solid line in the graph below represents the reaction profile for an uncatalyzed reaction, which line might represent the reaction profile for the catalyzed reaction?

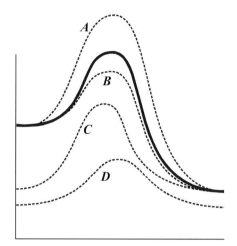

- **A.** A
- **B.** B
- **C.** C
- **D.** D

GO ON TO THE NEXT PAGE.

Passage III (Questions 38-44)

Peroxydisulfate (persulfate) ion reacts with the iodide anion according to Reaction 1.

$$S_2O_8^{2-}\,(aq) + 3I^-\,(aq) \rightleftharpoons 2SO_4^{2-}\,(aq) + I_3^-\,(aq)$$

Reaction 1

The amount of I_3^- formed can be determined by adding a known amount of $S_2O_3^{2-}$ and allowing it to react according to Reaction 2.

$$2S_2O_3^{2-}\,(aq) + I_3^-\,(aq) \rightleftharpoons S_4O_6^{2-}\,(aq) + 3I^-\,(aq)$$

Reaction 2

If starch is also added, any excess I_3^- will react to form a blue-black I_2 complex. The formation of this complex indicates the completion of Reaction 2. The rate of Reaction 1 can be determined by the following equation where t is the elapsed time from the addition of the last component to the formation of the blue-black starch, I_2 complex.

$$rate = \frac{\frac{1}{2}[S_2O_3^{2-}]}{t}$$

Equation 1

38. Why can Equation 1 be used to measure the rate of Reaction 1?

   A.   Reaction 2 must be much faster than Reaction 1, thus the rate in Equation 1 is the rate of formation of I_3^-.
   B.   Reaction 2 must be much slower than Reaction 1, thus the rate in Equation 1 is the rate of formation of I_3^-.
   C.   Reactions 1 and 2 must occur at the same rate, thus the rate in Equation 1 is the rate of formation of I_3^-.
   D.   Equation 1 can be derived directly from the rate laws of Reactions 1 and 2.

39. What would happen to the time and the rate in Equation 1, if the temperature were reduced?

   A.   Time would increase and rate would decrease.
   B.   Time would decrease and rate would increase.
   C.   Time would increase and rate would remain unchanged.
   D.   Time would remain the same and rate would increase.

40. The following table gives the relative concentrations and rates found using the method described in the passage. What is the rate law for Reaction 1?

	1	2	3
$[I^-],(M)$	0.060	0.030	0.030
$[S_2O_8^{2-}],(M)$	0.030	0.030	0.015
Rate,(M/sec)	6.0×10^{-6}	3.0×10^{-6}	1.5×10^{-6}

   A. $k[I^-]^2[S_2O_8^{2-}]^2$
   B. $k[I^-]\text{fi}[S_2O_8^{2-}]^2$
   C. $k[I^-]^3[S_2O_8^{2-}]$
   D. $k[I^-][S_2O_8^{2-}]$

41. The rate expression for the reaction of H_2 with Br_2 is:

   rate $= k[H_2][Br_2]$.

   A.   The rate is first order with respect to H_2, and first order overall.
   B.   The rate is first order with respect to H_2, and second order overall.
   C.   The rate is second order with respect to H_2, and first order overall.
   D.   The rate is second order with respect to H_2, and second order overall.

42. A student is performing the kinetic study described in the passage and forgets to add starch. What will be the result of the experiment?

   A.   The rates of both reactions as measured by the student will increase because the starch slows the reactions.
   B.   The rate of Reaction 1 as measured by the student will decrease because starch speeds up the reaction.
   C.   The rate of Reaction 1 as measured by the student will stay the same because starch has no effect on the rate.
   D.   The rate of Reaction 1 as measured by the student will not be able to be determined by the method described in the passage.

GO ON TO THE NEXT PAGE.

43. What would happen to the time and the rate in Equation 1, if more $S_2O_3^{2-}$ were added, and all other conditions remained the same?

    A.   Time would increase and rate would decrease.
    B.   Time would decrease and rate would increase.
    C.   Time would increase and rate would remain unchanged.
    D.   Time would remain the same and rate would increase.

44. What would happen to the time and the rate in Equation 1, if a catalyst is added to Reaction 1, and all other conditions remain the same?

    A.   Time would increase and rate would decrease.
    B.   Time would decrease and rate would increase.
    C.   Time would increase and rate would remain unchanged.
    D.   Time would remain the same and rate would increase.

> Questions 45 through 46 are **NOT** based on a descriptive passage.

45. Which of the following are true concerning any reaction at equilibrium?

    I.   The concentration of products is equal to the concentration of reactants.
    II.   The rate of change in the concentration of the products is equal to the rate of change in the concentration of reactants.
    III.   The rate constant of the forward reaction is equal to the rate constant of the reverse reaction.

    A.   II only
    B.   I and II only
    C.   II and III only
    D.   I, II, and III

46. Equal concentrations of hydrogen and oxygen gas are placed on side 1 of the container shown below. Side 2 contains a vacuum. A small pin hole exists in the barrier separating side 1 and side 2. Which of the following statements is true?

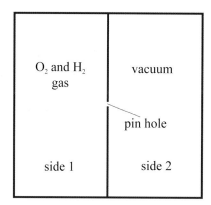

    A.   The partial pressure of oxygen on side 1 will increase.
    B.   The partial pressure of hydrogen on side 1 will increase.
    C.   The mole fraction of oxygen on side 1 will increase.
    D.   The mole fraction of hydrogen on side 1 will increase.

STOP. IF YOU FINISH BEFORE TIME IS CALLED, CHECK YOUR WORK. YOU MAY GO BACK TO ANY QUESTION IN THIS TEST BOOKLET.

30-MINUTE IN-CLASS EXAM FOR LECTURE 3

Passage I (Questions 47-52)

Nickel is purified by the Mond process, which relies on the equilibrium:

$$Ni(s) + 4CO(g) \rightleftharpoons Ni(CO)_4(g)$$

$$\Delta H^\circ = -160.8 \text{ kJ}, \Delta S^\circ = -409.5 \text{ JK}^{-1} \text{ at } 25°C$$

Reaction 1 The Mond process

Two chemists analyze the equilibrium.

Chemist A

Chemist A argues that Reaction 1 will be spontaneous in the forward direction because the product is more stable than the reactants. Furthermore, if the temperature is raised, the reaction will run in reverse because it is an exothermic reaction.

Chemist B

Chemist B argues that Reaction 1 will be spontaneous in the reverse direction because the entropy is higher for the reactants than for the products. Furthermore, if the temperature is raised, the spontaneity of the reverse reaction will increase.

47. The ΔH°_f for Ni(s) is:

- **A.** 0 kJ/mol
- **B.** −160.8 kJ/mol
- **C.** 160.8 kJ/mol
- **D.** 409.5 kJ/mol

48. Which of the following is a logical conclusion of Chemist *A*'s argument?

- **A.** The enthalpy change of a reaction is an indicator of the relative stability of the reactants and products.
- **B.** The entropy change of a reaction is an indicator of the relative stability of the reactants and products.
- **C.** At higher temperatures, the reactants of Reaction 1 will be more stable than the products.
- **D.** Reactions do not necessarily need to increase the entropy of the universe in order to be spontaneous.

49. What are the most efficient conditions for purifying nickel when using the Mond process?

- **A.** low pressure and low temperature
- **B.** low pressure and high temperature
- **C.** high pressure and low temperature
- **D.** high pressure and high temperature

50. Which of the following explains the error in Chemist *B*'s argument?

- **A.** Higher temperatures favor a reaction that decreases entropy.
- **B.** The entropy change of a reaction is the entropy change of the universe.
- **C.** A positive entropy of reaction does not necessarily indicate an entropy increase for the universe.
- **D.** The reaction will only run in the reverse direction until entropy is maximized for the reaction system.

51. What is the change in Gibbs free energy for Reaction 1 at standard state and 25°C?

- **A.** −38 kJ
- **B.** 38 kJ
- **C.** −150.5 kJ
- **D.** 150.5 kJ

52. Consider the reaction below:

$$C(s) + O_2(g) \rightarrow CO_2(g)$$

$$\Delta H^\circ \text{ is } -393.51 \text{ kJ and } \Delta S^\circ \text{ is } 2.86 \text{ JK}^{-1} \text{ at } 25°C$$

If solid carbon is exposed to 1atm of oxygen and 1 atm of carbon dioxide gas at room temperature, will carbon dioxide gas form spontaneously?

- **A.** No, because the enthalpy of formation for CO_2 is negative.
- **B.** No, because the change in Gibbs energy is negative.
- **C.** Yes, because the enthalpy of formation for CO_2 is negative.
- **D.** Yes, because the change in Gibbs energy is negative.

Passage II (Questions 53-58)

A heat engine converts heat energy to work via a cyclical process which necessarily results in some of the heat energy being transferred from a higher temperature heat reservoir to a lower temperature heat reservoir. A heat engine obeys the *First Law of Thermodynamics*. The efficiency e of a heat engine is the fraction of heat energy input converted to useful work and is given by:

$$e = \frac{W}{Q_h}$$

where W is the work done by the heat engine on the surroundings and Q_h is the heat removed from the higher temperature reservoir. Work on the surroundings can also be represented by:

$$W = Q_h - Q_c$$

where Q_c is the heat energy expelled into the cold reservoir.

Figure 1 A schematic diagram of two heat engines operating between the same two heat reservoirs. (Not drawn to scale.)

The *Carnot theorem* states: no engine working between two heat reservoirs can be more efficient than a reversible engine working between those same reservoirs. Such a reversible engine is called a Carnot engine. This theorem can be proven with the *Second Law of Thermodynamics*, which states that for any process other than a reversible process the entropy change of the universe is greater than zero, and for a reversible process the entropy change of the universe is zero. Thus a Carnot engine obeys the following equation:

$$\Delta S = \frac{Q_c}{T_c} - \frac{Q_h}{T_h} = 0$$

Figure 1 shows a schematic representation of two heat engines working between the same two reservoirs. Engine 1 is absorbing heat energy from the hot reservoir and doing work while emitting heat energy into the cold reservoir. Engine 2 is a Carnot engine and is being run backwards removing heat energy from the cold reservoir and rejecting heat energy into the hot reservoir.

53. If both Engines 1 and 2 are operating at the same time as shown in Figure 1, and the rate of heat energy being removed from each reservoir is equal to the rate of heat energy being added then:

A. $W' > W$.
B. $W' < W$.
C. Engine 1 is a Carnot engine.
D. The efficiency of Engine 2 is greater than the efficiency of Engine 1.

54. Which of the following is true of the engines in Figure 1 if Engine 1 is not a Carnot engine and the work from Engine 1 is used to run Engine 2?

A. $Q_c < Q_c'$ and $Q_h < Q_h'$.
B. $Q_c > Q_c'$ and $Q_h < Q_h'$.
C. $Q_c > Q_c'$ and $Q_h > Q_h'$.
D. The work from Engine 1 cannot be used to run Engine 2.

55. Assume Engine 2 is running in the opposite direction as shown in Figure 1. Which of the following changes to Engine 2 will increase its efficiency as a heat engine?

A. increasing Q_h'
B. decreasing Q_c'
C. decreasing the temperature difference between the reservoirs
D. increasing the temperature difference between the reservoirs

56. Which of the following would allow a Carnot engine to operate at 100% efficiency where $e = 1$.

A. The work on the surroundings must be very large.
B. The engine must be reversible.
C. The hot reservoir must be at the same temperature as the cold reservoir.
D. The cold reservoir must be at a temperature of absolute zero.

57. What is the minimum power required for a heat engine to lift a 80 kg mass 5 m in 20 s if it releases 1000 J of heat energy from its exhaust each second?

A. 200 W
B. 500 W
C. 1200 W
D. 3000 W

58. A certain Carnot engine requires 18 kg of water in the form of steam as its working substance. When 5×10^5 J of heat energy are added at a constant temperature of 400 K the gas expands to 4 m^3. What is the approximate pressure of the gas after the initial expansion? (The ideal gas constant is $R = 8.314$ J/K mol)

   A. 8.3×10^5 Pa
   B. 8.3×10^7 Pa
   C. 1.3×10^6 Pa
   D. 1.3×10^8 Pa

Passage III (Questions 59-65)

As shown in Figure 1, Reaction 1 is thermodynamically favored because the products are at a lower energy state than the reactants. However, at low temperatures this reaction will be too slow to be observed because the reactant molecules do not have enough energy to form the activated complex.

$$NO_2 + CO \rightleftharpoons NO + CO_2$$

Reaction 1

Figure 1 Energy diagram for Reaction 1.

As shown in Figure 2, Reaction 2 is not thermodynamically favored, but it has a smaller reaction barrier. The reactants require less energy to form the activated complex.

$$H_2 + Br \rightleftharpoons H + HBr$$

Reaction 2

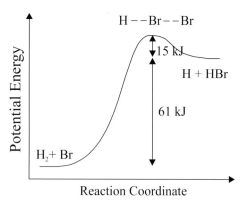

Figure 2 Energy diagram for Reaction 2

59. What does the symbol H--Br--Br represent in Figure 2?

A. an intermediate
B. a transition state
C. a reactant of the second step of the reaction
D. a product of the first step of the reaction

60. What is E_a for Reaction 2 as written?

A. 15 kJ/mole
B. 61 kJ/mole
C. 76 kJ/mole
D. 132 kJ/mole

61. Which reaction is most kinetically favored?

A. $NO_2 + CO \rightarrow NO + CO_2$
B. $NO + CO_2 \rightarrow NO_2 + CO$
C. $H_2 + Br \rightarrow H + HBr$
D. $H + HBr \rightarrow H_2 + Br$

62. Which reaction is most thermodynamically favored?

A. $NO_2 + CO \rightarrow NO + CO_2$
B. $NO + CO_2 \rightarrow NO_2 + CO$
C. $H_2 + Br \rightarrow H + HBr$
D. $H + HBr \rightarrow H_2 + Br$

63. If a catalyst were added to Reaction 1, what would happen?

A. E_1 would be less than 132 kJ but E_2 would remain unchanged.
B. E_1 would be less than 132 kJ and E_2 would be less than 226 kJ.
C. E_2 would be less than 226 but E_1 would remain unchanged.
D. A catalyst doesn't affect the thermodynamic properties of the reactants and products. E_1 and E_2 would remain unchanged but the reaction rate would increase.

64. What is ΔE for Reaction 2 as written?

A. 15 kJ/mole
B. 61 kJ/mole
C. 76 kJ/mole
D. –76 kJ/mole

65. For the reaction,

the ratio of products changes with temperature. At –80°C, 80% of 1 and 20% of 2 form. At 40°C, 15% of 1 and 85% of 2 form. Assuming the relative stability of products vs. reactants does not change significantly with the change in temperature, which product is the kinetically favored one?

A. 1
B. 2
C. both 1 and 2
D. neither 1 nor 2

GO ON TO THE NEXT PAGE.

66. An iron skillet is laid on a hot stove. After a few minutes the handle gets hot. The method of heat transfer described is:

- **A.** convection.
- **B.** conduction.
- **C.** radiation.
- **D.** translation.

67. A man straightens up his room. His action does not violate the second law of thermodynamics because:

- **A.** the entropy of his room increased.
- **B.** energy of the universe was conserved.
- **C.** the entropy increase by the breakdown of nutrients in his body is greater than the entropy decrease by the straightening of his room.
- **D.** his action does violate the second law of thermodynamics.

68. A metal rod is in thermal contact with two heat reservoirs both at constant temperature, one at 100 K and the other at 200 K. The rod conducts 1000 J of heat from the warmer to the colder reservoir. If no energy is exchanged with the surrounws, what is the total change of entropy?

- **A.** –5 J/K
- **B.** 0 J/K
- **C.** 5 J/K
- **D.** 10 J/K

69. Two ideal gases, A and B, are at the same temperature, volume and pressure. Gas A is reversibly expanded at constant temperature to a volume V. Gas B is allowed to expand into an evacuated chamber until it also has a total volume V, but without exchanging heat with its surroundings. Which of the following most accurately describes the two gases?

- **A.** Gas A has a higher temperature and enthalpy than gas B.
- **B.** Gas A has a higher temperature but a lower enthalpy than gas B.
- **C.** Gas B has a higher temperature and enthalpy than gas A.
- **D.** Gas A and B have equal temperatures and enthalpies.

STOP. IF YOU FINISH BEFORE TIME IS CALLED, CHECK YOUR WORK. YOU MAY GO BACK TO ANY QUESTION IN THIS TEST BOOKLET.

30-MINUTE IN-CLASS EXAM FOR LECTURE 4

Passage I (Questions 70-75)

The following tests were carried out on samples of an unknown solution in order to identify any presence of nitrate and nitrite ions.

Experiment 1

In acidic solution nitrites react with sulfamic acid (HNH_2SO_3) according to the following reaction:

$$NO_2^- + NH_2SO_3^- \rightarrow N_2(g) + SO_4^{2-} + H_2O$$

Barium sulfate is insoluble while barium sulfamate is soluble.

In a test tube, $BaCl_2$ is added to a few drops of a sample of the unknown solution. No precipitate is formed. A few crystals of sulfamic acid are then mixed into the sample.

No visible reaction occurs.

Experiment 2

Active metals such as aluminum and zinc in alkaline solution reduce nitrate to ammonia. Nitrite ion will also form ammonia under these conditions. Devarda's alloy (50% Cu, 45% Al, 5% Zn) gives the following reaction with nitrate ion:

$$Al + NO_3^- \rightarrow Al(OH)_4^- + NH_3(g)$$

Several drops of the unknown solution are mixed with an equal amount of 6 *M* NaOH and placed into a dry test tube. Care is taken not to wet the walls of the tube. Devarda's alloy is then added and a loose cotton plug pushed one third of the way down the tube. The tube is warmed briefly in a water bath and removed. A bent strip of red litmus with a moistened fold is then placed at the top of the tube as shown in Figure 1. The moistened section of the litmus turns blue.

 Litmus paper

Cotton filter

Figure 1

70. The unknown solution contains which of the following ions:

A. nitrite but not nitrate
B. both nitrite and nitrate
C. nitrate but not nitrite
D. neither nitrite nor nitrate

71. In Experiment 1, why is $BaCl_2$ added before the sulfamic acid crystals?

A. to acidify the solution
B. to remove any sulfate ions existing prior to the reaction with nitrite
C. to prevent sulfamic acid from reacting with $BaCl_2$
D. $BaCl_2$ is needed to react with nitrite and form the precipitate.

72. If the unknown solution contained nitrite what would be the expected result of Experiment 1?

A. A precipitate would be formed before the addition of sulfamic acid.
B. Bubbles and precipitate would be observed after the addition of sulfamic acid.
C. Bubbles but no precipitate would be observed after the addition of sulfamic acid.
D. No visible reaction would be observed after the addition of sulfamic acid.

73. If carbonate ion is present in the unknown, which of the following reactions might interfere with Experiment 1?

A. $2H^+ + CO_3^{2-} \rightarrow CO_2(g) + H_2O$
B. $Ba^{2+} + 2OH^- + CO_2 \rightarrow BaCO(s) + H_2O$
C. $NH_4^+ + CO_3^{2-} \rightarrow NH_3 + HCO_3^-$
D. $H_2CO_3 \rightarrow CO(g) + O_2(g) + H_2(g)$

74. When the solution in Experiment 2 is warmed in the water bath, all of the following may be true EXCEPT:

A. The equilibrium constant K of the reaction changes.
B. The rate constant k of the reaction changes.
C. The rate of the reaction decreases.
D. The rate of the reaction increases.

75. Which of the following represents the reaction taking place in the litmus paper in Experiment 2?

A. $NO_3^- + H_2O \rightarrow OH^- + HNO_3$
B. $HNO_3 + H_2O \rightarrow H_3O^+ + NO_3^-$
C. $NH_4^+ + H_2O \rightarrow H_3O^+ + NH_3$
D. $NH_3 + H_2O \rightarrow NH_4^+ + OH^-$

180

Passage II (Questions 76-82)

When $Ca(IO_3)_2$ dissolves in a solution containing H+ the following two reactions occur.

$$Ca(IO_3)_2 \rightleftharpoons Ca^{2+} + 2IO_3^-$$

Reaction 1

$$H^+ + IO_3^- \rightleftharpoons HIO_3$$

Reaction 2

HIO_3 is a weak acid. The K_{sp} for $Ca(IO_3)_2$ and the K_a for HIO_3 can be determined from the solubility (S) of $Ca(IO_3)_2$ for solutions of varying [H$^+$]. The solubility is related to the initial hydrogen ion concentration [H$^+$] by the following equation:

$$2(S)^{\frac{3}{2}} = K_{sp}^{\frac{1}{2}} + \left[\frac{K_{sp}^{\frac{1}{2}}}{K_a}\right][H^+]$$

A student prepared four saturated solutions by mixing $Ca(IO_3)_2$ with a strong acid. Excess solid was filtered off. The student found the S for each solution with constant ionic strength, using iodometric titrations. The resulting data are shown in Table 1.

Solution	[H$^+$] (mol/l)	S (mol/l)
1	1.0×10^{-7}	5.4×10^{-3}
2	2.5×10^{-1}	9.9×10^{-3}
3	5.0×10^{-1}	1.4×10^{-2}
4	1	2.0×10^{-2}

Table 1 Solubility data for $Ca(IO_3)_2$

76. The K_{sp} for $Ca(IO_3)_2$ and the K_a for HIO_3, respectively are:

A. $[Ca^{2+}][IO_3^-]^2$ and $\dfrac{[H^+][IO_3^-]}{[HIO_3]}$

B. $\dfrac{[Ca^{2+}][IO_3^-]^2}{[Ca(IO_3)_2]}$ and $\dfrac{[H^+][IO_3^-]}{[HIO_3]}$

C. $[Ca^{2+}][IO_3^-]^2$ and $[H^+][IO_3^-]$

D. $[Ca^{2+}][IO_3^-]^2$ and $\dfrac{[HIO_3]}{[H^+][IO_3^-]}$

77. As [H$^+$] increases, the solubility of $Ca(IO_3)_2$:

A. increases and K_{sp} increases.
B. decreases and K_{sp} decreases.
C. increases and K_{sp} does not change.
D. does not change and K_{sp} increases.

78. The graph of $2(\underline{S})^{3/2}$ versus [H$^+$] for the data shown in Table 1 would most closely resemble which of the following?

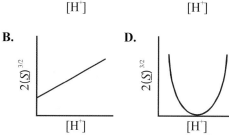

79. After filtering out excess solid, a student adds HCl to Solution 1 in Table 1. He then adds a small amount of $CaSO_4$, which dissolves completely. Which of the following also occurs in the new solution?

A. Some $Ca(IO_3)_2$ precipitates when the $CaSO_4$ is added.
B. Undissociated HIO_3 increases when the HCl is added.
C. Aqueous IO_3^- decreases when $CaSO_4$ is added.
D. Aqueous Ca^{2+} decreases when $CaSO_4$ is added.

80. According to Table 1, what is the value of K_{sp} for $Ca(IO_3)_2$?

A. 1.0×10^{-14}
B. 6.4×10^{-7}
C. 5.4×10^{-3}
D. 1.1×10^{-1}

81. If $Ca(OH)_2$ is added to the Solution 3 in Table 1:

A. the concentration of H$^+$ will increase.
B. the concentration of HIO_3 will increase.
C. the concentration of IO_3^- will increase
D. $Ca(IO_3)_2$ will precipitate.

82. How will the addition of HIO_3 affect Solution 2 from Table 1?

A. The lower pH will shift Reaction 2 to the right.
B. The increased hydrogen ion concentration will dissolve more $Ca(IO_3)_2$.
C. The common ion effect will shift Reaction 1 to the left.
D. The lower pH will balance out the common ion effect and the equilibrium will not change.

GO ON TO THE NEXT PAGE.

Many carbonate minerals are found in the earth's crust. As a result, the waters of several lakes, rivers, and even oceans are in contact with these minerals. $CaCO_3$ is the primary component of limestone and marble, while dolomite $(CaMg(CO_3)_2)$ and magnesite $(MgCO_3)$ are minerals found in other rock formations.

Limestone lines many of the river and lake beds resulting in contamination of the fresh water supply with Ca^{2+} and Mg^{2+}. The amount of these minerals present in water can be measured in parts per million (ppm). The "hardness" of water is determined by the ppm of Ca^{2+} and Mg^{2+} present. Hard water is the cause of many problems in the home. Scale buildup in pipes, on pots and pans, and in washing machines are just a few of the problems.

The hardness of water can be measured by titrating a sample of water with the ligand ethylenediamine tetraacetic acid (EDTA) and the indicator eriochrome black T. This ligand forms a coordination complex with metal cations (M) in a one-to-one stochiometry in the following association reaction:

$$EDTA + M \rightarrow EDTA-M$$

The structure of EDTA is shown in Figure 1. It has six binding sites to form a very stable complex ion with most metal ions.

Figure 1 The structure of EDTA

The association constants for EDTA with several metal ions are listed in Table 1.

Metal	K_{assoc}
Hg^{2+}	6×10^{21}
Mg^{2+}	5×10^{8}
Ca^{2+}	5×10^{10}
Al^{3+}	1×10^{16}
Fe^{2+}	2×10^{14}
Fe^{3+}	1×10^{25}
Cu^{2+}	6×10^{18}

Table 1 Association constants for EDTA with metal ions

Many households soften hard water using ion exchange resins. These resins replace the Ca^{2+} and Mg^{2+} ions with smaller cations such as Na^+ and H^+.

83. A scientist determines how hard the tap water is in the laboratory, using an EDTA titration. If the pipes in the building are old and some rust dissolves into the tap water, how will the results of the test change?

   A. The results will not change because the EDTA titration only works with Ca^{2+} and Mg^{2+}.
   B. The titration will not be able to be carried out because the tap water will be colored.
   C. The tap water will appear to have less Ca^{2+} and Mg^{2+} present.
   D. The tap water will appear to have more Ca^{2+} and Mg^{2+} present.

84. When EDTA reacts with a metal ion to form a complex ion, EDTA is acting as a(n):

   A. oxidizing agent.
   B. reducing agent.
   C. Lewis base.
   D. Lewis acid.

85. Salt water contains a high concentration of Cl^- ions. These ions form complexes $(CaCl^+)$ with Ca^{2+}. How will the solubility of limestone change in ocean water compared to fresh water?

   A. It will increase.
   B. It will decrease.
   C. It will remain the same.
   D. The change in solubility cannot be determined.

86. A 25 mL sample of hard water is titrated with a 0.001 solution of EDTA, and the endpoint of the titration is reached at 50 mL of EDTA added. What is the concentration of Ca^{2+} and Mg^{2+} ions in solution?

   A. 0.0005 M
   B. 0.001 M
   C. 0.002 M
   D. 0.006 M

87. The EDTA titrations are carried out at a pH of 10. Why is it necessary to buffer the pH at 10?

A. A low pH will cause metal hydroxides to form.
B. $CaCO_3$ requires a high pH in order to dissolve.
C. The indicator requires pH 10 to change color.
D. The coordinating atoms must be deprotonated in order to bond with the metal ion.

88. Why does replacing the cations found in hard water with Na^+ or H^+ soften the water (i.e. reduce the unwanted residue produced by hard water)?

A. The smaller cations do not form insoluble mineral deposits.
B. Twice as many smaller ions are necessary to react with soaps and other ligands.
C. No minerals contain Na and H.
D. H is found in water so there is no addition of new atoms.

89. 9 ppm is equivalent to an aqueous concentration of approximately 5×10^{-4} mol/L. If a water sample were reduced from 18 ppm Mg^{2+} to 9 ppm Mg^{2+} by the addition of EDTA, according to Table 1 what would be the concentration of the remaining unbound EDTA?

A. 2×10^{-9} mol/L
B. 5×10^{-4} mol/L
C. 1×10^{-3} mol/L
D. 5×10^{-3} mol/L

Questions 90 through 92 are **NOT** based on a descriptive passage.

90. The vapor pressure of pure water at 25°C is approximately 23.8 torr. Which of the following is the vapor pressure of pure water at 95°C?

A. 10 torr
B. 23.8 torr
C. 633.9 torr
D. 800 torr

91. Benzene and toluene form a nearly ideal solution. If the vapor pressure for benzene and toluene at 25°C is 94 mm Hg and 29 mm Hg respectively, what is the approximate vapor pressure of a solution made from 25% benzene and 75% toluene at the same temperature?

A. 29 mm Hg
B. 45 mm Hg
C. 94 mm Hg
D. 123 mm Hg

92. When volatile solvents *A* and *B* are mixed in equal proportions heat is given off to the surroundings. If pure *A* has a higher boiling point than pure *B*, which of the following could NOT be true?

A. The boiling point of the mixture is less than pure *A*.
B. The boiling point of the mixture is less than pure *B*.
C. The vapor pressure of the mixture is less than pure *A*.
D. The vapor pressure of the mixture is less than pure *B*.

STOP. IF YOU FINISH BEFORE TIME IS CALLED, CHECK YOUR WORK. YOU MAY GO BACK TO ANY QUESTION IN THIS TEST BOOKLET.

STOP.

30-MINUTE IN-CLASS EXAM FOR LECTURE 5

Two students performed the following experiment to calculate the molecular weight of an unknown substance. The apparatus shown in Figure 1 was used.

Figure 1 Freezing point apparatus

Both students placed 10.00 mL of cyclohexane into the test tube at room temperature. Next 0.500 gram of an unknown solid was dissolved in the cyclohexane. The test tube and contents were lowered into the ice bath, which was maintained at a temperature of $-5.0°C$ by adjusting the relative amounts of NaCl, ice, and water. The students monitored the temperature of the cyclohexane mixtures by taking readings from the thermometer at 30 seconds intervals. The freezing point of the solution for a given trial is the temperature maintained for four consecutive readings. The experiment was repeated two more times by warming the cyclohexane to room temperature then freezing it again.

The results obtained by the students are recorded in Table 1.

Time, seconds	30	60	90	120	150	180	210	240
Student 1	22.0	6.0	4.0	-3.5	-3.5	-3.5	-3.5	-3.5
Student 2	22.0	12.0	6.0	0.6	0.6	0.6	0.6	0.4

Table 1 Solution temperature ($°C$) with time

(The K_f for cyclohexane is $20.2°C$ kg/mol, the freezing point is $6.6°C$, and the density is 0.78 g/mL. The K_f for water is $1.86°C$ kg/mol.)

93. Why was NaCl added to the ice bath?

A. To lower the freezing point of the water and cool the cyclohexane solution more quickly.
B. To lower the freezing point of the cyclohexane solution below the freezing point of the water.
C. To lower the freezing point of the water below the freezing point of the cyclohexane solution.
D. To raise the freezing point of the water.

94. Which salt is the most efficient per gram at lowering the freezing point of water?

A. $Ba(OH)_2$
B. $MgSO_4$
C. NaCl
D. $CaCl_2$

95. The purpose of the copper stirrer is:

A. to ensure that the solid stays in solution.
B. to create heat to offset the chilling effect of the ice bath.
C. to ensure that the solution temperature remains homogenous.
D. to allow the student to see when crystals begin to form.

96. According to the results in Table 1, which student had the unknown with the greatest molecular weight? (Assume no dissociation of the unknown solids occurs.)

A. Student 1
B. Student 2
C. The molecular weights were the same.
D. It cannot be determined based on the given information.

97. Student 1 recorded a lower freezing point for the experiment because:

A. the concentration of particles in Student 1's crushed ice solution was lower than in Student 2's crushed ice solution.
B. the concentration of particles in Student 1's crushed ice solution was greater than in Student 2's crushed ice solution.
C. the concentration of particles in Student 1's cyclohexane solution was lower than in Student 2's cyclohexane solution.
D. the concentration of particles in Student 1's cyclohexane solution was greater than in Student 2's cyclohexane solution.

98. In order to calculate the molecular weight of their unknown solid the students probably used all of the following data EXCEPT:

A. the mass of the unknown solid added to the solution.
B. the time required for the cyclhexane solution to freeze.
C. the temperature at the freezing point of the cycloexane solution.
D. the volume of the cyclohexane solution.

99. A professor must choose the unknown from the following solutes. Which of the following would be the most appropriate for the experiment in the passage?

A. NaCl
B. $Mg(OH)_2$
C. CH_3OH
D. $C_{10}H_8$

100. Why does the temperature in Student 2's experiment begin to drop after 210 seconds?

A. Student 2 used too much ice in the ice bath.
B. Student 2's cyclohexane solution was completely frozen at 210 seconds.
C. Student 2 stopped stirring the solution at 180 seconds.
D. Student 2 stopped dissolving the unknown solid.

Passage II (Questions 101-106)

A series of experiments are performed using the calorimeter shown in Figure 1.

Figure 1 Coffee Cup Calorimeter

A volume of 0.5 M NaOH is placed near the calorimeter, which contains an equal volume of 0.5 M HCl. The temperatures of both solutions are monitored until they equilibrate to room temperature.

The NaOH solution is added to the HCl solution through the funnel. The temperature is recorded every 30 seconds for 5 minutes. The experiment is repeated three times with three different volumes of HCl and NaOH. The results of one of these experiments are shown in the graph in Figure 2. The data for all experiments are recorded in Table 1.

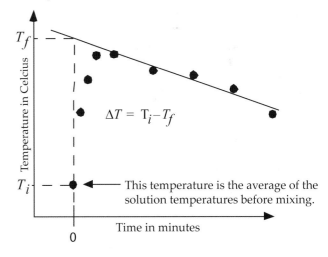

Figure 2 Temperature change of solution over time

GO ON TO THE NEXT PAGE.

Trial	Volume of HCL and NaOH (ml)	Initial Temperature °C	Initial Temperature °C
1	30	22.0	25.3
2	40	20.0	23.3
3	50	21.0	24.3

Table 1

101. What reaction is taking place in the calorimeter to cause the temperature change?

   A. $H^+ + OH^- \rightarrow H_2O$
   B. $Na^+ + Cl^- \rightarrow NaCl$
   C. $NaCl \rightarrow Na^+ + Cl^-$
   D. $Na^+ + 1e^- \rightarrow Na$

102. The reaction in the calorimeter is an:

   A. endothermic reaction.
   B. exothermic reaction.
   C. oxidation reaction.
   D. isothermic reaction.

103. Assuming that the heat capacity of the solution is the same as the heat capacity of water, what is the enthalpy change for the reaction in Trial 2 as recorded in Table 1? (The heat capacity for water is 1.0 cal $°C^{-1}$ mL^{-1})

   A. −132 cal
   B. 132 cal
   C. −330 cal
   D. 330 cal

104. If 0.5 M NH_4OH (a weaker base) were used instead of NaOH, how would this affect the results of the experiment?

   A. The temperature change would be greater because more energy is required to dissociate NH_4OH.
   B. The temperature change would be less because more energy is required to dissociate NH_4OH.
   C. The temperature change would be greater because less energy is required to dissociate NH_4OH.
   D. It would not change the results because both bases are ionic compounds and the energy required to separate equal charges is always the same.

105. Which trial would be expected to result in the greatest heat of solution per mole of reactants?

   A. 1
   B. 2
   C. 3
   D. They should all be the same.

106. If the solutions in the experiment began at room temperature, which of the following explains the heat transfer between the calorimeter and its surroundings for the experiment shown in Figure 2?

   A. Initially heat is transferred from the surroundings to the calorimeter, and then heat is transferred from the calorimeter to the surroundings.
   B. Initially heat is transferred from the calorimeter to the surroundings, and then heat is transferred from the surroundings to the calorimeter.
   C. Heat is transferred from the surroundings to the calorimeter throughout the experiment.
   D. Heat is transferred from the calorimeter to the surroundings throughout the experiment.

Passage III (Questions 107-113)

Phase diagrams show the changes in phase of a material as a function of temperature and pressure. Student A prepared a phase diagram for CO_2. After observing the phase diagram, he concluded that raising the pressure isothermally promotes a substance to change from a gas to a liquid to a solid as demonstrated by the dashed line in Figure 1.

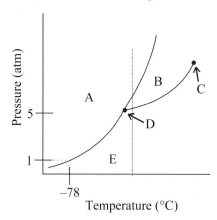

Figure 1 Phase diagram of CO_2

Student B chose to make a phase diagram of H_2O. She observed that raising the pressure isothermally promotes a substance to convert from vapor to solid then to liquid as indicated by the dashed line in Figure 2.

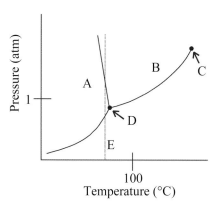

Figure 2 Phase diagram of H_2O

107. Which of the following explains the discrepancy between the observation the two students?

    A.   Water expands when going from liquid to solid, whereas CO_2 contracts.

    B. CO_2 expands when going from liquid to solid, whereas water contracts.

    C.   The two chemists observed the phase changes at different temperatures.

    D. CO_2 is a gas at room temperature, while H_2O is a liquid.

108. According to Figure 1, at $-78°C$ and 1 atm CO_2 will:

    A.   exist as a liquid.

    B.   exist in equilibrium as a gas and liquid.

    C.   exist in equilibrium as a gas and solid.

    D.   exist in equilibrium as a liquid and solid.

109. The temperature and pressure above which the gas and liquid phases of a substance can not be distinguished is called the:

    A.   critical point

    B.   triple point

    C.   boiling point

    D.   super point

110. At temperatures and pressures greater than point C in Figure 1:

    A. CO_2 is a vapor.

    B. CO_2 is a liquid.

    C. CO_2 is in both liquid and vapor phase.

    D.   the vapor and liquid phases of CO_2 cannot be distinguished.

111. According to Figure 2, as the pressure increases the melting point of H_2O:

    A.   increases.

    B.   decreases.

    C.   does not change.

    D.   increases than decreases.

112. The normal boiling point for O_2 is 90.2 K. Which of the following could be the triple point for O_2?

    A.   1.14 mmHg and 54.4 K

    B.   1.14 mmHg and 154.6 K

    C.   800 mmHg and 54.4 K

    D.   37,800 mmHg and 154.6 K

113. Describe the phase change for H_2O as the pressure is raised at 100°C.

    A.   sublimation

    B.   vaporization

    C.   condensation

    D.   melting

GO ON TO THE NEXT PAGE.

Questions 114 through 115 are **NOT** based on a descriptive passage.

114. During a solid to liquid phase change, energy is:

    A. absorbed by bond breakage.
    B. released by bond breakage.
    C. absorbed by increased kinetic energy of the liquid molecules.
    D. released by increased kinetic energy of the liquid molecules.

115. On his honeymoon the chemist, Joule, took with him a long thermometer with which to measure the temperature difference between the waters at the top and the bottom of Niagra Falls. If the height of the falls is 60 meters and the specific heat of water is approximately 4200 J kg^{-1} K^{-1}, what is the expected temperature difference?

    A. 1/7 K
    B. 7 K
    C. 70 K
    D. 700 K

STOP. IF YOU FINISH BEFORE TIME IS CALLED, CHECK YOUR WORK. YOU MAY GO BACK TO ANY QUESTION IN THIS TEST BOOKLET.

30-MINUTE IN-CLASS EXAM FOR LECTURE 6

Passage I (Questions 116-121)

The solubility of $Ca(OH)_2$ (Reaction 1) can be determined by titrating the saturated solution containing no precipitate against a standardized HCl solution and determining $[OH^-]$.

$$Ca(OH)_2 \rightleftharpoons Ca^{2+} + 2OH^-$$

Reaction 1

Once $[OH^-]$ is determined, the solubility (S) of $Ca(OH)_2$ is calculated using the following equation:

$$S = \frac{1}{2}[OH^-]_{Ca(OH)_2}$$

Equation 1

where $[OH-]_{Ca(OH)_2}$ is the concentration of hydroxide ion due only to $Ca(OH)_2$. The solubilities of $Ca(OH)_2$ in a variety of solutions of varying $[OH^-]$ concentrations were determined by the above method, but the calculation of S had to be altered slightly due to the presence of additional hydroxide ions.

$$S = \frac{1}{2}\{[OH^-]_{total} - [OH^-]_{solvent}\}$$

Equation 2

The results of the experiment are summarized in Table 1.

Trial	Solution	Solubility
1	H_2O	0.0199 M
2	0.01793 M NaOH	0.0100 M
3	0.03614 M NaOH	0.0047 M
4	0.07119 M NaOH	0.0015 M

Table 1 Solubility data for $Ca(OH)_2$

116. How does the solubility of $Ca(OH)_2$ change as the $[OH^-]$ in the solvent increases?

   A. It decreases because the increase in OH^- shifts Reaction 1 toward the left.

   B. It decreases because the increase in OH^- interferes with the acid titration.

   C. It increases because the increase in OH^- shifts Reaction 1 toward the left.

   D. It increases because the increase in OH^- interferes with the acid titration.

117. How do the titrations in Trials 1 and 3 compare?

   A. The pH of the equivalence points are the same, but more HCl is required to reach the equivalence point in Trial 3.

   B. The pH of the equivalence point in Trial 1 is higher, and less HCl is required to reach it.

   C. The pH of the equivalence point in Trial 3 is higher, and less HCl is required to reach it.

   D. The pH of the equivalence point in Trial 3 is higher, and more HCl is required to reach it.

118. The K_{sp} for Reaction 1 in the presence of NaOH is:

   A. $[Ca^{2+}][OH^-]^2_{Ca(OH)_2}$

   B. $[Ca^{2+}][OH^-]^2_{Total}$

   C. $[Ca^{2+}][2OH^-]^2_{Ca(OH)_2}$

   D. $[Ca^{2+}][2OH^-]^2_{Total}$

119. What is the pH of the solution in Trial 3 before the titration?

   A. 1.1

   B. 7.0

   C. 9.3

   D. 12.7

120. Which indicator would be best for the titration in this experiment?

   A. Phenolphthalein: (acid color is colorless, base is red, and the transition pH is $8.0 - 9.6$).

   B. Thymolphthalein: (acid color is colorless, base is blue, and the transition pH is $8.3 - 10.5$).

   C. Bromocresol purple: (acid color is yellow, base is purple, and the transition pH is $5.2 - 6.8$).

   D. Neutral red: (acid color is red, base color is yellow, and the transition pH is $6.8 - 8.0$).

121. If a pH meter were placed into the titration beaker, what would be the resulting curve for Trial 1?

A.

Volume of Titrant Added

B.

Volume of Titrant Added

C.

Volume of Titrant Added

D.

Volume of Titrant Added

Passage II (Questions 122-127)

The reaction for the autoionization of water is shown below:

$$2H_2O \rightarrow H_3O^+ + OH^-$$

The equilibrium constant (K_w) is temperature dependent. Table 1 lists the value of K_w at several temperatures.

Temperature (°C)	K_w
0	0.114×10^{-14}
10	0.292×10^{-14}
20	0.681×10^{-14}
25	1.01×10^{-14}
30	1.47×10^{-14}
40	2.92×10^{-14}
50	5.47×10^{-14}
60	9.61×10^{-14}

Table 1 Equilibrium constants for water at different temperatures

Water has a leveling effect on acids. Any acid stronger than H_3O^+ appears to have the same behavior in aqueous solution. For example, 1 M HCl and 1 M HClO$_4$ have the same concentration of H_3O^+ even though in anhydrous acetic acid, HClO$_4$ is a stronger acid.

122. What is the pH of H_2O at 40°C?

A. 7.5
B. 7.0
C. 6.7
D. 6.0

123. At 10°C, the concentration of OH$^-$ in 1 M HCl is approximately:

A. $1 \times 10^{-7} M$
B. $1 \times 10^{-14} M$
C. $3 \times 10^{-15} M$
D. $1 \times 10^{-15} M$

124. As temperature increases, the pH of pure water:

A. increases.
B. decreases.
C. becomes less than the pOH.
D. becomes greater than the pOH.

GO ON TO THE NEXT PAGE.

125. What is the conjugate base of H_2SO_4?

    A. H_2O
    B. OH^-
    C. HSO_4^-
    D. SO_4^{2-}

126. Why can the relative strength of HCl and $HClO_4$ be determined in acetic acid but not in water?

    A.   because acetic acid is a weaker acid than H_3O^+
    B.   because acetic acid is a stronger acid than H_3O^+
    C.   because acetic acid is a weaker Bronsted-Lowry base than H_2O
    D.   because acetic acid is a stronger Bronsted-Lowry base than H_2O

127. The equation for K_w at 50°C is:

    A. $[OH^-][H_3O^+]$

    B. $\dfrac{[OH^-][H_3O^+]}{[H_2O]^2}$

    C. $\dfrac{[OH^-][H_3O^+]}{[H_2O]}$

    D. $[H_3O^+]$

Passage III (Questions 128-134)

Acid rain results when $SO_3(g)$, produced by the industrial burning of fuel, dissolves in the moist atmosphere.

$$SO_3(g) + H_2O(l) \rightarrow H2SO_4(aq)$$

The rain formed from the condensation of this acidic water is an environmental hazard destroying trees and killing the fish in some lakes. (The pH of the water varies depending upon the level of pollution in the area. The pK_a values are about –2 for H_2SO_4 and 1.92 for HSO_4^-.)

Another pollutant which dissolves in water vapor and reacts to form acid rain is $SO_2(g)$. This gas forms $H_2SO_3(aq)$ which can be oxidized to H_2SO_4. (The pK_a values are 1.81 for H_2SO_3 and 6.91 for HSO_3^-.)

The table below gives the color changes of many acid base indicators used to test the pH of water.

Indicator	Color Change	pH of Color Change
Malachite green	yellow to green	0.2 – 1.8
Thymol blue	red to yellow	1.2 – 2.8
Methyl orange	red to yellow	3.2 – 4.4
Methyl red	red to yellow	4.8 – 6.0
Phenolphthalein	clear to red	8.2 – 10.0
Alizarin yellow	yellow to red	10.1 – 12.0

Table 1

128. A sample of rainwater tested with methyl orange results in a yellow color, and the addition of methyl red to a fresh sample of the same water results in a red color. What is the pH of the sample?

    A.   between 1.2 and 1.8
    B.   between 3.2 and 4.4
    C.   between 4.4 and 4.8
    D.   between 4.8 and 6.0

129. If there is no oxidant present in the air and the same number of moles of SO_2 and SO_3 are dissolved, which gas would produce acid rain with a lower pH?

    A. SO_2 because H_2SO_3 has a higher pK_a than H_2SO_4.
    B. SO_2 because HSO_3^- has a higher pK_a than HSO_4^-.
    C. SO_3 because H_2SO_4 has a lower pK_a than H_2SO_3.
    D. SO_3 because HSO_4^- has a lower pK_a than HSO_3^-.

130. What is the pK_b for HSO_3^-?

    A. 0
    B. 6.91
    C. 7.09
    D. 12.19

131. H_2SO_4 is a stronger acid than:

    I. H_2O
    II. H_3O^+
    III. H_2SO_3

    A. III only
    B. I and II only
    C. I and III only
    D. I, II, and III

132. What is the oxidation state of sulfur in H_2SO_4 and H_2SO_3 respectively?

    A. +6, +4
    B. +4, +6
    C. –6, –4
    D. –4, –6

133. What is the pH of a 5.0×10^{-8} M aqueous solution of H_2SO_4 at room temperature?

    A. 8.3
    B. 7.3
    C. 6.8
    D. 6.0

134. A sample of rainwater polluted with SO_3 is titrated with NaOH. Which of the following most resembles the shape of titration curve.

    A.

Volume of Titrant Added

    B.

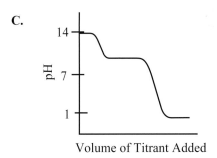

Volume of Titrant Added

    C.

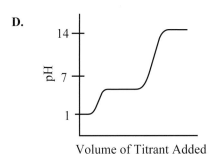

Volume of Titrant Added

    D.

Volume of Titrant Added

GO ON TO THE NEXT PAGE.

135. Which of the following is the strongest base?

    A. ClO^-
    B. ClO_2^-
    C. ClO_3^-
    D. ClO_4^-

136. A weak acid is titrated with a strong base. When the concentration of the conjugate base is equal to the concentration of the acid, the titration is at the:

    A.   stoichiometric point.
    B.   equivalence point.
    C.   half equivalence point.
    D.   end point.

137. A buffer solution is created using acetic acid and its conjugate base. If the ratio of acetic acid to its conjugate base is 10 to 1, what is the approximate pH of the solution? (The K_a of acetic acid is 1.8×10^{-5})

    A.   3.7
    B.   4.7
    C.   5.7
    D.   7.0

138. NH_3 has a K_b of 1.8×10^{-5}. Which of the following has a K_a of 5.6×10^{-10}?

    A. NH_3
    B. NH_4^+
    C. NH_2^-
    D. H^+

STOP. IF YOU FINISH BEFORE TIME IS CALLED, CHECK YOUR WORK. YOU MAY GO BACK TO ANY QUESTION IN THIS TEST BOOKLET.

30-MINUTE IN-CLASS EXAM FOR LECTURE 7

When Fe^{2+} is titrated with dichromate ($Cr_2O_7^{2-}$) according to Reaction 1, the titration curve similar to the one shown in Figure 1 results. The curve was generated by measuring the potential difference between the reaction solution and a standard solution after each addition of a known volume and concentration of dichromate. The potential is measured using a voltmeter attached to an *orp* electrode.

$$6Fe^{2+} + Cr_2O_7^{2-} + 14H^+ \rightleftharpoons 2Cr^{3+} + 7H_2O + 6Fe^{3+}$$

$$E° = 1.33 \text{ V}$$

Reaction 1

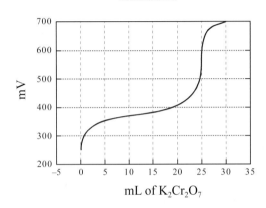

Figure 1. Titration curve for Reaction 1

Chromium (III) is green in color, and dichromate solution is orange. The orange is not intense enough to be used as an indicator. Instead, the endpoint of the titration can be indicated by the redox indicator diphenylamine sulfonic acid (DAS), which changes from colorless to violet when oxidized. The color change observed during the titration is from green to violet. After all the Fe^{2+} ions have been oxidized, the dichromate ion oxidizes DAS. However, the formal potential of the Fe^{2+} solution must be lowered in order to match the endpoint with the equivalence point of the titration. This is accomplished by the addition of H_2SO_4 and H_3PO_4 immediately before titration.

139. Which of the following is true concerning Reaction 1?

A.   Cr is oxidized and $Cr_2O_7^{2-}$ is the oxidizing agent.
B.   Cr is reduced and $Cr_2O_7^{2-}$ is the reducing agent.
C.   Cr is reduced and $Cr_2O_7^{2-}$ is the oxidizing agent.
D.   Cr is oxidized and $Cr_2O_7^{2-}$ is the reducing agent.

140. What is the oxidation state of Cr in $Cr_2O_7^{2-}$?

A.   +12
B.   +7
C.   +6
D.   +3

141. What is the volume of dichromate added to the titration at the equivalence point?

A.   13 mL
B.   15 mL
C.   25 mL
D.   30 mL

142. Which of the following expressions gives the concentration of Fe^{2+} in the unknown solution in terms of the volume of dichromate added $V_{Cr_2O_7^{2-}}$, the molarity of dichromate $M_{Cr_2O_7^{2-}}$, and the original volume of Fe^{2+} solution V_{Fe}?

A. $$\dfrac{\left(V_{Cr_2O_7^{2-}}\right)\left(M_{Cr_2O_7^{2-}}\right)}{V_{Fe}}$$

B. $$\dfrac{\left(6V_{Cr_2O_7^{2-}}\right)\left(M_{Cr_2O_7^{2-}}\right)}{V_{Fe}}$$

C. $$\dfrac{\left(V_{Cr_2O_7^{2-}}\right)\left(M_{Cr_2O_7^{2-}}\right)}{6V_{Fe}}$$

D. $$\dfrac{\left(2V_{Cr_2O_7^{2-}}\right)\left(M_{Cr_2O_7^{2-}}\right)}{V_{Fe}}$$

143. If the formal potential of the solution is not lowered, which of the following will be the result of the titration when DAS is used as the indicator?

A.   The solution will turn violet before the equivalence point is reached.
B.   The solution will turn violet after the equivalence point is reached.
C.   Dichromate ion will not be able to oxidize DAS.
D.   Dichromate ion will reduce DAS to its colorless form.

144. Which of the following statements is true at the equivalence point of the titration in the passage?

A.   Each iron ion has lost one electron and each chromium ion has gained three electrons.
B.   Each iron ion has lost one electron and each chromium ion has gained six electrons.
C.   Each iron ion has gained one electron and each chromium ion has lost three electrons.
D.   Each iron ion has gained one electron and each chromium ion has lost six electrons.

Passage II (Questions 145-151)

Rechargeable batteries have become an essential part of our environmentally conscientious society. The nickel-cadmium cell battery is a rechargeable battery used in small electronic devices. The half reactions that take place in the nickel-cadmium battery during discharge are:

$$Cd(OH)_2(s) + 2e^- \rightarrow Cd(s) + 2OH^-$$

$$E° = -0.4 \text{ V}$$

Half Reaction 1

$$2NiO_2(s) + H_2O + 2e^- \rightarrow 2Ni(OH)_2(s) + 2OH^-$$

$$E° = 0.5 \text{ V}$$

Half Reaction 2

Other types of rechargeable batteries currently being developed are those using sodium or lithium metal as the anode and sulfur as the cathode. These batteries must operate at high temperatures because the metals must be in the liquid state, but they provide a high energy density, which means the batteries will be very light weight.

145. The reaction taking place at the anode when the nickel-cadmium batteries are discharging is:

  A. $Cd(s) + 2OH^- \rightarrow Cd(OH)_2(s) + 2e^-$
  B. $2NiO_2(s) + H_2O + 2e^- \rightarrow 2Ni(OH)_2(s) + 2OH^-$
  C. $Cd(OH)_2(s) + 2e^- \rightarrow Cd(s) + 2OH^-$
  D. $2Ni(OH)_2(s) + 2OH^- \rightarrow 2NiO_2(s) + H_2O + 2e^-$

146. When the nickel-cadmium battery is recharging, what is the reaction at the anode?

  A. $Cd(s) + 2OH^- \rightarrow Cd(OH)_2(s) + 2e^-$
  B. $2NiO_2(s) + H_2O + 2e^- \rightarrow 2Ni(OH)_2(s) + 2OH^-$
  C. $Cd(OH)_2(s) + 2e^- \rightarrow Cd(s) + 2OH^-$
  D. $2Ni(OH)_2(s) + 2OH^- \rightarrow 2NiO_2(s) + H_2O + 2e^-$

147. What is the oxidizing agent in the nickel cadmium battery during discharge?

  A. Cd
  B. $Cd(OH)_2$
  C. NiO_2
  D. $2Ni(OH)_2$

148. Which of the following is true concerning the nickel-cadmium battery when it is recharging?

  A. The cell is a nonspontaneous electrolytic cell.
  B. The cell is a nonspontaneous galvanic cell.
  C. The cell is a spontaneous electrolytic cell.
  D. The cell is a spontaneous galvanic cell.

149. In order to recharge the nickel-cadmium battery back to standard conditions, what is the minimum voltage that must be applied across its electrodes?

  A. 0.1 V
  B. 0.2 V
  C. 0.9 V
  D. 1.8 V

150. In a sodium-sulfur battery, what is the half reaction for sodium in the spontaneous direction?

  A. $Na^+ + e^- \rightarrow Na$
  B. $Na \rightarrow Na^+ + e^-$
  C. $Na \rightarrow Na^{2+} + 2e^-$
  D. $Na^+ + OH^- \rightarrow NaOH$

151. The nickel-cadmium battery is used to power a light bulb. The current in the light bulb flows:

  A. in the same direction as the flow of electrons, from the side with Half Reaction 1 to the side with Half Reaction 2.
  B. in the same direction as the flow of electrons, from the side with Half Reaction 2 to the side with Half Reaction 1.
  C. in the opposite direction to the flow of electrons, from the side with Half Reaction 1 to the side with Half Reaction 2.
  D. in the opposite direction to the flow of electrons, from the side with Half Reaction 2 to the side with Half Reaction 1

GO ON TO THE NEXT PAGE.

A pH meter is a concentration cell which measures the potential difference between a reference solution and a test solution and reports the difference in terms of pH. In a simplified version of a pH meter the half reactions are:

$$H_2 + 2H_2O \rightarrow 2H_3O^+ + 2e^-$$

$$2H_3O^+ + 2e^- \rightarrow H_2 + 2H_2O$$

The potential difference between the two solutions is derived from the Nernst equation as follows:

$$E = -\frac{0.0592}{2} \log\left(\frac{[H_3O^+]_{test\ solution}}{[H_3O^+]_{reference\ solution}}\right)^2$$

where E is given in volts. This equation can be rewritten in terms of the pH of the solutions as follows:

$$E = 0.059(pH_{test} - pH_{reference})$$

Because it is inconvenient to bubble H_2 gas through a solution, a more sophisticated pH meter is used in standard laboratory practice. Dilute hydrochloric acid is used as the reference solution. The test solution is in contact with a thin glass membrane in which a silver wire coated with silver chloride is imbedded. This glass membrane is dipped into the test solution and the potential difference between the solutions is measured and interpreted by a computer, which displays the pH of the test solution. The same equation holds for both pH meters.

152. What is the reaction quotient (Q) in the Nernst equation for the simple pH meter?

A. $\dfrac{[H_3O^+]^2_{test\ solution}}{[H_2]}$

B. $\dfrac{[H_2]}{[H_3O^+]^2_{test\ solution}}$

C. $\dfrac{[H_3O^+]^2_{test\ solution}[H_2]_{reference\ solution}}{[H_3O^+]^2_{reference\ solution}[H_2]_{test\ solution}}$

D. $\dfrac{[H_3O^+]^2_{test\ solution}}{[H_3O^+]^2_{reference\ solution}}$

153. What would be the approximate potential difference measured by a pH meter if the test solution had a pH of 2 and the reference solution had a pH of 4?

A. −118 mV
B. −59 mV
C. 59 mV
D. 118 mV

154. The potential difference measured by a pH meter is directly proportional to:

A. the difference in the hydrogen ion concentrations of the test and reference solution.
B. the difference in the pH of the test and reference solution.
C. the pH of the test solution.
D. the hydrogen ion concentration of the test solution.

155. If the reference solution of a pH meter were 1 M HCl, and the potential difference measured by the meter were 59 mV, what would be the pH of the test solution?

A. 0
B. 1
C. 2
D. 8

156. How would the potential difference registered by a pH meter change for a given test solution if the hydrogen ion concentration of the reference solution were increased by a factor of 10?

A. The potential difference would increase by 59 mV.
B. The potential difference would decrease by 59 mV.
C. The potential difference would increase by a factor of 10.
D. The potential difference would decrease by a factor of 10.

157. A galvanic cell is prepared by connecting two half cells with a salt bridge and a wire. One cell has a Cu electrode and 1 M $CuSO_4$, and the other has a Cu electrode and 2 M $CuSO_4$. Which direction will the current flow through the wire?

    A. toward the $1M$ $CuSO_4$ solution.
    B. toward the $2M$ $CuSO_4$ solution.
    C. current will not flow because the half reactions are the same for both sides.
    D. current will not flow because both half cells have Cu electrodes.

158. Which of the following is true for an acid-base concentration cell such as the one used by the pH meter?

    A. Current always flows toward the more acidic solution.
    B. Current always flows toward the more basic solution.
    C. Current always flows toward the more neutral solution.
    D. Current always flows away from the more neutral solution.

Questions 159 through 161 are **NOT** based on a descriptive passage.

159. Consider the reduction potential:

$$Zn^{2+} + 2e^- \rightarrow Zn(s) \qquad E^\circ = -0.76 \text{ V.}$$

When solid Zinc is added to aqueous HCl, under standard conditions, does a reaction take place?

    A. No, because the oxidation potential for Cl^- is positive.
    B. No, because the reduction potential for Cl^- is negative.
    C. Yes, because the reduction potential for H^+ is positive.
    D. Yes, because the reduction potential for H^+ is zero.

160. Chemicals are mixed in a redox reaction and allowed to come to equilibrium. Which of the following must be true concerning the solution at equilibrium?

    A. $K = 1$
    B. $\Delta G^\circ = 0$
    C. $E = 0$
    D. $\Delta G^\circ = \Delta G$

161. At 298 K all reactants and products in a certain oxidation-reduction reaction are in aqueous phase at initial concentrations of 1 M. If the total potential for the reaction is E = 20 mV, which of the following must be true?

    A. $K = 1$
    B. $E^\circ_{298} = 20 \text{ mV}$
    C. ΔG is positive
    D. $K < 1$

STOP. IF YOU FINISH BEFORE TIME IS CALLED, CHECK YOUR WORK. YOU MAY GO BACK TO ANY QUESTION IN THIS TEST BOOKLET.

STOP.

ANSWERS & EXPLANATIONS

FOR

30-MINUTE IN-CLASS EXAMINATIONS

ANSWERS FOR THE 30-MINUTE IN-CLASS EXAMS

Lecture 1	Lecture 2	Lecture 3	Lecture 4	Lecture 5	Lecture 6	Lecture 7
1. D	24. B	47. A	70. C	93. C	116. A	139. C
2. B	25. A	48. C	71. B	94. C	117. A	140. C
3. A	26. C	49. B	72. B	95. C	118. B	141. C
4. B	27. C	50. C	73. A	96. B	119. D	142. B
5. C	28. B	51. A	74. C	97. D	120. D	143. A
6. D	29. C	52. D	75. D	98. B	121. A	144. A
7. B	30. C	53. C	76. A	99. D	122. C	145. A
8. C	31. A	54. C	77. C	100. B	123. C	146. D
9. D	32. A	55. D	78. B	101. A	124. B	147. C
10. C	33. A	56. D	79. B	102. B	125. C	148. A
11. D	34. D	57. C	80. B	103. A	126. C	149. C
12. C	35. D	58. A	81. D	104. B	127. A	150. B
13. C	36. C	59. B	82. C	105. D	128. C	151. D
14. A	37. B	60. C	83. D	106. D	129. C	152. D
15. A	38. A	61. D	84. C	107. A	130. D	153. A
16. B	39. A	62. A	85. A	108. C	131. D	154. B
17. B	40. D	63. A	86. C	109. A	132. A	155. B
18. D	41. B	64. B	87. D	110. D	133. C	156. A
19. B	42. D	65. A	88. A	111. B	134. D	157. A
20. A	43. C	66. B	89. A	112. A	135. A	158. B
21. D	44. B	67. C	90. C	113. C	136. C	159. D
22. B	45. A	68. C	91. B	114. A	137. A	160. C
23. D	46. C	69. D	92. B	115. A	138. B	161. B

MCAT CHEMISTRY

Raw Score	Estimated Scaled Score
21	15
20	14
19	13
18	12
17	11
15-16	10
14	9
12-13	8

MCAT CHEMISTRY

Raw Score	Estimated Scaled Score
11	7
9-10	6
8	5
6-7	4
5	3
3-4	2
1-2	1

EXPLANATIONS TO IN-CLASS EXAM FOR LECTURE 1

Passage I

1. **D is correct.** If you get a boiling point question on the MCAT, look for hydrogen bonding. It increases the strength of intermolecular attractions. Stronger intermolecular attractions leads to higher boiling point.

2. **B is correct.** You should recognize this compound as ionic because alkaline earth metals like to form ionic compounds with halogens.

3. **A is correct.** In order to explain an increase in boiling point, we have to look for a reason that intermolecular bond strength would increase. The intermolecular bonds in noble gases are totally due to van der Waals forces. If the atoms are more polarizable, instantaneous dipoles can have greater strength. Larger atoms are more polarizable because the electrons can get farther from the nucleus and create a larger dipole moment.

4. **B is correct.** This is a periodic trend. Radius increases going down and to the left on the periodic table.

5. **C is correct.** Crystallization depends upon molecular symmetry as well as intermolecular bonding. Boiling point is strongly dependent upon intermolecular bond strength.

6. **D is correct.** Methane is nonpolar, so its only intermolecular bonding is through van der Waals forces.

7. **B is correct.** All intermolecular bonding is via electrostatic forces. The dipoles in van der Waals forces are temporary whereas dipole-dipole interactions may be due to permanent dipoles.

Passage II

8. **C is correct.** 'As' is just to the left of 'Se' on the periodic table. Therefore, its radius should be slightly larger than Se.

9. **D is correct.** Elements in the same family tend to be chemically similar. Hydrogen is an exception.

10. **C is correct.** Atomic radius is a periodic trend increasing down and to the left.

11. **D is correct.** Only D is a true statement. A is knowledge that would not be required by the MCAT.

12. **C is correct.** Electron affinity is a periodic trend increasing (becoming more exothermic) to the right and up.

13. **C is correct.** The answer we are looking for must explain shielding. With each new period, a new shell is added which shields the new electrons from the greater nuclear charge.

14. **A is correct.** If you substitute H for X in the equation for Δ in the passage, you can only arrive at zero.

15. **A is correct.** C and O are close together in electronegativity and will form a covalent bond.

Passage III

16. **B is correct.** Only water is caught in Chamber 1. The change in mass of chamber 1, 0.9 grams, is all water. 0.9 grams of water divided by 18 g/mol gives 0.05 mole of water. All the hydrogen came from the sample, and all the oxygen came from the excess oxygen. For every mole of water, there are 2 moles of hydrogens, so there is $0.05 \times 2 = 0.1$ mole of hydrogen in the sample. Doing the same with the carbon dioxide caught in Chamber 2 we have: $4.4/44.2 = 0.1$ of CO_2, or 0.1 mole of carbon from the sample. This is a 1:1 ratio. The empirical formula is CH.

17. **B is correct.** The molarity of O_2 is equal to the molarity of the welding gas or any other ideal gas at the same temperature and pressure. Density divided by molecular weight is molarity. Therefore, we can set the ratios of density to molecular weight for oxygen and the welding gas equal to each other. We get: $1.3/32 = 1.1/M.W.$

18. **D is correct.** CH_2O has a molecular weight of 30 g/mol. Thus, we must multiply this by 4 to get 120. So, for the molecular formula we need four times as many atoms of each element from the empirical formula.

19. **B is correct.** O_2 is the limiting reagent. Only 0.5 mole of propane can react, producing 2 moles of water.

20. **A is correct.** The passage says that $CaCl_2$ absorbs water. Thus if Chamber 2 were in front of Chamber 1, it would weigh more because it would absorb both water and carbon dioxide. The amount of carbon dioxide is calculated from the weight of Chamber 2, so the calculated value would be too high.

21. **D is correct.** All of the welding gas must be reacted because the mass of the original sample is divided by the moles of carbon and hydrogen to find the molecular weight. If all the gas were not reacted, the calculated molecular weight would be too large. Adding excess oxygen ensures that all of the welding gas reacts.

Stand Alones

22. **B is correct.** Chlorine takes on an additional electron to become an ion.

23. **D is correct.** This is the Heisenberg uncertainty principle.

EXPLANATIONS TO IN-CLASS EXAM FOR LECTURE 2

Passage I

24. **B is correct.** The definition of $Z = PV/(nRT)$ is always 1 for an ideal gas.

25. **A is correct.** If a and b are both zero, the van der Waals equation becomes $PV = nRT$, the ideal gas law.

26. **C is correct.** You can figure this out from the passage, but it's a lot easier to fall back on your previous knowledge: gases behave most ideally at high temperature and low pressures.

27. **C is correct.** Volume is inversely proportional to pressure. A: $K.E. = 3/2 \, kT$. B: $PV = nRT$, D: This is one of the assumptions underlying the derivation of the ideal gas law.

28. **B is correct.** Condensation is due to intermolecular attractions, which are neglected for ideal gases. For D, start with $K.E. = 3/2 \, kT$. Then $1/2 \, mv^2 = 3/2 \, kT$, so v is proportional to the square root of T.

29. **C is correct.** Equations involving products or ratios of temperature are meaningless if the zero of the temperature scale is not absolute zero. A and B are true statements, but they don't explain why absolute temperature must be used.

Passage II

30. **C is correct.** A catalyst acts to lower the activation energy of a reaction, so the catalyzed reaction will have a lower activation energy than the uncatalyzed reaction.

31. **A is correct.** A catalyst is neither produced nor consumed in a reaction and does not appear in the net reaction. The net reaction for the mechanism shown is:

$$O_3 + O \rightarrow 2O_2$$

The catalyst, Cl, does not appear. ClO also does not appear, but it is produced and consumed in the reaction making it an intermediate.

32. **A is correct.** See the Arrhenius equation:

$$k = zpe^{-Ea/RT}$$

You should also memorize the fact that temperature always increases the rate of a reaction. Even in the case of biologically catalyzed reactions, heat increases the reaction rate until the enzyme is denatured. Once the enzyme is denatured, although the reaction rate slows, the reaction takes a new pathway, and is no longer the same reaction.

33. **A is correct.** If a catalyst only affected the rate in one direction, the equilibrium would be affected. A catalyst doesn't change the equilibrium. This can also be seen from a reaction profile diagram as shown in question 37.

34. **D is correct.** The catalyst is not necessarily the only factor influencing pH.

35. **D is correct.** Choice I is seen from the standard form of the rate law: rate = k[A][B]. For choice II, imagine the saturation kinetics exhibited by enzyme catalysts:

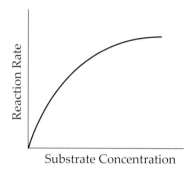

This should make it clear that the ratio of concentrations of the catalyst and the substrates affects the rate of a reaction. This ratio can be changed by changing the concentration of the catalyst. Thus the concentration of a catalyst can affect the rate of a reaction. For choice III, a heterogeneous catalyst is one that is not in the same phase as the reactants. Increasing the surface area of a heterogeneous catalyst is like increasing the concentration. The reaction is affected for the same reasons as in choice II. The reason that a heterogeneous catalyst is typically in the form of metal shavings as opposed to a solid metal bar is to increase surface area. Choice IV you should know from the Arrhenius equation: $k = zpe^{-Ea/RT}$

36. **C is correct.** The MCAT sometimes uses the phrase "van der Waals" forces as a synonym for London Dispersion Forces. A more modern meaning is as a synonym for intermolecular forces. In either case, this is a correct answer. Hydrogen bonding requires a hydrogen atom bonded to a nitrogen, fluorine, or oxygen. D is from an episode of Star Trek.

37. **B is correct.** Only the activation energy is changed by a catalyst. The initial and final states are not affected!

Passage III

In this experiment, Reaction 2 uses up I_3^- as it is formed. When all the $S_2O_3^{2-}$ is used up in Reaction 2, the I_3^- reacts with the starch to turn black. The black color signals the experimenter that all the $S_2O_3^{2-}$ is used up. The experimenter now knows that half as much I_3^- was used up in the same time, and can calculate the rate for Reaction 1. This depends upon Reaction 2 being the fastest reaction.

38. **A is correct.** If we look at Reactions 1 and 2 as two steps of a single reaction, we know that the rate of the slow step is equal to the rate of the overall reaction. Equation 1 measures the time necessary for a specific number of moles of I_3^- to be used by Reaction 2. (Notice that the rate of change of $1/2[S_2O_3^{2-}]$ will be equal to the rate of change of $[I_3^-]$) If Reaction 2 were not the fast step, then Equation 1 would not measure the rate of Reaction 1 accurately. Since Reaction 2 is the fast step, the time t required to use up $1/2[S_2O_3^{2-}]$ is equal to the time needed to produce $[I_3^-]$. The $[I_3^-]$ concentration produced divided by the time necessary to produce it is the rate of Reaction 1. Equation 1 is not derivable from the rate laws of Reactions 1 and 2.

39. **A is correct.** A temperature decrease reduces rate and makes the reaction take longer.

40. **D is correct.** The rate law is found by comparing the rate change from one trial to the next when the concentration of only one reaction is changed. Comparing trials 1 and 2, when the concentration of I⁻ is reduced by a factor of two, the rate is also reduced by a factor of two. This indicates a first order reaction with respect to I⁻. D is the only possible answer.

41. **B is correct.** The exponents in the rate law indicate the order of the reaction with respect to each concentration.

42. **D is correct.** The starch is used to measure the rate of Reaction 1, and does not affect the rate. Although C is true, it does not answer the question as well as D.

43. **C is correct.** Equation 1 gives the rate of Reaction 1. $S_2O_3^{2-}$ is not part of Reaction 1 and its concentration does not change the rate. If rate doesn't change, then, according to Equation 1, t must increase with $S_2O_3^{2-}$.

44. **B is correct.** A catalyst increases the rate of a reaction.

Stand Alones

45. **A is correct.** In a reaction at equilibrium, the rate of change in the concentrations of both products and reactants is zero. This does not mean that the concentrations of reactants and products are equal, nor that the rate constants are equal.

46. **C is correct.** Some of both gases will effuse from side 1 to side 2. This means that the partial pressures of both gases will decrease. (Remember, partial pressure is the pressure of the gas as if it were alone in the container. Thus if we reduce the number of moles of a gas at constant volume and temperature, we reduce its partial pressure.) Since hydrogen will diffuse more rapidly than oxygen, the mole fraction of oxygen will increase.

EXPLANATIONS TO IN-CLASS EXAM FOR LECTURE 3

Passage I

47. **A is correct.** Nickel is an element and is a solid in its natural state at 298 K. Thus, the enthalpy of formation of solid nickel at 298 K is zero.

48. **C is correct.** Chemist A chooses the direction of the reaction based upon chemical stability, and then says that the direction will change at higher temperatures. This is tantamount to saying that the stability will switch at higher temperatures, which, by the way, is also correct. D is, of course, a false statement. The entropy shown for Reaction 1 is the entropy of the reaction. In other words, it is the entropy of the system, and not the entropy of the universe. Chemist A's statement is correct, and does not contradict the second law of thermodynamics. A and B are contradicted because Chemist A says the direction is temperature dependent.

49. **B is correct.** Use Le Chatelier's principle. Read the first sentence of the passage carefully, and notice that to purify nickel, the reaction must move to the left. There are four gas molecules on the left side of the reaction and only one on the right. Pressure pushes the reaction to the right. The reaction is exothermic when moving to the right, so high temperature pushes the reaction to the left.

50. **C is correct.** The reaction is the system, and everything outside the reaction makes up the surroundings. The entropy change given in the passage refers to the system not the universe. The second law of thermodynamics says that a reaction is spontaneous when the entropy of the universe is positive. The entropy of the system may be positive or negative. A and B are false statements. D is a false statement as well. The reaction runs until the entropy of the universe is maximized.

51. **A is correct.** Use $\Delta G = \Delta H - T\Delta S$. Don't forget to convert J/K to kJ/K.

52. **D is correct.** Spontaneity is dictated by Gibbs energy. 1 atm. is standard state for a gas, so $\Delta G = \Delta G°$. When Gibbs energy is negative, a reaction is spontaneous. if enthalpy change is negative and entropy change is positive, then Gibbs energy change must be negative. You can use $\Delta G° = \Delta H° - T\Delta S°$. Check this as follows: If the partial pressures are 1, then the reaction quotient Q is 1, and the log of the reaction quotient is zero. From the equation $\Delta G = \Delta G° + RT\ln Q$ we see that $\Delta G = \Delta G°$. The reaction is spontaneous.

Passage II

Note: A heat engine obeys the first law of thermodynamics. It must expel the same amount of energy as it takes in.

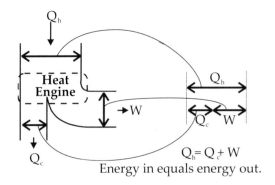

Energy in equals energy out.

53. **C is correct.** If $Q_h' = Q_h$ and $Q_c' = Q_c$ then $W' = W$. Thus the efficiencies of the engines must be equal. Since only a Carnot engine can be as efficient as another Carnot engine, Engine 1 must be a Carnot engine.

54. **C is correct.** If the all the work done by Engine 1 is done on Engine 2, the net work is zero. Since Engine 1 is not a Carnot engine, the entire process is not reversible. The result of any nonreversible process where no work is done must be that heat energy is transferred from the hot reservoir to the cold reservoir. Engine 1 has a lower e than Engine 2 and thus requires more heat energy to create as much work. According to conservation of energy, this extra heat energy input must be matched by extra heat energy output.

55. **D is correct.** Engine 2 is a Carnot engine, and, as the passage states, it has the highest possible efficiency of any engine working between the existing heat reservoirs. Thus only a change in the heat reservoirs will increase its efficiency. **The answer must therefore be C or D.** For greatest efficiency we want to remove the most heat energy possible from the hot reservoir and expel the least amount possible to the cold reservoir thus getting the most work with the least amount of wasted energy. Removing heat energy from the hot reservoir decreases its entropy, while adding heat energy to the cold reservoir increases its entropy. As the temperature of the hot reservoir increases, removing heat energy has less effect on the change in entropy, so more heat energy can be removed. The reverse is true for the cold reservoir. Since, in a Carnot engine, the change in entropy must be zero, the extra heat energy removed from the hot reservoir must be added to work. The engine becomes more efficient. Thus maximizing the temperature difference increases efficiency. This can be derived from the equation in the passage (the long method) as follows. Considering magnitudes only we have:

$$\frac{Q_h'}{T_h} = \frac{Q_c}{T_c} \qquad\qquad \frac{Q_c}{Q_h} = \frac{T_c}{T_h}$$

$$e = \frac{W}{Q_h} \qquad e = \frac{(Q_h - Q_c)}{Q_h} \qquad e = 1 - \frac{Q_c}{Q_h}$$

substituting $\dfrac{T_c}{T_h}$ for $\dfrac{Q_c}{Q_h}$ we have:

$$e = 1 - \frac{T_c}{T_h}$$

56. **D is correct.** From the derivation for efficiency in the previous explanation, if T_c is zero, $e = 1$. However, it is probably easier to eliminate the other answer choices insead. Choice A is wrong because by the equation for efficiency given in the passage, $e = W/Q_h$, a large W by itself won't give $e = 1$. Choice B is wrong because as per the passage all Carnot engines are reversible, but all Carnot engines are not 100% efficient. Choice C is wrong because from the entropy formula, if T_c and T_h were at the same temperature, Q_h and Q_c would also have to be at the same temperature, which gives $W = Q_h - Q_c = 0$, and an efficiency of zero. 100% efficiency is an impossibility.

57. **C is correct.** The exhaust is wasted energy. $Q_h = W + Q_c$. $P = Q_h/t = W/t + Q_c/t = (mgh)/ 20$ s $+ 1000$ J/s $= 4000/20 + 1000 = 1200$ J.

58. **A is correct.** $PV = nRT = (m/M.W.)RT$. $P = 1000 \times 8.314 \times 400/4 = 8.314 \times 10^5$ Pa. By the way, if the gas did not behave ideally, the real pressure would be lower. There is no answer lower than A, and the gas does behave very nearly ideally because it is at high temperature.

Passage III

59. **B is correct.** The transition state corresponds to the top of the energy curve.

60. **C is correct.** The energy of activation is given by the vertical displacement from the reactants to the top of the energy curve.

61. **D is correct.** The smallest energy of activation is the most kinetically favored.

62. **A is correct.** The largest drop in energy is the most thermodynamically favored.

63. **A is correct.** A catalyst lowers the energy of activation but does not change the energy difference between the reactants and products.

64. **B is correct.** The change in energy is energy of products minus reactants.

65.   **A is correct.** The kinetically favored product is the one with a lower energy of activation. The difference in their equilibrium is due to conflicting thermodynamics and kinetics. At a low temperature (T_2), the thermodynamically favored product does not have enough energy to reach the activated complex, so no reaction occurs. The kinetically favored reaction does reach the activated state and a reaction can occur. At the high temperature (T_1) both reactions occur but the reverse of the thermodynamically favored occurs only with a relatively lower probability. Thus the thermodynamically favored reaction predominates. This is not always true but is a concept of which you must be aware.

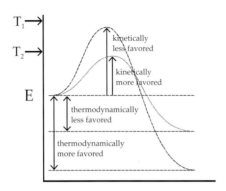

Stand Alones

66.   **B is correct.** Transfer by contact is conduction.

67.   **C is correct.** The second law of thermodynamics says that entropy of the universe increases for any process. By straightening up his room, the man increased the order in his room, and thus decreased its entropy. In order for the entropy of the universe to have increased, there must be a larger increase in entropy of the surroundings. Only C provides an explanation for this.

68.   **C is correct.** The entropy of the system is equal to change in entropy of the two reservoirs. $\Delta S = Q/T$ for each reservoir. The change in entropy of the first reservoir is negative because heat energy is leaving the system $(-1000/200 = -5)$, and the change in entropy of the second reservoir is positive because heat energy is entering the system $(1000/100 = 10)$. The sum of the two entropy changes is +5. You should have at least narrowed down the possibilities to C and D because the change in entropy for any isolated system must be positive for any irreversible process.

69.   **D is correct.** The temperature of Gas A remains constant because the question says so. Temperature is kinetic energy (due to random motion) per mole. Gas B does no work and doesn't exchange heat so its energy doesn't change; it has the same kinetic energy (due to random motion) per mole as when it began. Thus, its temperature doesn't change either.

        Enthalpy is $PV + U$. P and V are the same for both gases because they are at the same temp, volume and therefore pressure $(PV = nRT)$. U doesn't change for Gas A because any energy removed is replaced to keep the temperature the same. U doesn't change for Gas B because no energy is exchanged with the surroundings for Gas B.

EXPLANATIONS TO IN-CLASS EXAM FOR LECTURE 4

Passage I

70.   **C is correct.** The first experiment shows that no nitrite was in the solution. Had there been nitrite, nitrogen bubbles would have formed as per the reaction, and then barium sulfate would have precipitated upon the addition of barium chloride. The second experiment demonstrates that nitrates exist. The water in the moistened litmus paper reacted with ammonia gas to make OH^- ions turning the paper blue. Ammonia gas resulted from the reaction of nitrate with Devarda's alloy.

71.   **B is correct.** Any sulfate ions that exist in solution before sulfamic acid is added must be removed. They are removed by the addition of $BaCl_2$. Choice A is incorrect because $BaCl_2$ does not acidify the solution. Choice C is incorrect because $BaCl_2$ doesn't react with sulfamic acid, it reacts with sulfate. Choice D is incorrect because nitrite doesn't form a precipitate with $BaCl_2$, sulfate does.

72.   **B is correct.** The precipitate would result when the sulfate ion from the reaction reacts with the barium ion to form barium sulfate. The bubbles would be created by the formation of nitrogen gas.

73. **A is correct.** Choice A produces gas bubbles which could be confused with nitrogen gas bubbles. The $BaCl_2$ actually prevents this from happening by forming a precipitate with carbonate before the sulfamic acid-nitrite reaction. Choice B is incorrect because the solution in Experiment 1 is acidic not basic, and because the precipitate would come out before the sulfamic acid-nitrite reaction. Choice C is incorrect because there is no ammonium in solution. Choice D is not carbonate ion, and although carbonic acid is formed by carbonate ion in aqueous solution, you should know that it breaks down to water and carbon dioxide, not carbon monoxide, hydrogen, and oxygen. A reaction you should know: $H_2CO_3 \rightarrow CO_2(g) + H_2O$

74. **C is correct.** Change in temperature can change the rate constant and the equilibrium constant but it can only increase the rate of the reaction.

75. **D is correct.** The litmus paper is turned blue when the basic ammonia gas from the reaction in the experiment reacts with the water in the paper.

Passage II

76. **A is correct.** This is definitional: products over reactants excluding pure liquids and solids.

77. **C is correct.** K_{sp} is a constant; solubility of $Ca(IO_3)_2$ is not. By Reaction 2, as acidity increases, IO_3^- ions are used up, pulling Reaction 1 to the right. Or just look at Table 1. If you want to see why you can't just use Le Chatelier's principle on Reaction 2, simply add the two equations together to get:

$$Ca(IO_3)_2 + H^+ \rightarrow Ca^{2+} + IO_3^- + HIO_3$$

Now when you add H^+ to this equation, it moves to the right, dissolving $Ca(IO_3)_2$.

78. **B is correct.** You should recognize the $y = mx + b$ form of the equation. This is the equation of a line. The b in this case is not zero, but is (K_{sp}).

79. **B is correct.** You must realize that the new solution is no longer saturated. These means that Reaction 1 is not in equilibrium. No precipitate exists. New Ca^{2+} ions do not immediately create precipitate because the solution is not saturated. There is no leftward shift because there is no equilibrium. Thus A, C and D are wrong. Iodic acid is in equilibrium however. Increasing H^+ ions shifts Reaction 2 to the right, creating more HIO_3. This is, of course, why Solution 1 is no longer saturated after adding the acid.

80. **B is correct.** The easiest way to find the K_{sp} is to plug the value of S for Solution 1 into the equation. Notice that the $[H^+]$ value in Solution 1 is for neutral water. It is so small that the second term in the solubility equation becomes negligible. The equation becomes

$$2S^{3/2} = K_{sp}^{1/2}.$$

Squaring both sides gives: $4S^3 = K_{sp}$

$$\Rightarrow 4 \times (5.4 \times 10^{-3})^3 = K_{sp}.$$

The only answer that is even close is choice B at 10^{-7}.

81. **D is correct.** The net equation is $Ca(IO_3)_2(s) + H^+(aq) \rightarrow Ca^{2+}(aq) + IO_3^-(aq) + HIO_3(aq)$. $CaOH_2$ in aqueous solution will produce both OH^- and Ca^{2+}. The OH^- will reduce the H^+ in solution. Since the solution is saturated (in equilibrium), Le Chatelier's principle predicts that both of these changes will shift the reaction to the left producing $Ca(IO_3)_2(s)$.

82. **C is correct.** Reaction 2 will shift left via Le Chatelier's principle. The resulting increase in IO_3^- will shift Reaction 1 to the left due to the common ion effect, creating precipitate in the already saturated solution. The H^+ ion concentration in the formula for solubility is from hydrogen ions in solution before iodic acid is added. If a different acid were added (like HCl), the H^+ ion concentration would move Reaction 2 to the right and thus Reaction 1 to the right.

Passage III

A ligand is an ion or neutral molecule that can donate a pair of electrons to form a coordinate covalent bond with a metal ion. EDTA is a chelating agent (a ligand that makes more than one bond to a single metal ion). It wraps around its metal ion like a claw. Chele (χηλη) means claw in Greek.

83. **D is correct.** The passage states that EDTA reacts with other metal ions. If more EDTA is used up, the scientist will assume that it is being used up by calcium and magnesium ions. This will result in an over-estimation of these ions.

84. **C is correct.** EDTA is donating a pair of electrons in a coordinate covalent bond, so it is a Lewis Base.

85.   **A is correct.** This is LeChatelier's Principle. The chlorine ion will remove some of the Ca^{2+} pulling the reaction to the right.

86.   **C is correct.** The passage states that there is a one-to-one stoichiometry between EDTA and its metal ion. (50 mL)(0.001 mol/L) = (25 mL)x. $x = 0.002$ mol/L

87.   **D is correct.** D is the best explanation. Under high pH conditions, protons are stripped from the carboxylic acids allowing the ligand to bond to the cation. Indicators change color over a range so C is wrong. Calcium carbonate dissolves in an acid solution so B is wrong. A is irrelevant.

88.   **A is correct.** You should know that Na^+ is very soluble, and H^+ does not form mineral deposits.

89.   **A is correct.** The association constant from Table 1 is 5×108. The association reaction is:

$$Mg^{2+} + EDTA \rightarrow EDTA - Mg.$$

$$The\ K_{assoc} = 5 \times 10^8 = [EDTA - Mg]/[EDTA][Mg^{2+}]$$

Since half the magnesium is bound, [EDTA-Mg] is 9 ppm, which is 5×10^{-4}. The remaining half of $[Mg^{2+}]$ is 9 ppm, which is also 5×10^{-4}. Plugging these into the equilibrium expression leaves the remaining concentration [EDTA] = $1/(5 \times 10^8)$ or 2×10^{-9}.

Stand Alones

90.   **C is correct.** Water boils at 100°C and atmospheric pressure, 760 torr. Boiling point is where vapor pressure meets atmospheric pressure. Thus water vapor pressure must be below 760 at 95°C. But it must also rise with increasing temperature, so it must be above 23.8 torr.

91.   **B is correct.** No calculations are required since the vapor pressure would be somewhere between the vapor pressures of the pure liquids. The solution follows Raoult's law.

92.   **B is correct.** Since the reaction was exothermic, the vapor pressure deviated negatively from Raoult's law. Depending upon the ratios of the liquids in solution, the vapor pressure could be lower than either or just lower than B. (A has a higher boiling point thus a lower vapor pressure.) The boiling point must have gone up from B because the vapor pressure went down from B.

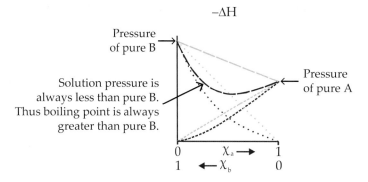

EXPLANATIONS TO IN-CLASS EXAM FOR LECTURE 5

Passage I

93.   **C is correct.** The salt lowers the freezing point of water. This is necessary in order to insure that the water can bring the unknown solution to its freezing point.

94.   **C is correct.** Even if the others completely dissociate, NaCl still releases more particles per gram than the others. (2 particles/58 grams) (A = 3/172, B = 2/120, and D = 3/115)

95.   **C is correct.** The copper stirrer acts to evenly distribute the heat throughout the solution by convection.

96.   **B is correct.** Since the freezing point depression was lower for Student 1, there must have been more particles for the same amount of mass. Thus Student 1 had an unknown with lower molecular weight.

97.   **D is correct.** A greater concentration of particles lowers freezing point more. The freezing point data was collected and recorded for the cyclohexane solution, not the crushed ice solution.

98.   **B is correct.** Time is not a factor in the calculation of the molecuar weight of the unknown solid. The molecular weight of the unknown solid can be calculated as follows:

$$\Delta T = K_f m:$$

$$m = (grams_{solute}/M.W.)/(volume_{solvent} \times density_{solvent} \times kg/gram)$$

plugging into $\Delta T = K_f m$ and rearranging we have:

$$M.W. = (K_f)(grams_{solute}) / \{(\Delta T)(volume_{solvent} \times density_{solvent} \times kg/gram)\}$$

$$K_f = 20.2,\ (grams_{solute}) = 0.5,\ \Delta T = (6.6 - -3.5) = 10.1,$$

$$volume_{solvent} = 10.0,\ density_{solvent} = 0.78,\ kg/gram = 1/1000$$

Thus

$$M.W. = (K_f)(grams_{solute}) / \{(\Delta T)(volume_{solvent} \times density_{solvent} \times kg/gram)\}$$

99.   **D is correct.** D is the only nonvolatile, nonpolar solute that is soluble in cyclohexane.

100.   **B is correct.** The only explanation is B. As long as some solution remains liquid, the energy removed by the ice bath creates bonds forming a solid. As soon as the entire solution is frozen, the energy removed from solution lowers the temperature.

Passage II

101.   **A is correct.** The acid and base are totally dissociated to begin with. This reaction takes high energy molecules and makes a low energy molecule, releasing heat.

102.   **B is correct.** Heat is released.

103.   **A is correct.** 40 mL × 1 cal/°C mL × –3.3°C = –132 cal. Since heat is released, we already know the answer is negative.

104.   **B is correct.** The ammonium nitrate would require energy to dissociate before releasing energy to form water.

105.   **D is correct.** Heat per mole is an intensive property.

106.   **D is correct.** The temperature of the calorimeter is higher than the surroundings throughout the experiment. Heat always moves from hot to cold.

Passage III

107.   **A is correct.** The negative slope on the phase diagram demonstrates that water expands when freezing.

108.   **C is correct.** The line between A and E represents equilibrium of gas and solid.

109.   **A is correct.** Point C in Figure 1 is the critical point, which is the temperature and pressure above which the gas and liquid phases cannot be distinguished.

110.   **D is correct.** Point C in Figure 1 is the critical point, which is the temperature and pressure above which the gas and liquid phases cannot be distinguished.

111.   **B is correct.** The negative slope between the solid and liquid phases of water in Figure 2 represents melting point at different temperatures and pressures. As pressure increases, the temperature decreases moving along the line.

112.   **A is correct.** The normal boiling point is the boiling point at local atmospheric conditions (1 atm). To have a normal boiling point, the triple point must be at a pressure below 1 atm. In that case, the temperature of the triple point will be below the temperature of the normal boiling point.

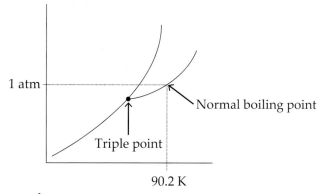

113.   **C is correct.** See the graph.

Stand Alones

114. **A is correct.** During a phase change, temperature, and thus molecular kinetic energy, is constant. Breaking bonds always absorbs energy. Ice cools things when it melts.

115. **A is correct.** The potential energy of the water at the top of the falls becomes kinetic energy as it drops, and then thermal energy at the bottom of the falls. Thus mgh = $Q = mc\Delta T$, or $\Delta T = gh/c$.

EXPLANATIONS TO IN-CLASS EXAM FOR LECTURE 6

Passage I

116. **A is correct.** This is the common ion effect in Reaction 1.

117. **A is correct.** For all trials, at the equivalence point there are Ca^{2+} ions, Na^+ and Cl^- ions. (Trial 1 has no Na^+ ions, but these don't affect pH anyway.) The Ca^{2+} started as a saturated solution. As OH^- ions are removed from solution by the acid, there is no precipitation of $Ca(OH)_2$. When all the OH^- ions are neutralized by the acid, the pH is 7 for all trials. The equivalence point is 7 for all trials. For trials with NaOH, the pH begins higher. More HCl is required to neutralize this extra base. The curves are exactly the same, but the trial one curve starts at a lower pH and requires less HCl.

118. **B is correct.** This is just the normal K_{sp}.

119. **D is correct.** pOH = $-\log[OH^-]$ In this case, the significant OH^- ion contribution comes completely from NaOH which dissociates completely. 1 > pOH > 2   The pH is 14 – pOH = between 12 and 13.

120. **D is correct.** The $Ca(OH)_2$ solution begins as basic, and when the $Ca(OH)_2$ is totally dissolved, it should be neutral. See answer to question #117.

121. **A is correct.** This is the titration of a strong base with a strong acid. See question #117.

Passage II

122. **C is correct.** Since the K_w is higher at 40°C, the hydrogen ion concentration will also be higher. Thus the pH will decrease. Note that the hydrogen ion concentration would have to be 10 times higher in order for the pH to be higher.

123. **C is correct.** Set K_w equal to 1 mole of hydrogen ions times the OH concentration.

124. **B is correct.** As T increases, the hydrogen ion concentration increases.

125. **C is correct.** A proton is lost to form the conjugate base of a Bronsted acid.

126. **C is correct.** The leveling effect in water occurs because water readily accepts all protons from both acids. The equilibrium in water is so far to the right for both reactions that no comparison can be made. Although acetic acid accepts protons from both HCl and $HClO_4$, it does not do so as readily as water (it is a weaker proton acceptor or Bronsted-Lowry base). Thus, an equilibrium is established for both reactions, and the equilibriums can be compared.

127. **A is correct.** Definitional.

Passage III

128. **C is correct.** The pH must be where both indicators can have the proper color.

129. **C is correct.** The lower pK_a of sulfuric acid demonstrates that it is a stronger acid than sulfurous acid. The second proton is not the major contributor to the acid strength, so D is wrong.

130. **D is correct.** The K_b is found by adding the base to water. If the pK_a is known, the pK_b of the conjugate base can be found by subtracting the pK_a from 14. HSO_3^- is the conjugate base of H_2SO_3. The pK_a of H_2SO_3 is given as 1.81. 14 – 1.81 = 12.19.

131. **D is correct.** The lowest pK_a is the strongest acid. You should know that sulfuric acid is stronger than the other acids.

132. **A is correct.** Minus eight for the oxygens, plus two for the hydrogens leaves minus six which must be counter balanced. Minus six for the oxygens, plus two for the hydrogens leaves minus four which must be counter balanced.

133. **C is correct.** We could never raise the pH by adding an acid. Water is the main contributor of H^+. To find the pH, we add the 5×10^{-8} ions contributed by H_2SO_4 to the 1×10^{-7} ions contributed by water. This leaves $1.5 \times 10^{-7}\ H^+$.

134. **D is correct.** This is the titration of a diprotic acid with a strong base.

Stand Alones

135. **A is correct.** Perchloric acid is the strongest acid, thus it has the weakest conjugate base. In oxy acids, the more oxygens, the greater the acid strength.

136. **C is correct.** This is the definition of the half equivalence point.

137. **A is correct.** Use the Henderson-Hasselbalch equation. $pH = pK_a + \log(A^-/HA) => pH = -\log(1.8 \times 10^{-5}) + \log(1/10) => pH = 4.7 - 1 = 3.7$

138. **B is correct.** The conjugate acid has the K_a that equals K_w/K_b.

EXPLANATIONS TO IN-CLASS EXAM FOR LECTURE 7

Passage I

139. **C is correct.** $Cr_2O_7^{2-}$ is reduced to Cr^{3+}. Although this doesn't look like reduction from the charges, Cr in the dichromate has an original oxidation state of +6.

140. **C is correct.** Oxygen is –2. There are 7 oxygens which make –14. The 2– charge on the ion takes care of 2 of the 14 negatives. The 2 chromiums must take care of the other 12. That's +6 for each chromium.

141. **C is correct.** This is simply reading the graph.

142. **B is correct.** For each mole of dichromate that is reduced, 6 moles of Fe are oxidized. The top portion of B gives the number of moles of dichromate reduced times six, which is the number of moles of Fe oxidized. (The equivalence point is where all the iron has been oxidized.) We divide this by the original volume of Fe solution and get the molarity.

143. **A is correct.** The equivalence point is defined as the point when the Fe^{2+} is completely oxidized. Changing the formal potential won't change that definition. The endpoint is when the indicator changes color. This should be at the equivalence point, but it doesn't have to be. The passage says that the formal potential is *lowered* so that the equivalence point and endpoint will coincide. This indicates that the indicator will change color at a low potential. If the formal potential isn't lowered, the indicator will change color early (still at the low potential) before the equivalence point is reached. The passage states that the indicator changes from colorless to violet; choice A. Dichromate ion will still oxidize DAS, but it will do so before oxidizing Fe^{2+}, so choice C is incorrect. Dichromate ion is an oxidizing agent and will not reduce anything, so choice D is incorrect.

144. **A is correct.** Each iron goes from a +2 to a +3 oxidation state by losing one electron. Each chromium goes from a +6 to a +3 oxidation state by gaining 3 electrons.

Passage II

145. **A is correct.** The half reactions must be rearranged in such a fashion that the total voltage is positive (meaning the battery is discharging). This requires reversing the top half reaction. When reversed, this reaction becomes oxidation, which takes place at the anode.

146. **D is correct.** When we recharge the battery, the reactions are both reversed from the positions in question one.

147. **C is correct.** Ni is being reduced, so NiO_2 is the oxidizing agent. The compound with many oxygens is often the oxidizing agent.

148. **A is correct.** The cell has a negative potential and is forced to run in the nonspontaneous direction.

149. **C is correct.** The two half reaction potentials must be added after they have been rearranged to represent the galvanic cell. This means that the first half reaction is reversed. If this potential is applied, the cell can be recharged back to this potential which is the standard potential.

150. **B is correct.** The passage tells us that sodium is at the anode so it is oxidized. Sodium is not normally oxidized to a +2.

151. **D is correct.** Current moves opposite to electrons. Since electrons flow from Half Reaction 1 to 2, current flows from Half Reaction 2 to 1.

Passage III

152. **D is correct.** The reaction quotient is in the same form as the equilibrium constant. Pure solids and liquids should not be used in the law of mass action to solve for the equilibrium constant.

153. **A is correct.** Plug the numbers into the Nernst equation. $(10^2)^2$ is 10^4. The log of 10^4 is 4. Thus the potential is negative and the voltage is twice 0.0592 V.

154. **B is correct.** See the last equation in the passage.

155. **B is correct.** See the last equation in the passage. A 1 M solution of HCl has a pH of 0.

156. **A is correct.** An increase of H^+ by a factor of 10 is a decrease in pH of 1. $E = 0.059 \, (\text{pH}_{test} - \text{pH}_{reference})$ Each decrease in $\text{pH}_{reference}$ of 1 amounts to an increase in E of 0.059 V or 59 mV.

157. **A is correct.** The current will try to equalize the charges in the solutions. Since we have more positive charge on the concentrated side, the current moves to the less concentrated side.

158. **B is correct.** Again, current flows toward the less positive side, which is the basic side, which has less H+ ions.

Stand Alones

159. **D is correct.** You should know this one reduction potential: $2H^+ + 2e^- \rightarrow H_2 \quad E = 0$. When this is added to the oxidation of solid zinc, the potential is positive, which means spontaneous.

160. **C is correct.** At equilibrium, there can be no potential; neither direction of the reaction is favored.

161. **B is correct.** The products and reactants are at standard state, and therefore their potential defines the standard potential $E°$. A is wrong because they are not at equilibrium when $Q = 1$. C is wrong because the potential is positive. D is wrong because Q is at 1 and Q will move toward K. The reaction is spontaneous from here so products will increase, and Q will increase. Therefore, K must be greater than 1.

ANSWERS & EXPLANATIONS

FOR
QUESTIONS IN THE LECTURES

ANSWERS TO THE LECTURE QUESTIONS

Lecture 1	Lecture 2	Lecture 3	Lecture 4	Lecture 5	Lecture 6	Lecture 7
1. C	25. C	49. D	73. C	97. D	121. B	145. C
2. C	26. B	50. A	74. D	98. A	122. C	146. C
3. A	27. A	51. C	75. A	99. B	123. C	147. A
4. B	28. D	52. D	76. D	100. D	124. A	148. A
5. A	29. B	53. D	77. C	101. D	125. A	149. D
6. B	30. C	54. B	78. D	102. C	126. B	150. D
7. B	31. D	55. D	79. B	103. A	127. B	151. D
8. B	32. D	56. A	80. B	104. B	128. A	152. A
9. C	33. B	57. B	81. D	105. D	129. D	153. D
10. D	34. D	58. D	82. A	106. B	130. B	154. C
11. B	35. A	59. A	83. C	107. C	131. C	155. B
12. C	36. A	60. B	84. B	108. C	132. D	156. A
13. B	37. C	61. B	85. C	109. A	133. D	157. D
14. D	38. C	62. C	86. B	110. B	134. B	158. C
15. B	39. B	63. D	87. D	111. D	135. C	159. A
16. A	40. B	64. A	88. C	112. A	136. D	160. B
17. B	41. D	65. D	89. D	113. A	137. D	161. C
18. B	42. C	66. A	90. C	114. C	138. B	162. C
19. B	43. A	67. D	91. D	115. B	139. A	163. D
20. C	44. C	68. D	92. C	116. B	140. B	164. D
21. B	45. C	69. A	93. C	117. C	141. C	165. B
22. C	46. D	70. D	94. A	118. D	142. C	166. A
23. B	47. A	71. A	95. A	119. A	143. D	167. B
24. A	48. A	72. D	96. B	120. D	144. B	168. C

ANSWERS & EXPLANATIONS FOR LECTURE QUESTIONS

1. **C is correct.** A family or group is the name for any vertical column on the periodic table. Of the choices given, only atomic radius increases going down a column. Although electron affinity is a possible choice depending upon the definition used, atomic radius is an unambiguous choice.

2. **C is correct.** The dipole moment will be greatest for the atoms with greatest difference in electronegativity. Based upon periodic trends, H and F will have the greatest dipole moment.

3. **A is correct.** By definition there are 12 amu in one atom of ^{12}C.

4. **B is correct.** Metals are lustrous, but they are also malleable and good conductors of electricity and heat. Silicon is positioned along the diagonal of elements in the periodic table sometimes referred to as metalloids.

5. **A is correct.** This is an isoelectronic series, which means that the number of electrons on each ion is the same. In an isoelectronic series of ions, the nuclear charge increases with increasing atomic number and draws the electrons inward with greater force. The ion with fewest protons produces the weakest attractive force on the electrons and thus has the largest size.

6. **B is correct.** Don't do any complicated calculations. This is the type of problem that everyone will get right, but many will spend too much time trying to be exact. First assume that 100% of the sample is ^{12}C. Now use the formula: moles = grams/molecular weight. This is very close to 4. The 1% that is not ^{12}C is insignificant.

7. **B is correct.** We are looking for an answer that would allow for the prediction of the order of atomic number. If atomic number increases with atomic weight, the scientists could have made accurate predictions.

8. **B is correct.** Sulfur can form four bonds. In choice A, Cl has the wrong number of electrons. In choice C, Se is too large to form stable pi bonds, so it can't double bond. In choice D, fluorine cannot make more than one bond. This question may require a little too much detailed knowledge to be on the MCAT.

---

9. **C is correct.** We start by assuming a 100 gram sample. By dividing grams by molecular weight, we obtain moles. $58.6/16 \approx 3.6$, $2.4/1 = 2.4$, $39/32 = 1.2$. Now we divide through by the lowest number of moles:

   $3.6/1.2 = 3$; $2.4/1.2 = 2$; $1.2/1.2 = 1$. This gives you the molar ratio of each element. Just to reduce the necessary calculations, the question tells you that it is a _neutral_ compound. Nevertheless, MCAT questions with this much calculation occasionally come up, but they are few and far between. Maybe three on one entire exam.

10. **D is correct.** Silicon is too large to form pi bonds like carbon does. In order to complete its octet, it must make four bonds. It makes one bond with each of four oxygens. Each oxygen bonds with two silicon atoms.

11. **B is correct.** C has 12 g/mol and O has 16 g/mol. The total weight of CO_2 is 44 g/mol. Carbon's weight divided by the total weight is $12/44 = 0.27$. We multiply by 100 to get 27%.

12. **C is correct.** When one mole of sulfur dioxide is oxidized, one mole of sulfur trioxide is produced. One mole of sulfur trioxide has a mass of 80 g.

13. **B is correct.** Normally, 34 grams of ammonia (2 moles) could make 28 grams of nitrogen (1 mole), but here, only 26 grams were made. In a reaction that runs to completion, this must be due to lack of CuO.

14. **D is correct.** Each perchlorate ion has a 1– charge giving the copper ion a 2+ charge.

15. **B is correct.** This is an unusual looking reaction because it is a polymerization. Here it is drawn in a more representative form showing the repeated unit of the polymer as the product:

$$nCH_2\!=\!CH_2 \longrightarrow \left(\begin{array}{cc} H & H \\ | & | \\ C & \!-\!C \\ | & | \\ H & H \end{array}\right)_n$$

16. **A is correct.** This reaction has the form A + B → C. This is the form of a combination reaction.

17. **B is correct.** The quickest way to see this is by realizing that atoms like to form ions with electron configurations similar to the nearest noble gas. Of course a noble gas does not have any unpaired electrons. You should recognize that Ca likes to form a 2+ ion not a 1+ ion.

18. **B is correct.** This question borders on requiring too much specific knowledge for the MCAT. The knowledge that the $4s$ and $3d$ orbitals are at the same energy level for the first row transition metals is probably beyond the MCAT. Rather than memorize specific exceptions to the Aufbau principle, answer this question by eliminating that A, C, and D must be wrong. A is wrong because there is no reason to skip the s subshell entirely. C is wrong because it contains the wrong number of electrons. D is wrong because we should be in the $3d$ subshell, not the $4d$ subshell. You may be able to see that, by Hund's rule, each electron would rather take its own orbital than share an orbital at the same energy level with another electron. Thus for Chromium, electrons fill the orbitals like this:

Chromium looks like this: [Ar] $\frac{\uparrow}{4s}$ $\frac{\uparrow}{3d}\ \frac{\uparrow}{3d}\ \frac{\uparrow}{3d}\ \frac{\uparrow}{3d}\ \frac{\uparrow}{3d}$

not like this: [Ar] $\frac{\uparrow\downarrow}{4s}$ $\frac{\uparrow}{3d}\ \frac{\uparrow}{3d}\ \frac{\uparrow}{3d}\ \frac{\uparrow}{3d}\ \frac{}{3d}$

Copper is the only other first row transition metal that breaks the Aufbau principle. Its electron configuration is [Ar] $4s^1\, 3d^{10}$.

19. **B is correct.** According to the Heisenberg uncertainty principle, the kinetic energy of the electrons increases only when intensity is increased by increasing the frequency. Increasing the work function (a) would actually decrease the kinetic energy (see formula). A single photon must have enough energy, or else no electron will be emitted.

20. **C is correct.** The atom must absorb energy in order for one of its electrons to move to a higher energy level orbital.

21. **B is correct.** The principle quantum number (n) represents the energy level of the electron. The lowest energy shell is $n = 1$. As n increases, the shells move farther from the nucleus and energy increases.

22. **C is correct.** Because sulfur is larger than oxygen, sulfur has $3d$ subshells available that allow electrons to form bonds and break the octet rule of the Lewis structure.

23. **B is correct.** Hund's rule says that electrons added to the same subshell will occupy empty orbitals first and the unpaired electrons will have parallel spins.

24. **A is correct.** Since chromium forms more than one oxidation state and aluminum forms only one, chromium requires the variability in number of bonds formed. This means choices C and D are out. Chromium has electrons in the orbitals of the $2p$ subshell, but these are core electrons and not used for making bonds. Chromium has 6 valence electrons, 5 of which are in the orbitals of the $3d$ subshell.

LECTURE 2

25. **C is correct.** You should recognize that 1 mole of gas occupies 22.4 liters at STP, so there is 0.5 moles of gas in the sample. 13 g/0.5 mol = 26 g/mol.

26. **B is correct.** Since density (ρ) is mass (m) divided by volume (V), and mass is moles (n) times molecular weight (MW), we have $(nMW)/V = \rho$. After some algebra we have: MW = $(\rho V)/n$. From the ideal gas law we know that $V/n = RT/P$. Substituting we have answer B.

27. **A is correct.** The number of moles of gas is extra information. If the container began at 11 atm then each gas is contributing a pressure in accordance with its stoichiometric coefficient. When the reaction runs to completion, the only gas in the container is nitrogen dioxide, so the partial pressure of nitrogen dioxide is the total pressure. The volume of the container remains constant, so the pressure is in accordance with the stoichiometric coefficient of nitrogen dioxide.

28. **D is correct.** An ideal gas has a *PV/RT* equal to one. Real volume is greater than predicted by the ideal gas law, and real pressure is less than predicted by the ideal gas law. Volume deviations are due to the volume of the molecules, and pressure deviations are due to the intermolecular forces. Thus, a negative deviation in this ratio would indicate that the intermolecular forces are having a greater affect on the nonideal behavior than the volume of the molecules. (see the graph on page 27)

29. **B is correct.** The force does work on the gas, which means that the internal energy of the gas is increased. Since the internal energy of the gas is increased, and the number of moles remains the same, the temperature, which is average kinetic energy per mole, also increases.

30. **C is correct.** From Graham's law we know that the effusion rate for hydrogen is four times that of oxygen.

$$\frac{H_{2 \text{ effusion rate}}}{O_{2 \text{ effusion rate}}} = \sqrt{\frac{\text{M.W.}_{\text{oxygen}}}{\text{M.W.}_{\text{hydrogen}}}} = \sqrt{\frac{32}{2}} = 4$$

Since we don't know how many moles of gas were initially in container A, nor how many moles effused out, we don't know the ratio of hydrogen to oxygen. However, since we know that four times as many moles of hydrogen effused from container A into B, we know that container B contains four times as many moles of hydrogen. We can neglect any effusion in the reverse direction since the question says a "very short time".

31. **D is correct.** The diffusion rate for NH_3 is 1.5 times that of HCl. If HCl diffuses 4 cm, NH_3 will diffuse 6 cm. 4 cm + 6 cm = 10 cm.

$$\frac{\text{diffusion rate of } NH_3}{\text{diffusion rate of HCl}} = \frac{\sqrt{M_{\text{HCl}}}}{\sqrt{M_{\text{NH}_3}}} = \sqrt{\frac{36.5}{17}} = 1.5$$

32. **D is correct.** At STP, equal volumes of any gas behaving ideally contain the same number or moles.

---

33. **B is correct.** Changing the concentration of the reactants will not change the rate constant. Increasing the concentration of a catalyst will only increase the rate of the reaction if the supply of catalyst is so small that the reactants are waiting for a catalyst. Most of the time on the MCAT, you can assume that the supply of catalyst is large enough so that a change in concentration will not change the reaction rate. (See Biology Lecture 2 for the graph relating reaction rate to enzyme catalysts.) Increasing the amount of catalyst never increases the rate constant. Increasing the temperature will always increase the rate constant, and the rate of the reaction. If the reaction is catalyzed by an enzyme, the enzyme may denature, slowing the reaction; however, the reaction without the enzyme is considered a different reaction.

34. **D is correct.** Catalysts do not directly affect the equilibrium of a reaction. Catalysts do increase the rate of the reverse reaction as well as the forward reaction.

35. **A is correct.** When the concentration of B is doubled, the rate doesn't change. When the concentration of A is doubled, the rate doubles. The reaction is first order overall, and first order with respect to A. By choosing a trial and plugging the values into the rate law, we find that the rate constant has a value of 0.1.

36. **A is correct.** The slow step determines the rate of a reaction.

37. **C is correct.** Exothermicity concerns the thermodynamics of the reaction, and not the rate. You can ignore it. The energy of activation is the energy required for a collision of properly oriented molecules to produce a reaction. This does not change with temperature.

38. **C is correct.** A first order reaction has a constant half life. In the first 15 minutes, 16 out of 33 white dots (compound *X*) turned black, so 15 minutes represents approximately one half life. In the next 15 minutes, the second half life, half of the remaining 17 white dots should turn black. This represents choice C where there are 9 white dots left. Once you identify that 15 minutes is the half life, you should be able to eliminate answer A because there is no change and answer choice B and D because there are very few dots left. Even if you didn't know that a first order reaction has a constant half life, you should know that the reaction will be proportional to the concentration of white dots. In choice B and D, the rate of the reaction hasn't changed in the second 15 minutes even though the concentration of white dots has been reduced after the first 15 minutes, so this can't be right.

39. **B is correct.** For a first order reaction the reaction rate is directly proportional to the concentration of reactant, according to the equation, rate = k[A]. So if the concentration of *cis*-2-butene is doubled, the reaction rate will also double. The rate constant is not affected by changes in the concentrations of reactants.

40. **B is correct.** The concentration of reactants decreases exponentially in a first order reaction. Another way of saying that is that the graph of ln[reactants] will be linear.

41. **D is correct.** Equilibrium will probably shift with temperature. The direction is dictated by thermodynamics. We need more information.

42. **C is correct.** The activation energy is dictated by the reaction itself and doesn't change during the reaction. We will see later that the Gibbs free energy is at a minimum when a reaction is at equilibrium.

43. **A is correct.** By Le Chatelier's principle the equilibrium would shift to the right causing an increase in the forward reaction.

44. **C is correct.** The equilibrium constant is products over reactants with the coefficients as exponents. However, reactants and products in pure liquid and solid phases generally have an exponent of zero, so they are not included in the equilibrium expression.

45. **C is correct.** Initially there are no products, so the reverse reaction begins at zero. As the reactants are used up, the forward reaction slows down. Equilibrium is the point where the rates equalize.

46. **D is correct.** A must be false because some of both solids must be present in order for equilibrium to exist. B and C are false because, as part of a solid molecule, calcium atoms have no way of leaving their respective beakers (other than a negligible amount of vapor pressure from their respective solids). D is true because when CaO in Beaker II combines with CO_2 gas in the container, $CaCO_3$ is formed in Beaker II. An equilibrium is achieved in both beakers.

47. **A is correct.** Pure solids are not included in the equilibrium expression.

48. **A is correct.** "K_p is equal to the partial pressure of CO_2" is the equilibrium expression for this reaction. If K_p were less than the partial pressure of CO_2, the reaction would want to go to the left, but there would be no CaO to react to form $CaCO_3$. Regarding choice D, although solid CaO is required to achieve equilibrium, solid CaO could be formed with the decomposition of $CaCO_3$.

LECTURE 3

49. **D is correct.** The second law of thermodynamics states that a heat engine cannot have 100% efficiency in converting heat to work in a cyclical process. An air conditioner is a heat engine running backwards. Thus an air conditioner must expel more heat than it takes in when it runs perpetually. A specially made air conditioner could initially cool the room, but to cool the room permanently, it must expel the heat to a heat reservoir.

50. **A is correct.** I. The temperature difference is directly proportional to the distance between two points of the same material.

$$\frac{Q}{t} = kA \frac{T_h - T_c}{L}$$

II. The rate of heat flow is constant throughout the blocks, or else heat would build up at the point of slowest flow. III. Since heat flow rate is constant, changing the order of the blocks won't change the rate of heat flow.

51. **C is correct.** There is no type of heat transfer called transduction. Conduction through the air would take a very long time and be very inefficient. Convection would require some type of air current or breeze. Radiation is as fast as light, and is the correct explanation.

52. **D is correct.** Unless the box and the incline are at different temperatures, there can be no heat. Energy transfer due to friction is work.

53. **D is correct.** Work is not a state function, thus we must know the path in order to calculate it.

54. **B is correct.** The rate at which heat is conducted is directly proportional to the difference in temperatures between the hot and cold reservoirs. In December, the difference is $25 - 5 = 20$ degrees. That's the largest difference on the table.

55. **D is correct.** Since the container is at rest and has constant volume, no work is done.

56. **A is correct.** The efficiency of a thermodynamic process describes what percent of the input energy is converted into work. No thermodynamic process can be 100 percent efficient.

---

57. **B is correct.** To find the enthalpy of the reaction we use the following formula:

$$\Delta H^\circ_{\text{reaction}} = \Delta H^\circ_{f\ \text{products}} - \Delta H^\circ_{f\ \text{reactants}}$$

The table gives these enthalpies. Don't forget that enthalpy is an extensive process, so quantity matters. We must multiply the enthalpies by the number of moles formed for each molecule. The enthalpy of formation of O_2 is zero, like that of any other molecule in its elemental form at 298 K.

58. **D is correct.** The definition of enthalpy is: $H \equiv U + PV$

59. **A is correct.** A catalyst affects the kinetics of a reaction and not the thermodynamics.

60. **B is correct.** Altering the ratio of the rates of a reaction will change the equilibrium. Removing thermal energy from an exothermic reaction will <u>probably</u> push it forward according to Le Chatelier's principle, since heat is a product. Answer C and D concern catalysts and will not change the ratio of the forward and reverse reaction.

61. **B is correct.** This is Hess's law. We reverse the equation for graphite, so that graphite is a product. In doing so, we must also reverse the sign of the enthalpy. Now we add the two equations and their enthalpies. Don't forget that we must multiply by two for the two moles. Enthalpy is an extensive property.

62. **C is correct.** Condensation must occur to form liquid water. Condensation is an exothermic process, so the formation of liquid water should be more exothermic than the formation of water vapor. The standard enthalpy of formation of water vapor will not be an endothermic process, so D is wrong.

63. **D is correct.** The reaction coordinate diagram below shows the energy of activation for an endothermic reaction is greater than for an exothermic reaction.

64. **A is correct.** Increasing the temperature increases the energy available to both the forward and the reverse reactions, enabling both to more easily overcome the activation energy. Just so you know, because the reverse reaction is endothermic, its rate will increase more. That's what causes the increase in the concentration of reactants predicted by LeChatelier's law.

---

65. **D is correct.** According to the equation $\Delta G = \Delta H - T\Delta S$, to guarantee that a reaction is spontaneous, enthalpy of the system must decrease and entropy of the system must increase.

66. **A is correct.** The entropy of the universe will increase in a spontaneous reaction. The entropy of a system may or may not increase.

67. **D is correct.** Energy is always required to break a bond.

68. **D is correct.** The process of building a bridge is an ordering process.

69. **A is correct.** Since the number of moles of gas is decreasing with the forward reaction, positional entropy is decreasing. This almost always means that overall system entropy is decreasing. Since the MCAT doesn't distinguish between positional entropy and any other kind of entropy, you can always view a reaction with decreasing number of gas particles as decreasing in entropy and vice versa.

70. **D is correct.** Bonds are formed when water condenses, so energy is released and ΔH is negative. The water molecules become less random, so ΔS is negative. Condensation occurs spontaneously at 25°C (room temperature), so ΔG is negative. Notice that you can answer this question without being given any numbers.

71. **A is correct.** $\Delta G = \Delta H - T\Delta S$. For a spontaneous reaction, ΔG must be negative. As T is increased, the negative part of the equation increases in magnitude. If T is increased enough, eventually ΔG will switch from positive to negative. Changing the pressure will have no effect on a nongaseous reaction that takes place in a solution.

72. **D is correct.** At the boiling point, benzene is in equilibrium between the liquid and gas phases. At equilibrium, ΔG for a reaction is equal to zero. S is positive for the reaction shown because gases are more random than liquids.

LECTURE 4

73. **C is correct.** One liter of water weighs 1 kg; one liter of this solution weighs 1.006 kilograms. If we assume that the volume of water changes very little when NaCl is added, then about 0.006 kg, or 6 g, of NaCl are in each liter of solution. The molecular weight of NaCl is 58.6. 6 grams is about 0.1 moles. (By the way, even if the salt increased the volume of 1 liter of solution by 10 cubic centimeters, the molarity would still be slightly greater than 0.099 M. So this is a good approximation. Remember, for dilute solutions, the volume of the solute is negligible.)

74. **D is correct.** Remember that like dissolves like. Water is polar, and will dissolve polar and ionic substances. A, B, C are ions, ionic compounds, or capable of hydrogen bonding. Carbon tetrachloride is a nonpolar molecule.

75. **A is correct.** For all practical purposes, choices A and B are the same. However, since the question asks you to compare them, a one molar solution is 1 mole of NaCl in slightly less than a liter of water. This is because the NaCl requires some volume. A one molal solution is one mole in one full liter of water. (This question assumes that a liter of water has a mass of 1 kg. This is true at 1 atm and approximately 3°C. Water at 1 atm is at its most dense state at a temperature of slightly over 3°C.) There are 55.5 moles of water in a liter (grams/molecular weight = moles). $1/100 = 0.01$ and $1/50 = 0.02$. Thus a solution with a mole fraction of 0.01 is closer to a 0.5 molar solution than a 1 molar solution. The last answer choice is less than one mole of NaCl in one liter of water.

76. **D is correct.** You should know that 1 atm is equal to 760 torr. Since the partial pressure of nitrogen is 600, the mole fraction of nitrogen is 0.79. This means that the percentages given are by particle and not by mass. D would be true if the percentages were based on mass. If you chose B, you need to go back to Lecture 3 and review standard molar volume.

77. **C is correct.** No solution is formed, so either B or C must be correct. B is not true.

78. **D is correct.** First calculate the number of moles of $MgCl_2$

$$\text{moles} = \text{grams/MW} = 19\ g/95\ g/mol = 0.2\ mol$$

0.2 moles of $MgCl_2$ will dissociate to produce 0.4 moles of Cl^- ions.

$$[Cl^-] = \text{moles/liters} = 0.4\ mol/0.5\ L = 0.8\ M$$

79. **B is correct.** First find the number of moles of HCl.

$$\text{moles} = (mol/L)(L) = (3\ mol/L)(0.8\ L) = 2.4\ moles$$

Now find the number of liters needed to make the solution 1 molar

$$L = mol/mol/L = 2.4\ mol/1\ M = 2.4\ L$$

Now be careful. You already have 0.8 liters of solution, so in order to get 2.4 L, you have to add 1.6 L of water.

80. **B is correct.** A strong electrolyte is a substance that dissociates completely in water to form ions, which can then conduct electricity. Carbon dioxide does not dissociate to form ions so it is not an electrolyte.

---

81. **D is correct.** The change in entropy is positive in solution formation and Gibbs free energy is negative in a spontaneous reaction. From $\Delta G = \Delta H_{sol} - T\Delta S$ we see that the heat of solution may be either positive or negative in this case. The heat of hydration is the separation of water molecules (which requires energy) and the formation of bonds between the ions and water molecules (which releases energy). Thus, the value of the heat of hydration could be either positive or negative. The actual heat of hydration is –783 kJ/mol making the heat of solution +3 kJ/mol.

82. **A is correct.** At constant pressure, change in enthalpy is equal to heat.

83. **C is correct.** The vapor pressure of solution might be lower than just one of the pure substances but not the other. You can see this from the graph below.

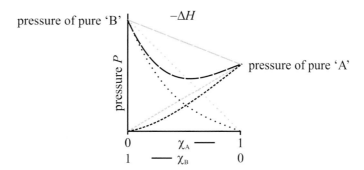

84. **B is correct.** You should notice that B and C are opposites, so one of them must be the answer. Molecules break free of the surface of a liquid and add to the vapor pressure when they have sufficient kinetic energy to break the intermolecular bonds.

85. **C is correct.** The solution had to deviate from Raoult's law and therefore could not be ideal. Since it deviated negatively from Raoult's law, the heat of solution is exothermic.

86. **B is correct.** In an ideal solution, the vapor pressure will be somewhere in between the vapor pressures of the solute and the solvent, depending on their relative mole fractions.

87. **D is correct.** Try testing the answer choices to see which one is right.

$$(0.2)(800 \text{ mmHg}) + (0.8)(300 \text{ mmHg}) = 400 \text{ mmHg.}$$

88. **C is correct.** If heat is released, the solvation process must be exothermic. The breaking of bonds is an endothermic process and the forming of bonds is an exothermic process, so in order for the process to be exothermic overall, the bonds formed must be stronger than the bonds that were broken.

---

89. **D is correct.** Think in terms of mole fraction. The concentration of solvent is at a minimum when the concentration of solute is at a maximum.

90. **C is correct.** This is the common ion effect (very important for the MCAT).

91. **D is correct.** We can compare the solubilities in one liter of water. For the compounds that dissociate into two parts, the smallest K_{sp} will be the least soluble and first to precipitate. This is $BaSO_4$. We don't have to compare $BaSO_4$ with Ag_2SO_4 because Ag_2SO_4 dissociates into three particles. This means that if their K_{sp}s were equal, then Ag_2SO_4 would be more soluble than $BaSO_4$. However, the K_{sp} for $BaSO_4$ is much lower, so we know for sure that it is less soluble.

92. **C is correct.** Gases become more soluble under greater pressure and lower temperatures. The pressure must be the partial pressure of the soluble gas. Adding an inert gas would not change the partial pressure of oxygen in this example. Shaking the can is adding energy, and is similar to heating the can. Think about shaking a can of soda.

Lecture Question Expls.

93. **C is correct.** The solubility of $BaCO_3$ in 3 liters of water is found from the equilibrium expression:

$$K_{sp} = [Ba^{2+}][CO_3^{2-}]$$
$$1.6 \times 10^{-9} = [x][x]$$
$$x = 4 \times 10^{-5}$$

This is the saturated concentration in mol/L. We multiply this by 3 liters to get the total number of moles.

94. **A is correct.** The solubility product is created by multiplying the concentrations of the products of the solvation while turning the coefficients into exponents.

95. **A is correct.** The K_{sp} expression is as follows.

$$K_{sp} = [Pb^{2+}][Cl^-]^2$$

For every $PbCl_2$ in solution, there is 1 Pb^{2+} and 2 Cl^-. So $[Pb^{2+}] = x$ and $[Cl^-] = 2x$.

$$K_{sp} = (x)(2x)^2 = (x)(4x^2) = 4x^3$$

96. **B is correct.** NaF is very soluble, so when it is added to the solution, it will introduce more Na^+ and F^- ions. The introduction of extra F^- ions will shift the CaF_2 equilibrium toward solid CaF_2, which removes Ca^{2+} ions from the solution.

LECTURE 5

97. **D is correct.** First figure out the heat evolved by the reaction using $q = mc\Delta T$ =>

$$q = 250 \text{ grams} \times 4.18 \text{ J/g } ^\circ C \times 1 \,^\circ C \approx 1050 \text{ joules}$$

Next divide by moles of NaCl (20 grams is about ⅓ of a mole). This gives you 3150 joules, which is equal to 3 kJ. Since the temperature went down, the reaction is endothermic with positive enthalpy. Notice all the rounding. This problem should have been done with very little math.

98. **A is correct.** Remember, $\Delta E = w + q$. There is no work done because there is no change in volume in a bomb calorimeter. Thus, the total change in energy is heat. Heat is not enthalpy. Heat equals enthalpy at constant pressure. The pressure is not constant in a bomb calorimeter.

99. **B is correct.** I is false because objects cannot contain heat, and because the same amount of the same substance can have the same amount of energy and be at different temperatures. Nevertheless, this is treading the MCAT edge of required knowledge. Don't feel too bad if you chose C. II is false. Different phases will have different specific heats. III is true.

100. **D is correct.** A, B, and C are false. Temperature is proportional to kinetic energy not just velocity, so more mass per molecule does not make a difference. Boiling point does not make sense; substance A might be water and substance B ice. Answer C mistakenly relies upon speed and not kinetic energy for temperature. D is the correct choice by process of elimination. The more ways that a substance has to absorb energy, the more heat it can absorb with the least change in temperature.

101. **D is correct.** No energy transfer takes place, so there is no heat or work.

102. **C is correct.** Aluminum has the largest value for specific heat, which means that it can absorb the most energy while showing the smallest temperature change.

103. **A is correct.** Since the specific heat for Au is one-third as large as the specific heat for Cu, one-third as much heat will be required to get the same temperature change.

104. **B is correct.** Use the equation $q = mc\Delta T$. The change in temperature is $31 - 26 = 5$. Don't forget to convert 1.8 kJ into 1800 J.

$$m = q/c\Delta T = (1800)/(0.90)(5) = 400 \text{ g.}$$

---

105. **D is correct.** We can solve this problem by summing the q's on the heat curve. The heat is positive because heat is added to the system.

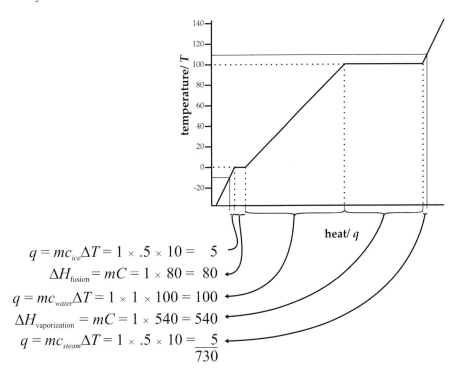

$$q = mc_{ice}\Delta T = 1 \times .5 \times 10 = 5$$
$$\Delta H_{fusion} = mC = 1 \times 80 = 80$$
$$q = mc_{water}\Delta T = 1 \times 1 \times 100 = 100$$
$$\Delta H_{vaporization} = mC = 1 \times 540 = 540$$
$$q = mc_{steam}\Delta T = 1 \times .5 \times 10 = \underline{5}$$
$$730$$

106. **B is correct.** The added energy goes into breaking bonds, and as is demonstrated by the heat curve above, the temperature remains constant until all the ice is melted. Entropy increases moving to the right on the heat curve.

107. **C is correct.** This is just a phase diagram with pressure on a log scale. There are many ways to manipulate the phase diagram. Don't be intimidated. Try to compare it to what you know.

108. **C is correct.** Above the critical point, liquid and vapor water have the same density. The critical temperature will be the highest temperature on the graph where the two lines meet.

109. **A is correct.** The area in the dashed line is the point where water is changing phase. Like along line RS, in the dashed line area water and steam exist in equilibrium.

110. **B is correct.** The heat of fusion is the amount of heat that must be added to convert one mole of a substance completely from solid to liquid. Benzene has a molecular mass of 78, so the sample contains 1 mole. The flat line on the heating curve represents the heat being added while the phase changes from solid to liquid, so the heat of fusion can be found by measuring the length of the flat line. So 14.4 kJ – 3.5 kJ = 10.9 kJ.

111. **D is correct.** At the boiling point, any added energy is used to break intermolecular bonds and not to increase kinetic energy, so while the water is boiling, there is no temperature increase.

112. **A is correct.** Heating the solid will raise its temperature which will eventually melt it. Compressing the solid will raise the pressure on the solid which will most likely keep it a solid. A few substances like water will melt under pressure, but for most solids, pressure changes a liquid to a solid. It is the random kinetic energy of the molecules of a solid and not the uniform translational motion kinetic energy of the solid that increases its temperature and would make it melt.

---

113. **A is correct.** Boiling point elevation is a colligative property. The more particles the higher the boiling point. NaCl dissociates so that the normality is twice the molarity. Thus, the least number of particles will be in 0.5 M glucose solution.

114. **C is correct.** The osmotic pressure will not create a difference in the buoyant force. The equation for buoyant force ($F_b = \rho Vg$) does not include osmotic pressure. Seawater has greater density because salts are heavier than water, and the salt added does not create an appreciable difference in volume.

115. **B is correct.** You must recognize from the formula that glycerol does not dissociate; it is not ionic. Then use $\Delta T = K_f m$, which gives you a molality of 10. Molality is moles of solute divided by kg of solvent. Assume that 1 liter of water has a mass of 1 kg. Thus 100 moles of glycerol are required. Glycerol has a molecular weight of 62 g/mol. 6200 g = 6.2 kg.

116. **B is correct.** The reaction is exothermic because the temperature increased. An exothermic reaction makes stronger bonds. Stronger bonds lower vapor pressure. A lower vapor pressure means more energy is needed to raise the vapor pressure to equal atmospheric pressure. Thus, a lower vapor pressure means a higher boiling point.

117. **C is correct.** The question has a lot of extra information to mislead you. A high value for h indicates a high osmotic pressure in the solution. From the formula for osmotic pressure, $\Pi = iMRT$, we know that a high osmotic pressure corresponds to a high molarity. A high molarity means many particles per gram of protein placed into the solution. Thus a high osmotic pressure means a low molecular weight.

118. **D is correct.** The freezing point depression formula is $\Delta T = kmi$. We know that k is 1.86. The molar mass of $CaCl_2$ is 111, so there are 3 moles of salt in 1 kg of water and m is 3. $CaCl_2$ dissociates into 3 particles, so i is 3.

$$\Delta T = (1.86)(3)(3) = 16.7°C$$

119. **A is correct.** The freezing point expression is $\Delta T = kmi$. The solute is non-polar, so i is 1 and we can leave it out. Now let's remember the definition of molality.

$$m = \text{(moles of solute)/(kg of solvent)}$$

but (moles of solute) = (grams of solute)/(molar mass of solute)

Substituting, we get $\Delta T = (k)$(grams of solute)/(molar mass of solute)(kg of solvent)

If you solve for the molar mass, you get choice A.

120. **D is correct.** Boiling point is a colligative property, which means that it depends only on the number of particles in solution, not on their specific properties. Both NaF and KCl dissociate completely into 2 particles each, so they will have the same effect on the boiling point of water.

LECTURE 6

121. **B is correct.** The conjugate acid is the molecule after it accepts a proton.

122. **C is correct.** By definition, a Lewis base donates a pair of electrons.

123. **C is correct.** NH_4^+ is an acid. The strongest base is the conjugate of the weakest acid.

124. **A is correct.** An amino acid can act as an acid or a base depending upon the pH. Although the conjugate base of sulfuric acid is amphoteric, sulfuric acid cannot accept a proton and is not amphoteric.

125. **A is correct.** The electron withdrawing group will further polarize the O-H bond, and polarization increases acidity in aqueous solution.

126. **B is correct.** The pH of solution B is 7. The pH of solution A is between 4 and 5. The difference in pH must be between 7 – 5 = 2 and 7 – 4 = 3. Choice B is the only one in that range.

127. **B is correct.** In a coordinate covalent bond, one atom donates an electron pair to share with another atom. In this case, ammonia has the unbonded pair to donate to boron, so ammonia is the Lewis base and boron is the Lewis acid.

128. **A is correct.** In Reaction 1, water accepts a proton to become H_3O^+, so it is acting as a Bronsted-Lowry base. In Reaction 2, water gives up a proton to become OH⁻, so it acts as a Bronsted-Lowry acid.

129. **D is correct.** K_b is the reaction of the conjugate base with water.

130. **B is correct.** HBr dissociates completely, so the concentration of H⁺ ions will be equal to the concentration of solution. The $-\log(0.1) = 1$.

131. **C is correct.** The K_b for $NaHCO_3$ is $K_w/K_a = K_b \approx 0.25 \times 10^{-7}$. We can set up the equilibrium expression:

$$K_b = \frac{[OH^-][H_2CO_3]}{[HCO_3^-]}$$

$$0.25 \times 10^{-7} = \frac{[x][x]}{[1 - x]}$$ This x is insignificant.

$$2.5 \times 10^{-8} = x^2$$

$$1.5 \times 10^{-4} = x$$

Thus, the pOH = between 3 and 4. Subtracting from 14, the pH = between 10 and 11.

132. **D is correct.** Each unit of pH is a tenfold increase of acidity.

133. **D is correct.** You should recognize CN^- as the conjugate base of a weak acid. Choices A, B, and C are conjugates of strong acids, and thus weaker bases.

134. **B is correct.** BrO^- is the conjugate base of $HBrO$, so you can find the base dissociation constant K_b by dividing. $1 \times 10^{-14}/2 \times 10^{-9}$. You get 0.5×10^{-5}, which is the same as 5×10^{-6}.

135. **C is correct.** If the pH is 10, the pOH must be 4. If the pOH is 4, then the hydroxide ion concentration must be $10^{-4}\ M$.

136. **D is correct.** Acetate ion, $C_2H_3O_2^-$, is the conjugate base of a weak acid, so it will act as a base in solution. Sodium ion, Na^+, is the conjugate acid of a strong base, so it is neutral in solution.

---

137. **D is correct.** The pH starts basic so a base is being titrated. It ends very acidic so a strong acid is titrating.

138. **B is correct.** A buffer is made from equal amounts of an acid and its conjugate. The buffer works best when the pH = pK_a. $-\log(8.3 \times 10^{-7})$ = between 6 and 7. 8.3 is close to ten, making the pK_a closer to 6.

139. **A is correct.** An indicator generally changes color within plus or minus one pH point of its pK_a.

140. **B is correct.** The concentration of the conjugate base of the first acid is the greatest at the first equivalence point.

141. **C is correct.** The equivalence point of a titration of a weak acid with a strong base will always be greater than 7. It is the same as adding the conjugate base of the acid to pure water. 14 is way too basic. Pure 1 M NaOH has a pH of 14.

142. **C is correct.** A buffered solution is formed when equal amounts of a weak acid and its conjugate base are present in a solution. Acetic acid is a weak acid and the acetate ion is its conjugate.

143. **D is correct.** HCO_3^- can act as a Bronsted Lowry acid and give up a hydrogen ion to become CO_3^{2-}. It can also act as a Lewis base and donate an electron pair to a hydrogen ion to become H_2CO_3. It is amphoteric because it can act as an acid or base. It is not polyprotic because it has only one hydrogen.

144. **B is correct.** From the Henderson-Hasselbalch equation, you can see that when a weak acid and its conjugate base are present in a solution in equal amounts, the pH will be equal to the pK_a. If you take the negative logarithm of 8.0×10^{-5}, it will be between 4 and 5. That's choice B.

LECTURE 7

145. **C is correct.** Each oxygen has an oxidation state of –2, and hydrogen has an oxidation state of +1. In order for the ion to have a 1– charge, the sulfur must have a +6 oxidation state. (Notice that oxidation states are given as +n, and actual charges are given as n+.)

146. **C is correct.** Aluminum begins as +3 and ends as 0, while carbon begins as 0 and ends as +4.

147. **A is correct.** The Zn is oxidized from an oxidation state of 0 to +2. Thus, it is the reducing agent.

148. **A is correct.** Both A and D cannot be true, so the answer must be A or D. The trickiest part of this problem is to know that lead is comfortable at +2 and sulfur, being in the oxygen family, is comfortable at –2; thus these are their oxidation states when they are together. But when they are with oxygen, the –2 of the oxygen rules.

149. **D is correct.** An example of where this is false is:

$$2HCl + Zn \rightarrow ZnCl_2 + H_2$$

Here each atom of the reducing agent, zinc, loses two electrons, and the hydrogen atom of the oxidizing agent, HCl, gains one electron. Of course, there must be two hydrogens for each zinc.

150. **D is correct.** The two oxygens in NO_2^- have a total oxidation number of –4, so nitrogen must have an oxidation number of +3 to get a total of –1 on the polyatomic ion. The three oxygens in NO_3^- have a total oxidation number of –6, so nitrogen must have an oxidation number of +5 to get a total of –1 on the polyatomic ion. Since the oxidation state is increasing from +3 to +5, electrons are being lost and oxidation is taking place.

151. **D is correct.** None of the oxidation states are changed during the course of this acid-base neutralization reaction, so no redox takes place.

152. **A is correct.** Don't forget, the oxidation states for Cl and Br in Cl_2 and Br_2 are zero by definition because the two elements are in their uncombined states. Chlorine gains electrons, so it is reduced. Since it is reduced, it is the oxidizing agent. Bromine loses electrons, so it is oxidized.

---

153. **D is correct.** Positive ions move across the salt bridge to the cathode. You can remember this because the salt bridge is used to balance the charges. Since negative electrons move to the cathode, positive ions must balance the charge by moving to the cathode.

154. **C is correct.** The forward and reverse reaction rates are only equal at equilibrium, and their rate constants are rarely equal.

155. **B is correct.** This question requires knowledge of the equation: $\Delta G° = -RT \ln(K)$. This equation is a statement about the relationship between $\Delta G°$ and K at a specific temperature. If $\Delta G° = 0$, then $K = 1$. The standard state for an aqueous solution is $1\ M$ concentrations.

156. **A is correct.** The strongest reducing agent is the one most easily oxidized; thus we must reverse the equations and the signs of the potentials.

157. **D is correct.** Although a both a Galvanic cell and an electrolytic cell can have a positive potential, only an electrolytic cell can have a negative potential.

158. **C is correct.** The potential given are reduction potentials. Since copper is reduced, we can use its potential (0.15 V) as written. Tin is oxidized, so we have to change the sign before we calculate. The total potential is 0.15 V + 0.14 V = 0.29 V. Notice that we ignore the coefficients when we do cell potential calculations.

159. **A is correct.** You can use the Nernst equation here, or you can just think about LeChatelier's law. As the concentration of products increases, the reaction will become less spontaneous. The less spontaneous the reaction, the lower the reaction potential.

160. **B is correct.** A galvanic cell generates power via a spontaneous reaction, so $\Delta G°$ must be less than zero. From the expression $\Delta G° = -RT \ln(K)$, you can figure out that if $\Delta G°$ is negative, then K must be greater than 1.

161. **C is correct.** Reactions in galvanic cells are always spontaneous. To find the reaction for this cell we must flip the more negative half reaction. Now we have a spontaneous cell.

$$Al^{3+} + 3e^- \rightarrow Al \qquad -1.66$$
$$Mg \rightarrow Mg^{2+} + 2e^- \qquad \underline{2.37}$$
$$0.71$$

We also have to multiply the aluminum reaction by 2 and the magnesium reaction by 3. Notice, however, that we do not multiply their potentials.

$$2Al^{3+} + 3Mg \rightarrow 3Mg^{2+} + 2Al \qquad E° = 0.71 \text{ V}$$

Since the potential for this cell does not equal this, the conditions must not be standard.

162. **C is correct.** Reduction always takes place at the cathode in any cell. This means that the cathode gains electrons.

163. **D is correct.** A concentration cell is a special type of galvanic cell. It is always spontaneous. The concentrations in the cell even out at equilibrium.

164. **D is correct.** In this cell the cathode has the greater concentration because electrons flow toward it to reduce the number of cations. Also in a concentration cell $E° = 0$, since the reduction half reaction is simply the reverse of the oxidation half reaction. $n = 1$ because only one electron is transferred in each reaction. x/y must be a fraction so that the log will be negative and E will be positive. Thus we have:

$$E = -(0.06/1)\log(0.1/y) = 0.12$$

$$y = 10 \text{ so that } x/y = 10^{-2}.$$

165. **B is correct.** Use units to solve the problem. We want to go from current to grams. Current is C/s. F is coulombs per mole of electrons. For every mole of electrons there is one mole of silver. The molecular weight of silver is 107.8 g/mol

$$C/s \times s = C \quad \Rightarrow \quad C \times \text{mol/C} = \text{mol} \quad \Rightarrow \quad \text{mol} \times \text{grams/mol} = \text{grams}$$

so:

$$i \times t \times (1/F) \times 107.8 = \text{grams}$$

166. **A is correct.** Remember, $I = Q/t$. The charge Q is $(96,500)(0.01) = 965$ C. The time t in seconds is $(5)(60) = 300$. So $Q/t = 965/300 = 3$. The answer is rounded to 3 because there is only 1 significant digit in some of the numbers used in the calculation.

167. **B is correct.** If a voltage is applied to a solution containing Na^+ and H_2O, the H_2O will take the electrons first because it has a larger reduction potential. As long as there is H_2O present, the aqueous sodium will not react.

168. **C is correct.** Ag^{2+} gains an electron to become Ag^+, so it is reduced (LEO the lion says GER). Reduction takes place at the cathode (ANOX/REDCAT).

PHOTO CREDITS

Covers

Front cover, hydrogen fuel cell, Electrolysis concept: © TiaClara/iStockphoto.com

Back cover, Chemical reaction: © E. R. Degginger/Science Source

Chapter 1

Pg. 2, Mole of carbon: © Andrew Lambert Photography/ Photo Researchers, Inc

Pg. 3, Metals malleability: © Alexey Tkachenko/ iStockphoto.com

Pg. 3, Calcium: © Charles D. Winters/Photo Researchers, Inc

Pg. 3, Magnesium: © Charles D. Winters/Photo Researchers, Inc

Pg. 3, Lithium: © Charles D. Winters/Photo Researchers, Inc

Pg. 4, Phosphorus: © Charles D. Winters/Photo Researchers, Inc

Pg. 4, Granulated mineral sulfur: © Dean Turner/ iStockphoto.com

Pg. 5, Flasks containing bromine and iodine: © Charles D. Winters/Photo Researchers, Inc

Pg. 15, Potassium with water: © Charles D. Winters/Photo Researchers, Inc

Pg. 16, A decomposition reaction: © Andrew Lambert Photography/Photo Researchers, Inc

Pg. 17, Candle wax: © Krystian Kaczmarski/iStockphoto. com

Pg. 17, Amethyst: © Besedin/iStockphoto.com

Pg. 23, Max Planck: © Science Source/Photo Researchers, Inc

Pg. 24, Early photoelectric cell: © Sheila Terry/Photo Researchers, Inc

Chapter 2

Pg. 27, Crab Nebula: © European Southern Observatory/ Photo Researchers, Inc.

Pg. 28, Orange balloons: © David Taylor/Photo Researchers, Inc

Pg. 30, Scuba divers: © Miguel Angelo Silva/iStockphoto. com

Pg. 32, Ammonia reacting with hydrochloric acid: © Charles D. Winters/Photo Researchers, Inc

Pg. 33, Bad dog: © Diane Diederich/iStockphoto.com

Pg. 35, Particle collision: © Victor de Schwanberg/Photo Researchers, Inc

Pg. 36, Magnesium reacting with Hydrochloric Acid: © Charles D. Winters/Photo Researchers, Inc.

Pg. 37, Ignite a match: © Sunnybeach/iStockphoto.com

Pg. 41, The Dartford Crossing: © Ian Hamilton/Istockphoto. com

Pg. 44, Indigestion tablets: © Gusto Productions/Photo Researchers, Inc.

Pg. 47, Nitric acid and copper react: © E. R. Degginger/ Photo Researchers, Inc.

Pg. 49, Pouring cement: © DeepDesertPhoto/Veer.com

Pg. 52, Haber process: © Federico Rostagno/Istockphoto.com

Pg. 53, Sunglasses: © Krzysztof Gawor/Istockphoto.com

Chapter 3

Pg. 61, Hot cup of coffee: © Studiocasper/iStockphoto.com

Pg. 67, Sterling engine: © Used by permission of www.stirlingengine.com

Pg. 70, Glass of water: © Robert Payne/iStockphoto.com

Pg. 72, Thermometer: © alxpin/iStockphoto.com

Pg. 74, Heat of hydration of copper sulphate: © Martyn F. Chillmaid / Photo Researchers, Inc.

Pg. 76, Computer interface measuring temperature: © Martin Shields/Photo Researchers, Inc.

Pg. 80, Coffee cup and saucer falling to floor (multiple exposure): © Ryan McVay/Gettyimages.com

Chapter 4

Pg. 87, Solutions: © ElementalImaging/iStockphoto.com

Pg. 88, Aerosol spray: © Dorling Kindersley/Gettyimages. com

Pg. 88, Illuminating the cuvette: © Charles D. Winters/Photo Researchers, Inc

Pg. 89, Lightening: © Salih Külcü/iStockphoto.com

Pg. 90, Drinking too much water: © Jacom Stephens/ iStockphoto.com

Pg. 92, Iron (II) sulphate solution: © Martyn F. Chillmaid/ Photo Researchers, Inc.

Pg. 93, Cold pack: © Dana Kelley

Pg. 94, Puddle: © Patricia Hogan/iStockphoto.com

Pg. 95, Boiling water: © Dorling Kindersley/Gettyimages. com

Pg. 98, Salt cave: © MickyWiswedel/iStockphoto.com

Pg. 98, Chemical powder to a blue solution in a beaker: © ElementalImaging/iStockphoto.com

Pg. 100, Oil and water: © Charles D. Winters/Photo Researchers, Inc

Pg. 101, Soda pouring: © Arthur Carlo Franco/iStockphoto. com

Pg. 102, Manatees and power plants: © Mark Conlin/ Gettyimages.com

Chapter 5

Pg. 106, Vickers Machine Gun: © Olga Milkina/iStockphoto. com

Pg. 107, Low-key eye: © Knape/iStockphoto.com

Pg. 108, Beach buckets: © Daniela Andreea Spyropoulos/ iStockphoto.com

Pg. 109, Turkey frying in an outdoor deep fryer: © Thomas Shortell/iStockphoto.com

Pg. 110, Bomb calorimeter: © Charles D. Winters/Photo Researchers, Inc

Pg. 112, Three ice cubes: © Okea/iStockphoto.com

Pg. 113, Dry ice: © Charles D. Winters/Photo Researchers, Inc

Pg. 114, Heavy water: © Charles D. Winters/Photo Researchers, Inc

Pg. 118, Albumin: © Antonia Reeve/Photo Researchers, Inc

Chapter 6

Pg. 123, Acid rain: © David Woodfall/Gettyimages.com

Pg. 124, Facade of St. Bartholomews Church: © John Kaprielian/Photo Researchers, Inc.

Pg. 124, Batteries: © Dana Kelley

Pg. 124, Lemon: © Dana Kelley

Pg. 124, Apple: © Marek Mnich/iStockphoto.com

Pg. 124, Bananas: © Dana Kelley

Pg. 124, Milk: © craftvision/iStockphoto.com

Pg. 124, Water: © Dana Kelley

Pg. 124, Baking soda: © Dana Kelley

Pg. 124, Egg: © Anthia Cumming/iStockphoto.com

Pg. 124, Soap: © DNY59/iStockphoto.com

Pg. 124, Ammonia: © Dana Kelley

Pg. 124, Bleach: © Dana Kelley

Pg. 124, Drain cleaner: © Dana Kelley

Pg. 126, Common household acids and bases: © Dana Kelley

Pg. 127, Glass specimen jar: © Victor de Schwanberg/Photo Researchers, Inc.

Pg. 129, Calcium Hydride Reaction: © Charles D. Winters/Photo Researchers, Inc.

Pg. 132, Urine analysis: © Faye Norman/Photo Researchers, Inc.

Pg. 133, Various types of salts: © lunanaranja/iStockphoto.com

Pg. 135, Titration: © Charles D. Winters/Photo Researchers, Inc.

Pg. 137, Buffer Solution: © Charles D. Winters/Photo Researchers, Inc.

Pg. 138, Acid-base reaction with indicator: © Martyn F. Chillmaid/Photo Researchers, Inc

Pg. 139, Student using a digital pH meter: © SPL/Photo Researchers, Inc

Chapter 7

Pg. 148, Hydrogen electrode apparatus: © Martyn F. Chillmaid/Photo Researchers, Inc

Pg. 149, Iron-platinum electrochemistry: © Andrew Lambert Photography/Photo Researchers, Inc

Pg. 150, Voltaic cell: © Andrew Lambert Photography/Photo Researchers, Inc

Pg. 151, Voltmeter and Zinc-copper battery: © Andrew Lambert Photography/Photo Researchers, Inc

Pg. 153, Michael Faraday: © Sheila Terry/Photo Researchers, Inc

Pg. 156, Contractions of the heart: © Andrey Prokhorov/iStockphoto.com

Pg. 157, Copper refinery plant: © Maximilian Stock Ltd/Photo Researchers, Inc.

INDEX

Symbols

π-bonds 4, 5

A

acid dissociation constant 131, 134, 142
acids 5, 123-141
actinides 20
activation energy 35, 36, 42, 43
activity 48, 49
actual yield 16
aerosol 88
alkali metals 4, 100, 133, 144
alkaline earth metals 4, 5, 144
ammonium 14, 93, 100
amorphous 17, 105
amphipathic 88
amphoteric 5, 126
angstrom 1
anions 6, 14, 89
anode 150-160
aqueous phase 89, 117
Arrhenius 36, 42, 76, 123, 140
Arrhenius acid 123
Arrhenius equation 36, 42, 76
atmospheric pressure 95, 110, 113, 114, 117
atoms 1-10, 13, 17, 19-23
atomic mass units 2
atomic number 2, 6
atomic radius 8
atomic weight 2
ATP 12
Aufbau principle 20
autocatalysis 43
autoionization of water 131
Avogadro's law 28
Avogadro's number 2, 25, 73
azimuthal quantum number 19

B

Balancing Redox Reactions 143, 149
bases 4, 123, 126, 132
bimolecular 37
binary molecular compounds 14
blackbody radiator 63
Bohr, Neils 23
boiling point 72, 112, 117, 120-122,
boiling point elevation 117
bomb calorimeter 110
bond dissociation energy 12
bond energy 12, 96
bond length 12
bonds 4, 5, 8, 12, 17, 42, 44, 76, 77, 89, 92-94, 96, 108, 112, 114, 117

Boron 12
Boyle's law 28
Broglie, Louis de 23
bromine 5
Brønsted and Lowry 123
Brønsted-Lowry 16, 123, 140
buffered 136, 137
buffer solution 136

C

cage effect 44
calorimeter 110
carbon 2, 4, 5, 22, 44, 114
carbonates 100
carbon dioxide 15, 44
Carnot engine 67
catalyst 17, 42, 43, 76, 151
cathode 24, 150-152, 157
cations 4, 6, 14, 89, 123, 133
cell diagram 152
cell potential 150-157
celsius 73
centigrade 73
cesium 8
chalcogens 4
Charles' law 28, 29
chemical equilibrium 46
chlorine 5, 212
coagulate 88
coffee cup calorimeter 110, 111
cold reservoir 64, 66, 67
colligative 90, 117, 118
collision model 35, 39
colloid 88, 118
combination reaction 16
combustion reaction 15-16
common ion effect 99
compound 2, 12-15, 18, 53, 75, 87, 89, 94, 95, 117, 144, 145
concentration cell 156
condensation 112, 113
condense 95
conduction 61, 62, 151
conduction 61, 85
conjugate acid 125, 126, 215
conjugate base 125, 126, 128, 131, 134-138
conservation of energy 67, 70, 83
convection 62, 85
copper 14, 47, 74, 87, 149-152, 157
Coulomb's law 7, 8, 32
covalent bond 4, 5, 8, 12
critical point 114
critical pressure 114
critical temperature 114, 115
crystal 17, 98, 117

crystallization 98, 117

D

Dalton's law 30
decomposition 16
degenerate orbitals 22
degrees of freedom 72
delocalized electrons 17
deposition 112, 113
deuterium 2, 114
deviations from ideal behavior 32, 33
dialysis 88
diatomic 4, 5, 71
diffusion 31-32, 55
diprotic acid 127, 135
dispersion medium 88
dissolution 89, 90, 92, 98
DNA 17
d orbitals 4, 5
double bonds 4
double displacement 4
double replacement 16
Downs cell 157

E

Ea 36, 42
effective nuclear charge 7, 8
efficiency 67
effusion 31, 54, 55
Einstein 23, 24, 71
electrical work 63, 74, 83
electric potential 148, 150
electrochemical cell 157
electrodes 148, 150, 151, 157
electrolysis 157
electrolyte 150, 225
electrolytic cell 157
electromagnetic waves 62
electromotive force 150
electromotive force 158
electron affinity 8, 9, 25
electron configuration 25
electronegative 4, 5, 128
electronic charge 1
electronic energy 70, 71
electrons 1-9, 12, 17, 19-24, 143-153, 157
electron spin quantum number 19
electron units 1
electrostatic forces 7, 12, 17, 32, 44
elementary reaction 37, 47, 48
elements 2-6, 14, 19-22, 129, 144
Emf 158
emissivity 24, 62, 63
empirical formula 12, 13, 18
emulsion 88
endothermic 9, 75, 92-94, 113, 117
endpoint 138, 140
energy ladder 23
enthalpy 59, 70, 74, 84, 85

entropy 47, 52, 79-83, 93, 113
equilibrium 46-53, 60, 63-65, 67, 80-83, 94, 98, 99, 114, 118, 150, 153, 154
equilibrium approximation 42
equilibrium constant 42, 48, 50-52, 98, 99, 131, 154
equipartition theory 72
equivalence point 135-141, 145, 146
equivalents 90, 135
evaporation 15
exothermic 92, 93, 98
extensive properties 60

F

families 3
First Law of Thermodynamics 59, 64, 84, 85
fluorine 5, 6, 8, 128
foam 88, 101
free energy 76, 82-85, 118, 153
freezing 72, 112, 113
freezing point 72
freezing point depression 117, 119, 120

G

galvanic cell 150-154, 156, 157,
Gibbs Free Energy 59-60, 70, 82-83
glucose 12, 132
glycogen 17
Graham's law 31, 32
ground state 21, 25
groups 3, 4, 12, 20, 144

H

Haber Process 52
half cell 150, 156
half equivalence point 136, 137, 139, 145
half life 40
half reaction 148-152, 156
halides 5, 128
halogens 4, 5, 100, 144
HCl 124, 126
heat 60-67, 70, 71, 74, 75, 77, 80-85, 92-94, 96, 106-114
heat capacity 106-112, 120
heat engine 67
heating curve 112, 113
heat of fusion 112
heat of hydration 93, 97, 225
heat of solution 92, 93, 96, 102, 117
heat of vaporization 94, 112
heats of hydration 5
heats of reaction 110, 120
Heisenberg Uncertainty Principle 1, 20
helium 7, 29
Henderson-Hasselbalch equation 136-138, 140
Henry's law 101
Hess' law 75
heterogeneous catalyst 42, 170
hot reservoir 66, 67
Hund's rule 22
hydration 5, 74, 89, 93

P

partial pressure 30, 50, 52, 55, 94-96, 101, 113
parts per million 90, 103
path functions 60
Pauli Exclusion Principle 19
Pauling scale 8
percent yield 16
period 3, 5, 8, 20, 22
periodic table 2-9, 14, 15, 19, 20
periodic trends 8, 9
peroxides 4
phase 94, 95, 105, 106, 112-114, 117, 150, 152
phase changes 77, 106, 113, 114
phase diagram 114
pH meter 138, 139
phosphates 100
Phosphorous 4, 37
photoelectric effect 23, 24
photoelectrons 24
photon 23, 24
Planck, Max 23
Planck's constant 20, 23
Planck's quantum theory 23
platinum 149, 151
polymers 17
polyprotic acids 127, 139
p orbitals 5, 7
precipitation 98
principle for detailed balance 50
principle quantum number 19, 22
protein 17, 43, 118, 132
protium 2
proton 1, 2, 6, 7, 20, 123-128, 133, 139
protons 1, 2, 6, 7, 10, 90, 127, 133, 135, 136
purifying metals 157
PV work 63-65, 74, 75, 81-83, 85, 106, 107, 114

Q

quadratic equation 132
quantum mechanics 19, 23

R

radiation 62, 63, 85
range of an indicator 138
Raoult's law 95, 96, 101, 117
rate constant 36-40, 44, 47, 48, 222
rate determining step 41
rate law 36-43, 47, 48, 171
reaction coordinate 42
reaction quotient 51, 153
redox 143, 145, 146, 149
redox reaction 143-145, 148, 149, 153
reduced 143-147
reducing agent 144, 145, 149
reductant 144, 145
reduction 143-145, 148-152, 156, 157
reduction half reaction 148, 150-152, 156
reduction potentials 148, 149, 151, 159
reference form 75

representative elements 6
resonance 17
rest mass energy 71
reversible 37, 46, 57, 64, 67, 74, 80-83, 98, 170
root-mean-square (rms) 31
rotational energy 71
rotation of polarized light 15
runs to completion 15, 16, 18, 48

S

salt bridge 150-152, 159
salts 133, 140
saturated solution 98, 99
second ionization energy 8
second law of thermodynamics 66, 67, 79-81
SHE 148, 151
shell 6-8, 19, 20, 21, 106
shielding 7
silver 16, 53, 100, 149, 151
single Displacement 16
single replacement 16, 18
SI units 11
sodium 6, 7, 14, 24, 90, 134, 135, 157
solubility 87, 98, 100, 101, 103
solubility Guidelines 87, 100
solubility product 98, 99, 104
solute 87-90, 92, 95, 96, 98, 101, 102, 117, 118
solution 110, 117, 118
solvation 52, 89, 98, 99
solvent 87-98, 101, 102, 104, 118
specific heat capacity 109
spectator ions 99
spontaneous reaction 82, 83, 93, 102, 153, 165
standard enthalpy of formation 75
standard hydrogen electrode 148, 151
standard molar volume 29
standard solution 145, 198
standard state 17, 75, 151-154
standard state cell potential 151
standard temperature and pressure 27
standard Temperature And Pressure 55
state 20-22, 60, 61, 66, 67, 70-76, 79-83, 105, 107, 112, 144
state Functions 59, 60, 70, 85
steady state 42, 61
steady state approximation 42
Stefan-Boltzman law 62
steric factor 36, 42
sterling engine 67
stoichiometric point 135
STP 27, 29, 55, 75
strong nuclear force 1
sublimation 112, 113
subshell 6, 7, 19-22
sulfate 14
sulfides 4, 100
sulfur 4, 5, 18, 105
sulfuric acid 14
supercritical fluid 114
surroundings 59, 61, 64-66, 79-83
system 59-61, 63-67, 70-75, 78, 79-83

T

temperature 28, 29, 31, 33, 36, 37, 61-67, 71-75, 80-85, 93-95, 101, 102, 106-110, 112-114, 117, 118
terminals 150, 152
termolecular 37
theoretical yield 16
thermal conductivity 61, 62
thermodynamic functions 70
third law of thermodynamics 80
titration 135-139, 145
titration curve 135, 137, 139
transition metals 4, 6, 20, 22, 144
transition state 76
translational energy 71
triple bonds 4
triple point 114,
tritium 2
turnover number 43
Tyndall effect 88

U

unimolecular 37
universal gas constant 28

V

valence electrons 21
Van der Waals equation 33
Van der Waals forces 42, 102
Van't Hoff factor 117
vaporization 94, 112, 113, 120
vapor pressure 94-96, 101, 104, 113, 117
vibrational energy 70, 71
volatile solute 95, 101, 117
voltaic cell 150, 156
volume 54, 55, 60, 70, 72

W

water 15
water potential 118
work 63-67, 79, 81-83, 85, 101
work function 24

Z

z 36, 72
Z_{eff} 7, 8, 9
zeroth law of thermodynamics 72

An Unedited Student Review of This Book

The following review of this book was written by Teri R—. from New York. Teri scored a 43 out of 45 possible points on the MCAT. She is currently attending UCSF medical school, one of the most selective medical schools in the country.

"The Examkrackers MCAT books are the best MCAT prep materials I've seen-and I looked at many before deciding. The worst part about studying for the MCAT is figuring out what you need to cover and getting the material organized. These books do all that for you so that you can spend your time learning. The books are well and carefully written, with great diagrams and really useful mnemonic tricks, so you don't waste time trying to figure out what the book is saying. They are concise enough that you can get through all of the subjects without cramming unnecessary details, and they really give you a strategy for the exam. The study questions in each section cover all the important concepts, and let you check your learning after each section. Alternating between reading and answering questions in MCAT format really helps make the material stick, and means there are no surprises on the day of the exam-the exam format seems really familiar and this helps enormously with the anxiety. Basically, these books make it clear what you need to do to be completely prepared for the MCAT and deliver it to you in a straightforward and easy-to-follow form. The mass of material you could study is overwhelming, so I decided to trust these books—I used nothing but the Examkrackers books in all subjects and got a 13-15 on Verbal, a 14 on Physical Sciences, and a 14 on Biological Sciences. Thanks to Jonathan Orsay and Examkrackers, I was admitted to all of my top-choice schools (Columbia, Cornell, Stanford, and UCSF). I will always be grateful. I could not recommend the Examkrackers books more strongly. Please contact me if you have any questions."

Sincerely,
Teri R—

About the Author

Jonathan Orsay is uniquely qualified to write an MCAT preparation book. He graduated on the Dean's list with a B.A. in History from Columbia University. While considering medical school, he sat for the real MCAT three times from 1989 to 1996. He scored in the 90 percentiles on all sections before becoming an MCAT instructor. He has lectured in MCAT test preparation for thousands of hours and across the country. He has taught premeds from such prestigious Universities as Harvard and Columbia. He was the editor of one of the best selling MCAT prep books in 1996 and again in 1997. He has written and published the following books and audio products in MCAT preparation: "Examkrackers MCAT Physics"; "Examkrackers MCAT Chemistry"; "Examkrackers MCAT Organic Chemistry"; "Examkrackers MCAT Biology"; "Examkrackers MCAT Verbal Reasoning & Math"; "Examkrackers 1001 questions in MCAT Physics", "Examkrackers MCAT Audio Osmosis with Jordan and Jon".

Notes: